FUNDAMENTALS OF CELESTIAL MECHANICS

FUNDAMENTALS OF

CELESTIAL MECHANICS

J. M. A. DANBY

Yale University

NEW YORK - THE MACMILLAN COMPANY

A DIVISION OF THE CROWELL-COLLIER PUBLISHING COMPANY

© John M. A. Danby 1962

Second Printing 1964

Library of Congress catalog card number: 62-7032

The Macmillan Company, New York
Brett-Macmillan Ltd., Galt, Ontario

Printed in the United States of America

Preface

This text is based on courses given originally to students at the University of Minnesota and is intended for undergraduates in their third and fourth years and for graduate students who have not had the equivalent work. These students (not only astronomers, but also mathematicians, physicists, and engineers) are not always ready for analytical dynamics, upon which much of the theory of celestial mechanics is based. Consequently the approach has had to be elementary throughout, with individual topics pursued only so far as elementary methods permit. This has the advantage that long formulas are avoided, and that some basic qualitative properties show through more clearly; on the other hand it can make the subject appear deceptively easy.

Vector notation is used wherever possible. In my opinion this adds elegance and directness to the mechanics and geometry and, in the long run, makes the subject simpler. From experience it has been found necessary to include introductions to vectors and vectorial mechanics; it is expected that these chapters will principally be used for review, and perhaps only for reference. Nevertheless I have usually found it necessary to start from first principles when teaching the course, and the chapters on vectors have been made as complete as possible.

It has become the fashion to state at the beginning of a text for undergraduates that the only prerequisite is a little elementary calculus. However, in my opinion, no student is prepared for celestial mechanics until he has mastered elementary calculus, including the evaluation of simple integrals (without using tables of integrals, a regretable habit in students) and the solution of elementary differential equations. He should have spent at least one year on mechanics. He should be familiar with elementary two- and three-dimensional analytic geometry, and especially with the properties of conics. Since students who have completed courses on analytic geometry are often woefully ignorant of all but the very elementary properties of conics, a short review of these has been included in the appendix.

Celestial mechanics is a branch of astronomy. Its procedures are mathematical but its background and applications concern astronomy. A chapter on

"The Astronomical Background" has been included for the benefit of students new to the subject, but this does little more than introduce the vocabulary. Students cannot fail to benefit from additional reading.

Hardly any specific mention has been made of astronautics. This is because, in my opinion, the division between astronautics and celestial mechanics occurs at a more advanced level than that considered here. Problems of guidance, optimization, and so on require theories of their own, but frequently astronautics makes fresh (and exacting) demands on the techniques of classical celestial mechanics (as in the case of the motion of a satellite in the field of an oblate planet), so that it pays to have a grounding in the subject. It is hoped, therefore, that those students expecting to be associated with astronautics will find this book helpful as a text.

The text falls naturally into two parts: the solution of the two-body problem and its applications to the prediction of positions of celestial bodies and the determination of orbits from observations, and the numerical and analytical methods for the calculation of perturbations. Since important perturbations can be caused by the aspherical shape of a body such as the Earth, the potentials of such bodies are considered. Applications of the theory include elementary solutions for the precession, nutation, the physical libration of the Moon, and the figures of equilibrium of rotating and tidally distorted fluid masses. For completeness, there is also a chapter on the three-body problem. Some may object to the inclusion of a chapter on numerical procedures, suggesting that the student should wait until he has access to an automatic computing machine. But some undergraduates come to the subject with no experience in numerical methods at all, and a little knowledge of these is needed to appreciate some of the processes of celestial mechanics. It is this knowledge which Chapter 10 is intended to convey. Also I believe it is salutary for the student to perform some calculations by hand (such as the solution of Kepler's equation or the numerical integration of a differential equation) before he buries his sorrows in someone else's pre-programmed sub-routine!

From necessity, the text gives only an academic development of the subject. For instance, in the chapter on the determination of orbits the basic principles have been derived but no detailed instructions have been given. It is hoped that, as a result of a grounding in the basic principles, the student who wants to go further will be able better to understand the technical details of practical or advanced texts. Also, in the future, although he may not be immediately concerned with practical work, he will appreciate the problems of those who are. The student should at no time be under any illusion about the ultimate necessity of resorting to calculation in nearly all problems of celestial mechanics.

In the final stages of writing the text I continually resisted the temptation to include extra material, and in my eyes the greatest faults of the text are sins of omission. But, however important extra material may be, it can become confusing in an elementary text that aims to be direct rather than encyclopaedic. This is not intended to be a reference book. No attempt has been made to make the bibliography complete, but only books which seem to me to be most immediately helpful have been indicated. Also, little attempt has been made to describe the history of the subject. Throughout I have tried to consider the students' pockets as well as the publisher's stomach in limiting the contents of the book.

A large number of problems has been included. This represents an old-fashioned approach to teaching, but is deliberate. Progress in teaching techniques has been considerable, and to the traditional stages of learning—"read, mark, learn and inwardly digest"— have now been added "hear" and "see." But, in spite of this, and however clear a lecturer may be, the student still needs to "learn and inwardly digest" the material, and there is much to be said for the old-fashioned view that this is best achieved by working on many problems in private and by discussion later in class. There is a deliberate change of emphasis in the problems as the text proceeds. Early, they are exercises, usually short although not always easy; later, and particularly in Chapter 11 on perturbations, they may be longer than the average assignment and may be more appropriate to private thought followed by class discussion.

Although the text arose from a course given over two quarters, it now contains fully enough material for a year at the undergraduate level. For a short course I have found the material up to and including Chapter 7, but omitting much of Chapter 5, to be quite enough, so long as working on problems is emphasized. Certainly a thorough understanding of the undisturbed motion of two bodies is fundamental in celestial mechanics, and perturbations should not be considered until that part of the subject has been mastered.

Lack of space has made it impossible to acknowledge the authors of all the theorems and methods used. This neglect may be defensible where continuity of development is important, but I regret it none the less, and apologize to all those who are slighted. But I would particularly like to acknowledge a personal debt to the writings of Plummer, Ramsey, Smart, and Herget. No text of this nature can fail to be influenced by Moulton's classic, and if this present text resembles that of Moulton, it is not a coincidence.

Some of the problems are original, and some have been taken from other texts; many of these are classics, hallowed by age, which have appeared in many texts and examinations in the past. The texts from which problems have been immediately taken are:

L. A. Pars, *An Introduction to Dynamics* (Cambridge)

A. R. Ramsey, *Dynamics*, Parts 1 and 2 (Cambridge)

A. R. Ramsey, *Newtonian Attraction* (Cambridge)

W. M. Smart, *Spherical Astronomy* (Cambridge)

E. T. Whittaker, *Analytical Dynamics* (Cambridge)

F. R. Moulton, *An Introduction to Celestial Mechanics* (Macmillan)

K. P. Williams, *The Calculation of the Orbits of Asteroids and Comets* (Principia Press)

R. Kurth, *Introduction to the Mechanics of the Solar System* (Pergamon Press)

D. E. Rutherford, *Vector Methods* (Oliver and Boyd)

I am most grateful to the publishers and authors for their kind permission to reproduce the problems, and also to C. W. Allen and the London University Press, the author and publisher of *Astrophysical Quantities*, for permission to reproduce some of the tables appearing in the appendix.

I would also like to thank Professor Dirk Brouwer of Yale University who critically read the manuscript and made several suggestions that have materially increased its value as a text; the faults that remain are of course the responsibility only of the author. Much care has been devoted to the writing and proof reading of the book, but many errors must remain, and I will be grateful to hear of these.

J. M. A. DANBY

New Haven, Connecticut

Contents

*Problems will be found at the ends of sections marked with an asterisk.

FUNDAMENTALS OF CELESTIAL MECHANICS

Chapter 1 ** THE ASTRONOMICAL BACKGROUND

1.1 Introduction

Much of the theory in this text is that of conventional mechanics, but since its applications will concern celestial objects, we shall be using terms that may not be familiar to students who lack a background in astronomy. This chapter is intended for such students. It is confined to a bare introduction to the astronomical terms used in the text. Students are strongly advised to read, in addition, some general text in descriptive astronomy.

The fundamental law of celestial mechanics is Newton's law of gravitation. Most applications concern the solar system, but the theory can be applied anywhere in the universe. For very small distances, comparable with the size of the atom, and for very large distances, of the order of a billion light years, this law may, perhaps, not be useful, but we shall not be concerned with such extremes here. It is important to realize that, apart from some small modifications (as in the case of Mercury's orbit), Newton's law holds good in the sense that it gives the right answers; furthermore it is the only reasonable law in elementary mechanics that gives the right answers. In practice, the law is used not only in work on the solar system but also in the mechanics of multiple star systems, of the galaxy, and even of clusters of galaxies.

In celestial mechanics we are primarily concerned with things as we find them. We need to explain observed motion and to provide accurate predictions for the future. But when a rocket is launched, some control is exercised over its orbit, even if only by a judicious choice of the initial conditions of launching. An orbit is chosen in advance; in addition to the forces due to gravity, thrusts can be imposed; if the rocket does not follow its chosen orbit precisely, corrections must be applied. These circumstances fall into the province of *astronautics* (which can be said to include "experimental celestial mechanics"). Actually, the methods of celestial mechanics can be applied to the problems of astronautics, and the basic theory of the two subjects is the same.

1

1.2 Some Definitions

The *solar system* contains one star, the Sun, and various bodies that travel in orbits around the Sun.

A *star* is a celestial body that provides its own light.

A *planet* is a body, revolving around a star, that does not provide its own light. In the solar system the planets "shine" by virtue of light reflected from the Sun. A planet is much less massive than a star. Jupiter contains more mass than the remainder of the planets in the solar system put together, but it still has only about one-thousandth of the mass of the Sun. The orbits of the planets in the solar system (excepting that of Pluto) lie very roughly in the same plane and are very approximately circular. The names of the *major* planets in the solar system are: Mercury, Venus, the Earth, Mars, Jupiter, Saturn, Uranus, Neptune, and Pluto, in order of increasing distance from the Sun (but a part of Pluto's orbit lies within that of Neptune). The first four and Pluto are *terrestrial* planets and are much smaller and less massive than the remaining four, which are the *giants*. Planets with orbits outside that of the Earth are *superior*; Mercury and Venus are *inferior* planets.

In addition to the major planets there are countless *minor* planets (also called *asteroids* or *planetoids*), most of which have orbits lying between those of Mars and Jupiter. These are very much smaller than the major planets and, with few exceptions, have diameters of the order of a few kilometers or less.

There may be a continuous gradation between the minor planets and *meteorites*, but the latter are usually considered to be the size of large rocks at most, and to merge into the micrometeorites, which are microscopic. Billions of these strike the Earth in a day; some of them, possibly the ones that appear as *meteors* (or "shooting stars"), are certainly the remains of comets.

A *comet* is a loose aggregate of rocks traveling around the Sun. When observed, it is surrounded by a haze of gases that gives it a characteristically fuzzy appearance. When close to the Sun it may develop a tail which will point away from the Sun. Comets have pronouncedly elongated orbits, many being nearly parabolic; the orbits are not concentrated near any plane. Those comets with periods of the order of ten or one hundred years are called *periodic* comets. It is important to remember that all these objects belong to the solar system and travel in orbits that remain (by astronomical standards) close to the Sun.

A *satellite* is a body revolving around a planet. It is normally of negligible mass compared with its parent planet. The notable exception to this is the Moon, which has a mass of about one-eighteenth of the Earth's mass.

The word "revolve" will be used in this text to imply motion around a point. "Rotate" will imply motion about an axis. Thus the Earth revolves around the Sun but rotates on its axis.

The word "orbit" is sadly abused nowadays, both as a noun and as a verb. Here it will be used only as a noun. The operative definition is no more than "the course of a planet, comet, satellite, etc." It is entirely wrong to speak of a rocket fired from the Earth as "*starting* to move in orbit around the Sun *a few days later.*"

The Earth is nearly spherical, with a radius of about 4000 miles or 6400 km. It is flattened at the poles, the deviations from a sphere being slight (the difference between the polar and equatorial diameters is about 43 km) but important in precise work.

The fundamental problem in celestial mechanics is the *two-body problem*; this is concerned with the motion of two point masses which move subject only to their mutual gravitational attraction. This situation is nearly reproduced in the solar system for orbits of objects around the Sun. Deviations from it, caused, for instance, by the added attraction of Jupiter on a planet, are known as *perturbations*.

1.3 Orbital Definitions

In the orbit of one body about another the least and greatest separations are indicated by applying the prefixes "peri–" and "apo–" (or "ap–") respectively to the Greek word for the more massive of the two bodies. For instance, in the orbit of a satellite around the Earth, these positions are called *perigee* and *apogee*; for a planet revolving around the Sun, the positions are *perihelion* and *aphelion*; for motion around any star, "–astron" is used, and for any center of force, "–centron." (The use of roots that are not related to the Greek is increasing, and should be diminished.)

The time taken for a complete revolution in an orbit, with respect to the stars, is the *sidereal period* of that orbit. Since an orbit can itself revolve in space, the sidereal period need not be equal to the time between, say, one passage through perihelion to the next. Various qualifications of "period" will appear during the course of the text: it will only be used without qualification when all perturbations are ignored in the discussion, so that the orbit is constant and fixed in space; then the sidereal period will be implied.

Names of some of the positions with respect to the Earth in the orbits of the planets are illustrated in Figure 1.1, page 4. The student should note the differences between the names for the orbits of the inferior and superior planets. The average time taken for a planet to return to the same position relative to the Earth (for instance, the average time between one opposition and the next) is called the *mean synodic period* of the planet. The student should verify that the relation between the sidereal and mean synodic periods of a planet is

$$\frac{1}{\text{sidereal period}} + \frac{1}{\text{synodic period}} = 1$$

for a superior planet, or

$$\frac{1}{\text{sidereal period}} - \frac{1}{\text{synodic period}} = 1$$

for an inferior planet, the unit of time being the sidereal year (the sidereal period of the Earth).

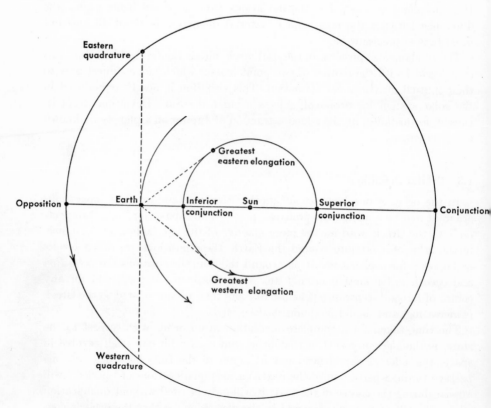

Figure 1.1 Here the orbits are illustrated as seen from the north pole of the ecliptic.

When observed from the north, most orbits around the Sun would be counter-clockwise; these are *direct* orbits. Some comets and a few satellites revolve in the opposite sense; their orbits are *retrograde*.

1.4 Kepler's Laws

The motion of the planets was found by Kepler to follow three laws:

1. The orbit of each planet is an ellipse, with the Sun at one of its foci.
2. Each planet revolves so that the line joining it to the Sun sweeps out equal areas in equal intervals of time. (This is the "law of areas.")

3. The squares of the periods of any two planets are in the same proportion as the cubes of their mean distances from the Sun. (This law requires modification; it will be described in Chapter Six.)

Motion following these laws is called "Keplerian motion," and the planets are said to move in "Keplerian orbits."

1.5 The Astronomical Unit

Consider Kepler's third law. The sidereal period of a planet can be calculated from its mean synodic period, which can be observed. If P is the sidereal period and a the mean distance from the Sun in the orbit of some planet, and if P_E and a_E are the corresponding values for the orbit of the Earth, we have

$$\frac{P^2}{P_E{}^2} = \frac{a^3}{a_E{}^3}.$$

Let P_E (the sidereal year) and a_E be chosen as units of time and length: a_E is the *astronomical unit*; it will be discussed more rigorously later. In these units

$$P^2 = a^3.$$

Hence a can be calculated for any planet, and a scale model can be constructed of the relative dimensions of the planetary orbits in the solar system. Any interplanetary distance can then be measured in terms of the astronomical unit. But if we want to find a distance in terms of some absolute unit, kilometers, say, we must first know the length of the astronomical unit in kilometers. The measurement of the astronomical unit is an extremely difficult problem; at present it is not known with sufficient accuracy, but better determinations will certainly be made very soon.

If any one interplanetary distance can be measured in absolute units, then the scale of the model of the solar system can be expressed in those units. One method for finding the astronomical unit uses the orbit of the minor planet Eros, which approaches close enough to the Earth for its distance to be measurable by the use of the principles of triangulation. A second method uses radar techniques to measure interplanetary distances; these have already been successfully applied to Venus. Another approach is to use the perturbations of the orbit of Eros; these are caused by the perturbing forces of the planets, which depend on the ratios of the masses of the planets to the mass of the Sun and on their distances from Eros. The results of these methods disagree, and the differences between them are larger than the probable errors of the determinations. There must be systematic errors which still remain to be cleared up. At present the value of the astronomical unit can be taken as 149,500,000 km, or 92,900,000 miles.

Instead of the astronomical unit, we sometimes refer to the *Sun's geocentric parallax*. This is the angle subtended at the mean distance of the Sun by the Earth's equatorial radius. The value corresponding to the figures quoted above is 8″.80.

1.6 Bode's Law

Consider the sequence of numbers

$$0, 3, 6, 12, \cdots$$

where, after the start, each number is doubled to give the next one. Add 4 to each, and divide the result by 10. We have the resulting sequence

$$0.4, 0.7, 1.0, 1.6, 2.8, 5.2, \cdots$$

and these numbers represent, with moderate accuracy, the mean distances of the planets from the Sun, with the exception of Neptune and Pluto. The number 2.8 corresponds to the average of the system of minor planets.

This rule, known as Bode's law, was actually noted earlier by Titius, in 1772. It acted as a stimulus for the search for a planet between Mars and Jupiter, although the existence of such a planet had been expected long before. It is sometimes a useful rule of thumb for recalling planetary distances. Table 1.1 indicates the degree of its success.

Table 1.1

Mean Distance from the Sun

Name	Bode's Law	True Value
Mercury	0.4	0.39
Venus	0.7	0.72
Earth	1.0	1.00
Mars	1.6	1.52
Minor planets (Ceres)	2.8	2.77
Jupiter	5.2	5.20
Saturn	10.0	9.54
Uranus	19.6	19.18
Neptune	38.8	30.06
Pluto	77.2	39.44

1.7 Astronomical Observations

The observations with which we shall be concerned consist of the direction of some object and the time of the observation. Each of these quantities requires careful definition and some discussion. The direction of an object is given by two angles. To describe completely its position in space relative to the observer, its distance must also be known; this cannot normally be observed and must be found by some indirect method. In a few instances, notably in astronautics, distances can be measured directly by radar or other electrical devices.

1.8 The Celestial Sphere

The direction of an object is given by two angles that fix its position on the *celestial sphere*. This is a spherical shell of arbitrarily large radius on which celestial objects appear projected. Normally the center of the Earth is at the center of the celestial sphere, but it may be convenient at times to have the observer or the Sun there. The "fixed" stars occupy nearly constant positions on the celestial sphere; the reasons for their inconstancies do not concern us here, but we note in passing that every star has its individual motion in space. The planets (literally "wanderers") and other bodies in the solar system move in paths on the celestial sphere, the most important of which is the path described by the center of the Sun, known as the *ecliptic*.

A *great circle* on the surface of a sphere is formed by the section with any plane passing through its center. Since the orbit of the Earth about the Sun takes place in a plane which contains the Sun, the ecliptic is a great circle on the celestial sphere. The line through the center of a sphere perpendicular to a great circle cuts the sphere in the *poles* of that great circle. If A and B are two points on a sphere that are not at opposite ends of a diameter, there is one and only one great circle passing through them. The angle written AB is the angle subtended by AB at the center of the sphere.

To define any coordinates, some system of reference is required. We illustrate this for the case of the surface of a sphere by considering the familiar coordinates of longitude and latitude on the surface of the Earth. The Earth's axis of rotation cuts the surface of the Earth in the *north* and *south poles*, and the great circle corresponding to these is the *equator*. The *latitude* of a point P is the angular distance of P measured north or south of the equator (see Figure 1.2, page 8). A great circle passing through the poles is called a *meridian*, and the meridian that passes through Greenwich (England) is the *prime meridian*. The angle between the meridian through P (there is only one, so long as P is not at a pole) and the prime meridian is the *longitude* of P; it is measured east or west.

Similar angles are used to fix position on the celestial sphere. Various reference systems are used, the most convenient of which, for practical purposes, is the *equatorial* system. The Earth's axis of rotation cuts the celestial sphere in the *celestial north* and *south poles*, the *celestial equator* being midway between them. The ecliptic cuts the celestial equator in two points known as the *equinoxes*. When the Sun crosses the equator, going north, it passes through the *vernal equinox*, or first point of Aries, written ♈. Great circles passing through the celestial poles are known as *hour circles*. The hour circle corresponding to the prime meridian passes through ♈, and the angle measured *eastward* from this to the hour circle through some star, X, is the *right ascension* of X, written α. α is usually measured in units of time such that twenty-four hours equals $360°$. δ, the *declination* of X, is the angle corresponding to latitude; it is measured positive north and negative south of the celestial equator. (See Figure 1.3.)

Celestial longitude and *latitude* are based on the ecliptic. Celestial latitude, β, is measured positive north and negative south of the ecliptic, and celestial

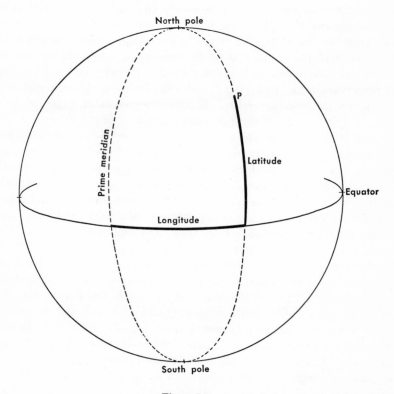

Figure 1.2

longitude, λ, is measured eastward from the vernal equinox. (See Figure 1.4, page 10.)

Several other coordinate systems are in use, but the two described here are the only ones needed in this text.

The angle between the celestial equator and the ecliptic is known as the *obliquity* of the ecliptic, and denoted by ϵ. Its value is about $23° \, 27'$. The Sun passes through the vernal equinox at the beginning of spring in the northern hemisphere and through the autumnal equinox (the corresponding point on the other side of the celestial sphere) at the beginning of autumn. The points of the ecliptic farthest north and south of the equator are the *summer* and *winter solstices*. The student is urged to consult any standard text for a description of the connection between these points and the seasons experienced on Earth.

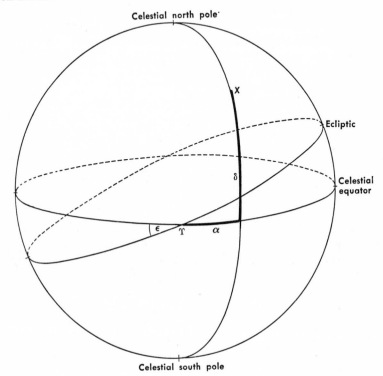

Figure 1.3

1.9 Precession, Nutation, and Variation of Latitude

A disadvantage of the coordinate systems described above is that the fundamental reference systems are not fixed. The causes of this will be very briefly described.

Variation of latitude. Consider the Earth's axis of rotation as remaining fixed in space, while the Earth slips about it. The effect of this is that the geographical poles "wander" within small areas of radius some fifteen meters, causing perceptible if small changes in the latitudes of points on the Earth.

Lunisolar precession. Due to the pull of the Moon and Sun on the Earth's equatorial bulge, the Earth's axis is slowly precessing, or describing a cone in space, a complete revolution occurring in a period of about 26,000 years. The obliquity remains approximately constant.

Nutation. The plane of the Moon's orbit about the Earth rotates, with respect to the ecliptic, with a period of just under nineteen years. This leads to an oscillation in that component of the pull on the Earth's equatorial bulge which is due to the Moon, causing an extra oscillation or "nodding" of the Earth's axis. This nutation is superimposed on the precessional motion.

Planetary precession. Due to perturbations from the other planets on the Earth's orbit, the ecliptic is not fixed in space, but is gradually changing.

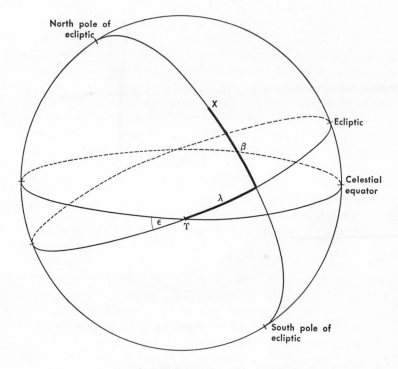

Figure 1.4

General precession is the combined effect of lunisolar and planetary precession.

A consequence of precession is that the celestial equator is not fixed on the celestial sphere, and the vernal equinox is slowly moving westward along the ecliptic (which changes much more sluggishly). It was named the "first point of Aries" when it actually lay in the constellation Aries, but it is now in Pisces. As a result of this, the coordinates of celestial objects are gradually changing; they must always be referred to some date or *epoch* for comparison with other observations.

Star positions are usually referred to a *mean equator* and *mean equinox* for some epoch, which are found by neglecting the periodic parts of the motion of the celestial equator. The resulting coordinates are *mean coordinates*.

1.10   The True and Apparent Places of a Celestial Object

When specifying the coordinates of a celestial object rigorously, it is necessary to make clear which point of the solar system is at the center of the celestial sphere, or the origin of coordinates.

The *true place* of a star is defined with the Sun at the origin and with respect to the *true equator* and *true equinox* at the instant of observation.

For the *apparent place*, the origin is moved to the center of the Earth. This move is bound to change the relative positions of the stars on the celestial sphere, the closer ones being affected more. These changes are ascribed to *annual parallax* (since they are periodic, the period of variation being the sidereal year); they are practically negligible for all but the nearest stars. More important changes are caused by *annual aberration*. Since light moves with finite velocity, the direction in which an object is observed will depend not only on its true geometrical direction but also on the velocities of the object and observer and on the velocity of light. For a star, which will have constant velocity over long periods, the changes are caused by the Earth's orbital velocity around the Sun, and this gives rise to annual aberration. If the object is in the solar system, its own velocity varies and must be taken into account together with the time lag caused by the light traveling from the object to the observer; in this case we have displacements due to *planetary aberration*.

An actual observation is made from the surface of the Earth, and in interpreting this we have to allow for an additional aberrational effect caused by the velocity of the observer that is due to the Earth's rotation; this is *diurnal aberration*. In addition we must take into account the fact that the origin has been moved again, introducing a further effect due to parallax.

Formulas for these various effects are given in standard texts on spherical astronomy; they are also given in most almanacs, together with the physical constants involved.

We remark in passing that the refraction of light in the Earth's atmosphere can affect considerably the apparent angle of a celestial object above the horizon; the effect is greater near the horizon where it is of the order of half a degree.

1.11   The Measurement of Time

The fundamental "clock" for the measurement of time has for centuries been the Earth, rotating on its axis. One complete rotation with respect to the celestial sphere measures one *sidereal day* or twenty-four hours of *sidereal time*. Because of the Sun's motion around the celestial sphere, a complete rotation of the Earth with respect to the Sun (which measures the *solar day* or twenty-four hours, *apparent solar time*) takes about four minutes longer than the sidereal day. For obvious reasons the sidereal day is not used for civil purposes.

Since the motion of the Sun around the celestial sphere is neither uniform nor along the celestial equator, the solar day is not of constant length. A fictitious sun called the *mean Sun* has been invented, moving uniformly along the celestial equator, for the measurement of *mean solar time*.

The time measured astronomically by an observer will depend on his longitude; it will be his *local time*. Since it would be impractical to have civil time varying continuously with longitude or to standardize it for the whole world, the Earth is divided into twenty-four *time zones*, bounded by meridians at 15° intervals and centered on longitudes that are integral multiples of 15°, except where civil convenience calls for slight irregularities. Within each time zone the civil time is the same, being dictated by the mean solar time at the central meridian, and the time in each zone differs from the times in its immediate neighbors by one hour. The meridian of longitude 180° (again with slight variations for practical convenience) is known as the *international date line*. When it is midnight at this longitude, the date is the same everywhere on the Earth. A traveler crossing this line experiences a discontinuity of one day in his calendar.

Astronomical observations are usually referred to *universal time*, or *U.T.*, which is the mean solar time at the meridian of Greenwich.

The *Julian date* is the number of days, and fraction of a day, measured from mean noon on January 1 of the year 4713 B.C. It is tabulated in almanacs for every day of the year.

As a clock, the Earth does not keep accurate time. Consider the prediction from theory of the position of some celestial object at some definite time. If observation does not confirm the prediction, it is possible that either the theory or the recorded time of observation may be in error. Toward the end of the nineteenth century it had become increasingly probable that observed deviations between observations and the gravitational theory of the Moon's motion were not caused by imperfections in the theory but by irregularities in the Earth's rate of rotation. Proof was lacking until, during the first half of the twentieth century, it was shown conclusively that the differences between observation and theory in the mean longitudes of Mercury, Venus, and the Sun exhibit fluctuations that are identical, if expressed in seconds of time, to those in the Moon's mean longitude. Over the past three centuries these fluctuations have ranged between ±30 seconds of time. A much smaller annual variation of around one-tenth of a second in the time given by the Earth's rotation has been established with the aid of terrestrial clocks, notably the quartz crystal clock and atomic clocks. In addition ancient observations of eclipses have shown that the day is gradually becoming longer (although only by about one-thousandth of a second per day per century).

To cope with this situation, *ephemeris time* has been introduced. This runs on uniformly with an invariable basic unit, and so corresponds with the theoretical notion of time used in mechanics. It is this time that should be used in celestial mechanics. The difference between ephemeris time and universal time is tabulated in the standard almanacs.

Chapter 2 ** INTRODUCTION TO VECTORS

2.1 Scalars and Vectors

A quantity that has magnitude only is called a *scalar*; it can be represented by a number with an associated sign. For example, distance and electric charge are scalars.

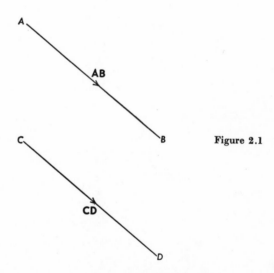

Figure 2.1

Consider two points A and B. The distance between them is AB, which is a scalar; if this distance is associated with the direction of A to B, it becomes a vector, **AB**. A vector can be thought of as a scalar with an associated direction (this is necessary but not sufficient; vectors must also satisfy the law of addition given in the following section); or, in this example, **AB** can be regarded as a displacement of amount AB in the direction A to B.

14

Notation for vectors varies widely. Some writers use an arrow, e.g., $\vec{AB}$, but the order in which the letters occur leaves no doubt as to the sense being from A to B and not from B to A. In everyday writing, the author prefers a line drawn underneath as being less likely to be confused with other uses of a line drawn above a symbol. In this text a vector will be denoted by a symbol in boldface type. The *modulus* of a vector **a** is its scalar value and this will be written as $|\mathbf{a}|$, or simply a; it is always positive. A *unit vector* has unit modulus; it will be written with a "cap" above it, e.g., **â**.   **â** is the unit vector along **a**; it may be referred to as the *direction* of **a** or as the *line of action* of **a**. A vector with zero modulus is a *null* or *zero vector* and is simply written "0." Considering **AB** as a displacement from A to B, we have

$$\mathbf{AB} + \mathbf{BA} = 0 \quad \text{or} \quad \mathbf{AB} = -\mathbf{BA}.$$

Vectors may be used in any of three senses:

1. *Free vectors.* Two free vectors, **AB** and **CD**, are equal if they have the same modulus and parallel directions. (See Figure 2.1.)

2. *Localized vectors.* These have their lines of action passing through some point. Examples are the force acting at a point and the velocity of a point.

3. *Position vectors.* Let O be any fixed origin and P a point that may vary. The vector

$$\mathbf{OP} = \mathbf{r}$$

is the position vector of P with respect to O. The symbol **r** will usually denote a position vector; it is always anchored to some origin. (See Figure 2.2.) The

Figure 2.2

possibility of three different senses may seem confusing, but in practice the context makes it quite clear which one is relevant.

From the definition, a vector may be multiplied by a scalar, only its modulus being affected (unless the scalar is negative, when the direction is reversed). For example, 2**AB** has the same direction as **AB** but twice its modulus. So we can write

$$\mathbf{r} = r\mathbf{\hat{r}},$$

an expression which will be used rather frequently, and

$$k\mathbf{r} = (kr)\hat{\mathbf{r}}.$$

It follows from the known properties of scalars that

$$k\mathbf{r} = \mathbf{r}k$$

and

$$(k+l)\mathbf{r} = k\mathbf{r} + l\mathbf{r}.$$

2.2 The Law of Addition

Considering $\mathbf{AB}$ as a displacement, we see that two vectors $\mathbf{AB}$ and $\mathbf{BC}$ can be added to give $\mathbf{AC}$. Any two free vectors can be added as shown in Figure 2.3.

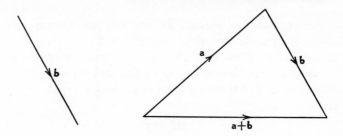

Figure 2.3

It follows from geometrical constructions (which are left to the student) that

$$\mathbf{a} + \mathbf{b} = \mathbf{b} + \mathbf{a} \qquad \text{(commutative law)}$$

and

$$(\mathbf{a} + \mathbf{b}) + \mathbf{c} = \mathbf{a} + (\mathbf{b} + \mathbf{c}) \quad \text{(associative law)}.$$

Subtraction can be considered in a similar way to addition, since $\mathbf{AB} = -\mathbf{BA}$.

To illustrate the use of vector addition, consider the straight line AD with direction $\hat{\mathbf{i}}$. Let B and C be any two points on AD, and let their position vectors with respect to any origin be $\mathbf{r}_0$ and $\mathbf{r}$. Then

$$\mathbf{OC} = \mathbf{OB} + \mathbf{BC}$$

or

$$\mathbf{r} = \mathbf{r}_0 + \lambda\hat{\mathbf{i}}, \tag{2.2.1}$$

where λ, the length BC, is a scalar. If λ varies, C traces out the whole line, so that (2.2.1) is the vector equation of the line AD. Now suppose that C is moving along the line at a constant speed v, and that at time $t = 0$, it is at B. Then at time t, $BC = \lambda = vt$, and

$$\mathbf{r} = \mathbf{r}_0 + vt\hat{\mathbf{i}}. \tag{2.2.2}$$

Conversely, if equations of motion yield this solution for the motion of C, then it must be moving in a straight line with constant speed.

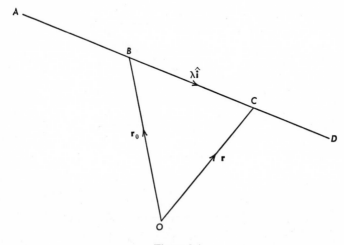

Figure 2.4

If $\hat{\mathbf{i}}$, $\hat{\mathbf{j}}$, and $\mathbf{r}$ are three coplanar vectors, and $\hat{\mathbf{i}}$ and $\hat{\mathbf{j}}$ are neither parallel nor antiparallel (pointing in opposite directions), then unique scalars x and y exist such that

$$\mathbf{r} = x\hat{\mathbf{i}} + y\hat{\mathbf{j}}.$$

(See Figure 2.5, page 18.) Similarly, if we add another vector $\hat{\mathbf{k}}$, which does not lie in this plane, and let $\mathbf{r}$ be any (three-dimensional) vector, then unique scalars x, y, and z exist such that

$$\mathbf{r} = x\hat{\mathbf{i}} + y\hat{\mathbf{j}} + z\hat{\mathbf{k}}.$$

$\mathbf{r}$ is said to be *resolved* along these three directions, and x, y, and z are its *components*. Resolution can be regarded as the reverse of addition.

$\hat{\mathbf{i}}$, $\hat{\mathbf{j}}$, and $\hat{\mathbf{k}}$ can be any three directions, but in the applications in this text they will be mutually perpendicular, forming a *right-handed triad*. This is such that if $\hat{\mathbf{k}}$ points away, then a rotation through $90°$ from $\hat{\mathbf{i}}$ to $\hat{\mathbf{j}}$ will be clockwise.

Let $\mathbf{r}$ have components x, y, and z with respect to some triad; then it may be written without ambiguity as

$$\mathbf{r} = (x,y,z).$$

If another triad is chosen, **r** will have different components. One great strength of the vector notation is that it is independent of any particular system of reference. The student should always beware of resolving too early; once a vector has been resolved, there are three quantities to cope with instead of one. Also, if a different triad is needed later, then all the paraphernalia of a change of origin and a rotation of axes are needed to change the components.

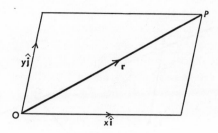

Figure 2.5a

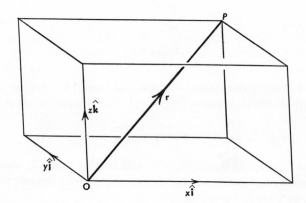

Figure 2.5b

Let **OP** $= $ **r** make an angle α with Ox (the x-axis). Then let

$$\cos \alpha = \frac{x}{r} = l.$$

If m and n are similarly defined, then l, m, and n are the *direction cosines* of **r** with respect to this triad. Since

$$l^2 + m^2 + n^2 = 1$$

the vector (l,m,n) has unit modulus and so is the unit vector $\hat{\mathbf{r}}$. In various notations we may write

$$\mathbf{OP} = \mathbf{r} = x\hat{\mathbf{i}} + y\hat{\mathbf{j}} + z\hat{\mathbf{k}} = (x,y,z) = (rl, rm, rn) = r(l,m,n) = r\hat{\mathbf{r}}.$$

If $\mathbf{r}_1 = (x_1, y_1, z_1)$ and $\mathbf{r}_2 = (x_2, y_2, z_2)$, then

$$\mathbf{r}_1 + \mathbf{r}_2 = (x_1 + x_2, y_1 + y_2, z_1 + z_2).$$

This form of the addition law must hold for any vector. Before anything can be called a vector, it must be shown to have magnitude and direction and to obey the vector addition law. A good example of something that has magnitude and direction but is not a vector is a finite rotation. The direction is that of the axis of rotation, and the magnitude is the angle through which the rotation turns, but two finite rotations cannot be added according to the vector addition law. *Infinitesimal* rotations, however, can be added in this way.

Problems

1. Construct geometrically: $\mathbf{OA} + \mathbf{OB}$, $\mathbf{OA} + \mathbf{BO}$, $-\mathbf{OA} + \mathbf{BO}$.
2. State the necessary and sufficient conditions for the sum of two vectors to vanish.
3. Show by similar triangles, or otherwise, that $l(\mathbf{a} + \mathbf{b}) = l\mathbf{a} + l\mathbf{b}$.
4. Show that the resolution of a vector along any three directions (where no two are parallel or antiparallel and all three do not lie in a plane) is unique. (Consider the consequences if this were not so.)
5. Find the moduli and direction cosines of the following vectors:

    $$(-a,0,0), \qquad (1,1,-1), \qquad (0,1,-1), \qquad (x,y,z)$$

    and of

    $$[(-a,b,0) + (a,b,0)], \qquad [(2,3,-5) + (3,-2,4)]$$

    and

    $$[(x,y,z) + (p,q,r)].$$

    All symbols may be assumed to represent positive numbers.
6. Assuming that forces are vectors, find the resultant of the two forces: P_1 along (l_1, m_1, n_1) and P_2 along (l_2, m_2, n_2).
7. Find the necessary and sufficient conditions for the sum of three nonzero vectors to vanish.
8. Prove that

    (a) $\dfrac{(\mathbf{OA} + \mathbf{OB})}{2}$ is the mid-point of AB;

    (b) $\dfrac{(n\,\mathbf{OA} + m\,\mathbf{OB})}{(m + n)}$ is the center of mass of masses n at A and m at B;

    (c) $\dfrac{(\mathbf{OA} + \mathbf{OB} + \mathbf{OC})}{3}$ is the centroid of the triangle ABC.

9. Prove by a vector method that the medians of a triangle are concurrent.

10. Two triangles ABC and $A'B'C'$ have centroids G and G'. Prove that

$$\mathbf{AA'} + \mathbf{BB'} + \mathbf{CC'} = 3\mathbf{GG'}.$$

11. Express the vector equation of the line (2.2.1), in cartesians, and eliminate the parameter λ.

12. Show that the equation of a plane can be written

$$\mathbf{r} = \mathbf{r}_0 + \lambda\hat{\mathbf{a}} + \mu\hat{\mathbf{b}},$$

where $\mathbf{r}_0$ is a point in the plane, $\hat{\mathbf{a}}$ and $\hat{\mathbf{b}}$ are any two nonparallel directions in the plane, and λ and μ are variable scalars. Show that this is equivalent to the usual cartesian equation of the plane.

13. If Ox points toward the vernal equinox, and Oz toward the celestial north pole, show that the direction cosines of a point (α, δ) are

$$(\cos\alpha\cos\delta, \quad \sin\alpha\cos\delta, \quad \sin\delta).$$

Find the direction cosines of the following points: the north pole of the ecliptic; the winter solstice; (12h, $+45°$); (15h, $-30°$); (4h 35m 53.2s, $-58°\ 16'\ 31''$). In each case verify that the sum of the squares of the direction cosines is one.

14. What is the equation of the plane of the ecliptic in the reference system of problem 13?

15. If Ox points toward the vernal equinox, and Oz toward the north pole of the ecliptic, find the direction cosines of the celestial north and south poles, the autumnal equinox, and (6h, $0°$).

2.3 The Scalar Product

The angle between two vectors is conventionally taken to lie between 0 and 180°. Let the angle between $\mathbf{a}$ and $\mathbf{b}$ be θ; then their *scalar* or "dot" product is defined by

$$\mathbf{a}\cdot\mathbf{b} = ab\cos\theta. \tag{2.3.1}$$

From the definition and the commutative law for scalars we have

$$\mathbf{a}\cdot\mathbf{b} = ab\cos\theta = ba\cos\theta = \mathbf{b}\cdot\mathbf{a},$$

so the commutative law holds for the scalar product. $\mathbf{a}\cdot\mathbf{b}$ may be considered as the length of $\mathbf{a}$ multiplied by the projected length of $\mathbf{b}$ on $\mathbf{a}$ (i.e., $b\cos\theta$). Then, since the projection of $(\mathbf{b} + \mathbf{c})$ on $\mathbf{a}$ is the sum of the separate projections of $\mathbf{b}$ and $\mathbf{c}$ on $\mathbf{a}$, it follows that

$$\mathbf{a}\cdot(\mathbf{b} + \mathbf{c}) = \mathbf{a}\cdot\mathbf{b} + \mathbf{a}\cdot\mathbf{c}$$

or that the distributive law holds. We also have, from the properties of scalars,

$$m(\mathbf{a}\cdot\mathbf{b}) = (m\mathbf{a})\cdot\mathbf{b} = \mathbf{a}\cdot(m\mathbf{b}).$$

The student should accept (2.3.1) as an arbitrary definition. Neither reason nor excuse need be offered for it, but there are plenty of reasons why it turns out to be useful in practice, and that is what matters.

One of the most important uses of the scalar product is in the resolution of vectors. In particular if $\hat{\imath}$, $\hat{\jmath}$, and $\hat{k}$ form a rectangular triad, the components of $\mathbf{r}$ in this triad are $\mathbf{r}\cdot\hat{\imath}$, $\mathbf{r}\cdot\hat{\jmath}$, and $\mathbf{r}\cdot\hat{k}$. Since the directions are mutually perpendicular, we have

$$\hat{\jmath}\cdot\hat{k} = \hat{k}\cdot\hat{\imath} = \hat{\imath}\cdot\hat{\jmath} = 0.$$

The square of a vector, $\mathbf{r}^2$, is defined by

$$\mathbf{r}^2 = \mathbf{r}\cdot\mathbf{r} = rr = r^2.$$

In particular

$$\hat{\imath}^2 = \hat{\jmath}^2 = \hat{k}^2 = 1.$$

Writing $\mathbf{r} = x\hat{\imath} + y\hat{\jmath} + z\hat{k}$, we find

$$\mathbf{r}^2 = x^2 + y^2 + z^2,$$

which is the usual formula for finding the modulus of a vector.

Problems

1. If the angle between **AB** and **CD** is θ, what are the angles between **AB** and **DC** and between **BA** and **DC**?
2. Find a formula for the cosine of the angle between the two vectors (x_1,y_1,z_1) and (x_2,y_2,z_2).
3. Prove by a vector method that for any triangle

$$a^2 = b^2 + c^2 - 2bc\cos A.$$

4. Solve, for the unknown vector **x**, the equations:

    (a) $\mathbf{x}\cdot\mathbf{a} = 0$.   (b) $\mathbf{x}\cdot\mathbf{a} = \mathbf{x}\cdot\mathbf{b}$ (where $\mathbf{a} \neq \mathbf{b}$).   (c) $\mathbf{x}\cdot\mathbf{a} = b$.

5. Evaluate $(\mathbf{a} + \mathbf{b})\cdot(\mathbf{a} - \mathbf{b})$ when $a = b$. Hence prove that the diagonals of a rhombus are perpendicular.
6. **a**, **b**, and **c** are three nonzero and non-coplanar vectors, and no two of them are parallel or antiparallel. Prove that if

$$\mathbf{x}\cdot\mathbf{a} = \mathbf{x}\cdot\mathbf{b} = \mathbf{x}\cdot\mathbf{c} = 0$$

    then $\mathbf{x} = 0$.
7. Assuming that forces are vectors, what relation must exist between P and Q such that forces P along $(1,0,0)$ and Q along $(0,1,0)$ have zero resultant along $(l,m,0)$?
8. Prove by a vector method that the altitudes of a triangle intersect in a point.

9. Prove by a vector method that the perpendicular bisectors of a triangle intersect in a point.

10. Show that the equation of a plane can be written

$$(\mathbf{r} - \mathbf{r}_0)\cdot\hat{\imath} = 0.$$

Interpret $\hat{\imath}$, and show that this equation is equivalent to that of problem 12, Section 2.2.

11. Find the shortest distances from the origin to the line

$$\mathbf{r} = \mathbf{r}_0 + \lambda\hat{\imath}$$

and to the plane

$$(\mathbf{r} - \mathbf{r}_0)\cdot\hat{\imath} = 0.$$

12. Find the shortest distances from the point $\mathbf{r}_1$ to the line and plane of problem 11.

13. Interpret the equation

$$(\mathbf{r} - \mathbf{r}_0)^2 = a^2,$$

where $\mathbf{r}$ is a variable vector.

2.4 The Vector Product

To rotate from a vector **a** to another vector **b**, the right-handed convention is adopted, so that a unique direction is associated with the rotation, as shown in Figure 2.6. Let this direction be $\hat{\imath}$; then the *vector* or "cross" product is defined by

$$\mathbf{a} \times \mathbf{b} = (ab \sin \theta)\hat{\imath}, \tag{2.4.1}$$

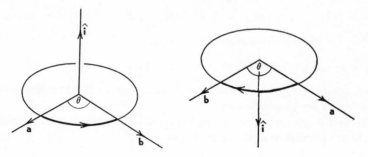

Figure 2.6

where θ is the angle between them. The order is important because, from the definition, it follows that

$$\mathbf{a} \times \mathbf{b} = -\mathbf{b} \times \mathbf{a}$$

so that the vector product is not commutative. (Notation for the vector product differs, but the symbol " $\times$ " seems to be nearly universal now. The author regrets the passing of the notation $\mathbf{a}_\wedge \mathbf{b}$ which is much safer than $\mathbf{a} \times \mathbf{b}$, since $\times$ has so many uses; in particular it is fatally easy to start to treat $\times$ as a variable!)

The distributive law does hold; i.e.,

$$\mathbf{a} \times (\mathbf{b} + \mathbf{c}) = \mathbf{a} \times \mathbf{b} + \mathbf{a} \times \mathbf{c}.$$

There are several proofs of this, all of which require careful reasoning. The proof given here is based on that given in Rutherford's *Vector Methods* (Ref. 14).

Let a plane perpendicular to $\mathbf{a}$ be called π, and let the projections of $\mathbf{b}$ and $\mathbf{c}$ on π be $\mathbf{b}'$ and $\mathbf{c}'$. Then the projection of $(\mathbf{b} + \mathbf{c})$ on π is $(\mathbf{b}' + \mathbf{c}')$. Now the length of $\mathbf{b}'$ is $b \sin \theta$, where θ is the angle between $\mathbf{a}$ and $\mathbf{b}$; so we have

$$\mathbf{a} \times \mathbf{b}' = \mathbf{a} \times \mathbf{b}$$

and similarly,

$$\mathbf{a} \times \mathbf{c}' = \mathbf{a} \times \mathbf{c} \quad \text{and} \quad \mathbf{a} \times (\mathbf{b}' + \mathbf{c}') = \mathbf{a} \times (\mathbf{b} + \mathbf{c}).$$

Now $\mathbf{a}$ is perpendicular to $\mathbf{b}'$, so $\mathbf{a} \times \mathbf{b}'$ lies in π and is a times the length of $\mathbf{b}'$. Similarly, $\mathbf{a} \times \mathbf{c}'$ lies in π and is a times the length of $\mathbf{c}'$. Then it follows that $(\mathbf{a} \times \mathbf{b}' + \mathbf{a} \times \mathbf{c}')$ lies in π, is a times the length of $(\mathbf{b}' + \mathbf{c}')$, and is perpendicular to $(\mathbf{b}' + \mathbf{c}')$. Then

$$\mathbf{a} \times \mathbf{b}' + \mathbf{a} \times \mathbf{c}' = \mathbf{a} \times (\mathbf{b}' + \mathbf{c}'),$$

from which the result follows.

It is important to remember that

$$\mathbf{r} \times \mathbf{r} = 0$$

and that if $\hat{\mathbf{i}}$, $\hat{\mathbf{j}}$, and $\hat{\mathbf{k}}$ form the conventional right-handed rectangular triad, then

$$\hat{\mathbf{j}} \times \hat{\mathbf{k}} = \hat{\mathbf{i}}, \qquad \hat{\mathbf{k}} \times \hat{\mathbf{i}} = \hat{\mathbf{j}}, \qquad \hat{\mathbf{i}} \times \hat{\mathbf{j}} = \hat{\mathbf{k}}, \quad \text{and} \quad \hat{\mathbf{k}} \times \hat{\mathbf{j}} = -\hat{\mathbf{i}}, \text{ etc.}$$

It follows from this and from the distributive law that if the components of $\mathbf{b}$ and $\mathbf{c}$ are (b_x, b_y, b_z) and (c_x, c_y, c_z), then

$$\mathbf{b} \times \mathbf{c} = (b_y c_z - b_z c_y, \quad b_z c_x - b_x c_z, \quad b_x c_y - b_y c_x)$$

or, in determinant notation,

$$\mathbf{b} \times \mathbf{c} = \begin{vmatrix} \hat{\mathbf{i}} & \hat{\mathbf{j}} & \hat{\mathbf{k}} \\ b_x & b_y & b_z \\ c_x & c_y & c_z \end{vmatrix}. \tag{2.4.2}$$

The *triple scalar product* is defined by $\mathbf{a} \cdot (\mathbf{b} \times \mathbf{c})$, and is often written as $[\mathbf{a}, \mathbf{b}, \mathbf{c}]$. If $\mathbf{a} = (a_x, a_y, a_z)$, then by (2.4.2),

$$[\mathbf{a}, \mathbf{b}, \mathbf{c}] = \begin{vmatrix} a_x & a_y & a_z \\ b_x & b_y & b_z \\ c_x & c_y & c_z \end{vmatrix}. \tag{2.4.3}$$

Students familiar with solid geometry will recognize from its determinant form that the triple scalar product is equal to the volume of the parallepiped with edges **a**, **b**, and **c**. A simple proof of this follows. In the notation of Figure 2.7 we have

$$\mathbf{b} \times \mathbf{c} = bc \sin \theta \, \hat{\mathbf{p}},$$

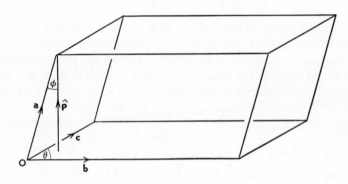

Figure 2.7

where $\hat{\mathbf{p}}$ is the unit vector perpendicular to **b** and **c**, as shown. Then

$$
\begin{aligned}
[\mathbf{a,b,c}] &= bc \sin \theta \hat{\mathbf{p}} \cdot \mathbf{a} \\
&= bc \sin \theta \, a \cos \phi \\
&= \text{area of base times the perpendicular height} \\
&= \text{the volume of the parallepiped.}
\end{aligned}
$$

It follows from this or from the properties of determinants that

$$[\mathbf{a,b,c}] = [\mathbf{b,c,a}] = [\mathbf{c,a,b}] = -[\mathbf{c,b,a}] = -[\mathbf{a,c,b}] = -[\mathbf{b,a,c}],$$

and that the triple scalar product of three nonzero vectors vanishes if any two are parallel or antiparallel or if all three vectors lie in a plane.

The *triple* or *continued vector product* is

$$\mathbf{a} \times (\mathbf{b} \times \mathbf{c})$$

in which the inclusion of parentheses is essential. It can be shown (most simply, if not most elegantly, by resolving the vectors) that

$$\mathbf{a} \times (\mathbf{b} \times \mathbf{c}) = (\mathbf{a \cdot c})\mathbf{b} - (\mathbf{a \cdot b})\mathbf{c}. \tag{2.4.4}$$

This formula is important and should be memorized.

Let P be any point on the line of action of a vector **Q**, and let **OP** $=$ **r**. Then the *moment* of **Q** about **O** is **r** $\times$ **Q**. The student should verify that this is independent of the position of P along **Q**.

It is important that the student should get the feel of the vector product, for it is largely through this that vectors have such considerable practical use. Various uses of the product will appear shortly, but one will be pointed out now. If a vector equation contains some term that the student does not like, he has only to multiply vectorially by its direction to eliminate it. For instance, the general equation of motion for a central orbit has the form

$$\frac{d^2\mathbf{r}}{dt^2} = -f\hat{\mathbf{r}}, \qquad (2.4.5)$$

where f is some scalar function. Vectorial multiplication by $\mathbf{r}$ gives

$$\mathbf{r} \times \frac{d^2\mathbf{r}}{dt^2} = 0, \qquad (2.4.6)$$

which yields an important integral for any central orbit. Another example of the elimination of unwanted terms occurs in a consideration of the equation of the plane. This may be put in the form

$$\mathbf{r} = \mathbf{r}_0 + \lambda\hat{\mathbf{a}} + \mu\hat{\mathbf{b}}, \qquad (2.4.7)$$

where $\mathbf{r}_0$ is any point in the plane and $\hat{\mathbf{a}}$ and $\hat{\mathbf{b}}$ lie in the plane. λ and μ are variable scalars that can be eliminated by scalar multiplication by $\hat{\mathbf{a}} \times \hat{\mathbf{b}}$. Then we have

$$(\mathbf{r} - \mathbf{r}_0)\cdot(\hat{\mathbf{a}} \times \hat{\mathbf{b}}) = 0. \qquad (2.4.8)$$

Problems

1. Let $\hat{\mathbf{i}}$ point toward the vernal equinox, $\hat{\mathbf{k}}$ toward the celestial north pole, $\hat{\mathbf{m}}$ toward the summer solstice, and $\hat{\mathbf{n}}$ toward the north pole of the ecliptic. Express $\hat{\mathbf{i}}$ in terms of $\hat{\mathbf{n}}$ and $\hat{\mathbf{k}}$; $\hat{\mathbf{m}}$ in terms of $\hat{\mathbf{n}}$ and $\hat{\mathbf{k}}$; $\hat{\mathbf{n}}$ in terms of $\hat{\mathbf{i}}$ and $\hat{\mathbf{k}}$; $\hat{\mathbf{k}}$ in terms of $\hat{\mathbf{i}}$ and $\hat{\mathbf{n}}$.
2. Prove the formula for the triple vector product.
3. If $\mathbf{a} + \mathbf{b} + \mathbf{c} = 0$, prove that

$$\mathbf{b} \times \mathbf{c} = \mathbf{c} \times \mathbf{a} = \mathbf{a} \times \mathbf{b},$$

and interpret geometrically.
4. What is the locus of $\mathbf{r}$ such that $[\mathbf{r},\mathbf{a},\mathbf{b}] = 0$?
5. If l, m, and n are three nonzero scalars, and

$$l\mathbf{a} + m\mathbf{b} + n\mathbf{c} = 0,$$

prove that $\mathbf{a}$, $\mathbf{b}$, and $\mathbf{c}$ are coplanar. If also

$$l'\mathbf{a} + m'\mathbf{b} + n'\mathbf{c} = 0,$$

prove that

$$\frac{l}{l'} = \frac{m}{m'} = \frac{n}{n'}.$$

6. If x, a, and b are coplanar, show that usually x can be expressed as

$$x = \lambda a + \mu b.$$

What is the exception to this?

7. Evaluate $(a + b) \times (a - b)$.

8. Choosing simple (but not trivial) numerical values for the components of a, b, and c, verify numerically that

$$a \cdot (b + c) = a \cdot b + a \cdot c, \qquad a \times (b + c) = a \times b + a \times c,$$
$$a \times (b \times c) = (a \cdot c)b - (a \cdot b)c.$$

Find the values of

$$|a \times c|, \quad [a,b,c], \quad (a \times b) \times c, \quad (a \times b) \cdot (a \times c), \quad (a \times b) \times (a \times c).$$

9. Find the equation to the plane through a, b, and c.

10. Prove that $(a \times b) \cdot (c \times d) = (b \cdot d)(c \cdot a) - (b \cdot c)(d \cdot a)$.

11. Prove that

$$(a \times b) \times (c \times d) = [a,b,d]c - [a,b,c]d$$
$$= (c \times d) \times (b \times a)$$
$$= [c,d,a]b - [c,d,b]a.$$

Hence show that

$$[a,b,c]d = [d,b,c]a + [a,d,c]b + [a,b,d]c$$

and deduce the conditions for the unique resolution of the vector d along the three directions a, b, and c.

12. Show that

$$[a,b,c](f \times g) = \begin{vmatrix} a & b & c \\ f \cdot a & f \cdot b & f \cdot c \\ g \cdot a & g \cdot b & g \cdot c \end{vmatrix}.$$

Hence, generalize equation (2.4.2).

13. Solve for X the equation $\quad X \times a = b$, $\quad$ where $a \cdot b = 0$.

14. Solve the equation $\quad X + a(X \cdot b) = c$. $\quad$ (Try $\cdot b$.)

15. Solve the simultaneous equations

$$\alpha X + \beta Y = a \quad \text{and} \quad X \times Y = b, \qquad \text{where } a \cdot b = 0.$$

16. Solve the equation $\quad X \times a + (X \cdot b)c = d$.

2.5 The Velocity of a Vector

A vector can vary as a function of a scalar, such as time, or as a function of another vector, such as position. Provided that the variation is suitably continuous (and this will normally be taken for granted), the vector can be differentiated. Here we shall mostly be considering vectors that vary with time, and the subject of differentiation will be approached in relation to the kinematics of a particle.

Let AB represent the path of a particle P, and let P and P' be positions of the particle at times t and $t + \delta t$. δt is a small time interval, and the arc PP' can be considered as linear because we are shortly to take the limit $\delta t \rightarrow 0$.

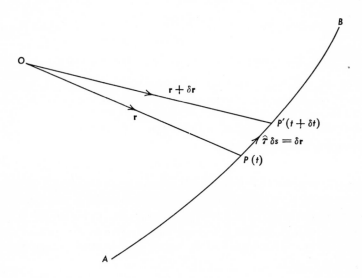

Figure 2.8

Choose any origin O, and let $\mathbf{OP} = \mathbf{r}$ and $\mathbf{OP}' = \mathbf{r} + \delta\mathbf{r}$, so that $\mathbf{PP}' = \delta\mathbf{r}$. Let $\hat{\boldsymbol{\tau}}$ be the unit vector along $\mathbf{PP}'$; in the limit, this will be the tangent at P. Then

$$\delta\mathbf{r} = \hat{\boldsymbol{\tau}}\,\delta s$$

where s is distance measured along the curve. Taking the limit we have

$$\lim_{\delta t \to 0} \frac{\mathbf{PP}'}{\delta t} = \lim_{\delta t \to 0} \frac{\delta\mathbf{r}}{\delta t} = \frac{d\mathbf{r}}{dt} = \hat{\boldsymbol{\tau}}\frac{ds}{dt}.$$

This is the *velocity* of the particle at P. It may also be written $\dot{\mathbf{r}}$ or $\mathbf{v}$. It has magnitude and direction, but we have to show that it obeys the vector law of addition, in order to establish that it is a vector.

Let P have its position changed in time δt by two increments, $\delta_1\mathbf{r}$ and $\delta_2\mathbf{r}$. These are vectors, so that the total displacement is $\delta\mathbf{r} = \delta_1\mathbf{r} + \delta_2\mathbf{r}$. Dividing by δt and taking the limit, we get

$$\frac{d\mathbf{r}}{dt} = \frac{d\mathbf{r}_1}{dt} + \frac{d\mathbf{r}_2}{dt},$$

which can be written as

$$\mathbf{v} = \mathbf{v}_1 + \mathbf{v}_2.$$

This is the required result.

The components of $\dot{\mathbf{r}}$ are $(\dot{x}, \dot{y}, \dot{z})$, and those of $\hat{\mathbf{t}}$ are $(dx/ds, dy/ds, dz/ds)$.

It is convenient to adopt the modern convention of using "velocity" only as the vector $\mathbf{v}$, and "speed" as the scalar value of the velocity. Thus the speed of P is $\dfrac{ds}{dt}$.

It is very important to realize that $\left|\dfrac{d\mathbf{r}}{dt}\right|$, or $|\dot{\mathbf{r}}|$, is not in general the same as $\dfrac{d|\mathbf{r}|}{dt}$, or $\dfrac{dr}{dt}$, or $\dot{r}$. The former is the speed of P, while the latter is only the component of the velocity of P along the radius vector: in general there will also be a *transverse* component of velocity, at right angles to the radius vector. We have

$$\mathbf{r} \cdot \mathbf{r} = r^2.$$

Differentiating each side, we get

$$\mathbf{r} \cdot \dot{\mathbf{r}} = r\dot{r}, \tag{2.5.1}$$

an important relation that will be used frequently in this text.

$\mathbf{r}$ is a position vector and the path traced out by P is the locus (or orbit, for our purposes) of P. $\dot{\mathbf{r}}$ is a localized vector, but if we let $\mathbf{OQ} = \dot{\mathbf{r}}$, then Q traces out a path called the *hodograph* of the motion. The rate of change of $\mathbf{OQ}$ measures the acceleration of P, which is a vector. It may be written $d^2\mathbf{r}/dt^2$, or $d\mathbf{v}/dt$, or $\ddot{\mathbf{r}}$.

In Figure 2.8 consider the product $\mathbf{OP} \times \mathbf{OP}' = \mathbf{r} \times \delta\mathbf{r}$. The modulus is equal to twice the area of the triangle OPP', and the rate of change of this area is the *areal velocity* of OP. The areal velocity is therefore

$$\tfrac{1}{2}|\mathbf{r} \times \dot{\mathbf{r}}|.$$

The direction of $\mathbf{r} \times \dot{\mathbf{r}}$ is perpendicular to the plane containing $\mathbf{r}$ and $\dot{\mathbf{r}}$. If the motion takes place in a plane, then this direction is constant. Consider Kepler's first two laws: the first specifies motion in a plane for a planet, and the second states that the areal velocity is constant. So, for Keplerian motion, we have

$$\mathbf{r} \times \dot{\mathbf{r}} = \mathbf{h}, \tag{2.5.2}$$

where $\mathbf{h}$ is a constant vector. The student should note that (2.5.2) is the first integral of (2.4.6) and that this means that the acceleration is entirely directed along $\hat{\mathbf{r}}$.

Problems

1. Solve the following equations of motion, and interpret their solutions:

(a) $\dot{\mathbf{r}} = \mathbf{a}$; (b) $\ddot{\mathbf{r}} = \mathbf{b}$; (c) $\mathbf{r} \cdot \dot{\mathbf{r}} = 0$; (d) $\mathbf{r} \cdot \dot{\mathbf{r}} = c$; (e) $|\dot{\mathbf{r}}| = \dot{r}$; (f) $\mathbf{r} \times \ddot{\mathbf{r}} = 0$; (g) $\dot{\mathbf{r}} = \mathbf{r} \times \ddot{\mathbf{r}}$.

2. Show that $\dfrac{d(a\mathbf{r})}{dt} = \mathbf{r}\dfrac{da}{dt} + a\dfrac{d\mathbf{r}}{dt}$.

3. Show that $\dfrac{d(\mathbf{a}\cdot\mathbf{b})}{dt} = \mathbf{a}\cdot\dfrac{d\mathbf{b}}{dt} + \mathbf{b}\cdot\dfrac{d\mathbf{a}}{dt}$.

4. Show that $\dfrac{d(\mathbf{a}\times\mathbf{b})}{dt} = \mathbf{a}\times\dfrac{d\mathbf{b}}{dt} + \dfrac{d\mathbf{a}}{dt}\times\mathbf{b}$.

5. Describe the hodograph of uniform circular motion with radius a and speed v. Hence show that the acceleration is (v^2/a) directed toward the center.

6. A particle describes an equiangular spiral with constant areal velocity A. Show that for the motion $r\dot{r} = 2A\cot\theta$, where θ is the (constant) angle between the radius vector and the tangent, and solve this equation to show how r varies with the time.

2.6 Angular Velocity

A vector can change its direction as well as its modulus, so that it is possible to differentiate a unit vector, $\hat{\imath}$, say. Let $\hat{\imath}$ be rotated through a small angle, $\delta\theta$, the new vector being $\hat{\imath} + \delta\hat{\imath}$. Since this must still be a unit vector, $\hat{\imath}\cdot\delta\hat{\imath} = 0$.

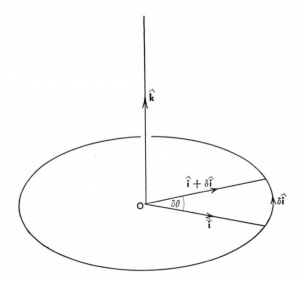

Figure 2.9

(Squares of small quantities, such as $\delta\hat{\imath}^2$, are, of course, neglected.) Let the direction of the rotation, taken in the right-handed sense, be $\hat{\mathbf{k}}$. Then the direction of $\delta\hat{\imath}$ is $\hat{\mathbf{k}}\times\hat{\imath}$ and its length is $\delta\theta$, so

$$\delta\hat{\imath} = \delta\theta\,\hat{\mathbf{k}}\times\hat{\imath},$$

and

$$\frac{d\hat{\imath}}{dt} = \left(\hat{k}\, \frac{d\theta}{dt} \right) \times \hat{\imath}$$

$$= \boldsymbol{\omega} \times \hat{\imath},$$

where $\boldsymbol{\omega}$ is an *angular velocity*. It is useful to remember that the derivative of a unit vector is always perpendicular to that vector.

More generally, let $\mathbf{OP} = \mathbf{r}$ be any vector, making an angle θ with $\hat{k}$, the axis of rotation. Then, since P is at a distance $r \sin \theta$ from $\hat{k}$, the rate of change of $\mathbf{r}$ due *solely* to the angular velocity $\boldsymbol{\omega}$ is $\boldsymbol{\omega} \times \mathbf{r}$.

$\boldsymbol{\omega}$ has magnitude and direction. To show that it is a vector, we must prove that it obeys the vector addition law. Suppose $\mathbf{r}$ to be subjected to two infinitesimal rotations, $\delta\theta_1$ about $\hat{k}_1$ and $\delta\theta_2$ about $\hat{k}_2$. Taking these in order, we have $\mathbf{r}$ becoming first

$$\mathbf{r} + \delta\mathbf{r}_1 = \mathbf{r} + \delta\theta_1\, \hat{k}_1 \times \mathbf{r}$$

and then

$$\mathbf{r} + \delta\mathbf{r}_{12} = (\mathbf{r} + \delta\theta_1 \hat{k}_1 \times \mathbf{r}) + \delta\theta_2 \hat{k}_2 \times (\mathbf{r} + \delta\theta_1 \hat{k}_1 \times \mathbf{r}).$$

Neglecting the second order small quantity $\delta\theta_1\, \delta\theta_2$ (this is all right since we are to take a limit; it is this step which is not possible when dealing with finite rotations), we have

$$\delta\mathbf{r}_{12} = \delta\theta_1\, \hat{k}_1 \times \mathbf{r} + \delta\theta_2\, \hat{k}_2 \times \mathbf{r} = \delta\mathbf{r}_{21},$$

showing that infinitesimal rotations are commutative. Dividing by δt and taking the limit, we see that the same is true for angular velocities. If

$$\hat{k}_1 \frac{d\theta_1}{dt} = \boldsymbol{\omega}_1 \quad \text{and} \quad \hat{k}_2 \frac{d\theta_2}{dt} = \boldsymbol{\omega}_2,$$

then

$$\dot{\mathbf{r}} = (\boldsymbol{\omega}_1 + \boldsymbol{\omega}_2) \times \mathbf{r},$$

so that the effect is the same as that produced by a single angular velocity $(\boldsymbol{\omega}_1 + \boldsymbol{\omega}_2)$. Hence angular velocities are vectors; they can be added according to the vector law and they can also be resolved.

Problems

1. Find expressions for the modulus and direction of the angular velocity of the mean Sun.

2. Find the angular velocity of the apparent Sun, assuming that the Earth's orbit is circular, with constant angular velocity. Resolve this angular velocity along an equatorial system of axes and hence find the components of the Sun's motion on the celestial sphere along these axes.

Compare the component in right ascension with the angular velocity of the mean Sun.

3. Assuming the Earth to be fixed and the celestial sphere (of unit radius) to be rotating around the Earth, consider the apparent motion of the stars as seen by an observer at latitude l. If $\hat{\mathbf{z}}$ points to the observer's zenith (the direction vertically above him), resolve the motion of a star at declination δ along and at right angles to $\hat{\mathbf{z}}$.

2.7 Rotating Axes

Writing $\mathbf{r} = r\hat{\mathbf{r}}$ and differentiating, we have

$$\dot{\mathbf{r}} = \dot{r}\hat{\mathbf{r}} + r\frac{d\hat{\mathbf{r}}}{dt}. \tag{2.7.1}$$

This expresses $\dot{\mathbf{r}}$ as the sum of two vectors, one along and one perpendicular to $\mathbf{r}$. The first gives the rate of change of the length of $\mathbf{r}$, and the second can be considered as being due to a rotation.

Frequently (as on the Earth) we observe phenomena with respect to rotating axes. Suppose a vector $\mathbf{r}$ to be observed to have rates of change $\dfrac{d\mathbf{r}}{dt}$ with respect to a fixed frame of reference F_1, and $\dfrac{\partial\mathbf{r}}{\partial t}$ with respect to a frame F_2, rotating with respect to F_1 with angular velocity $\boldsymbol{\omega}$, which need not be constant. The formula (2.7.1) applies to a simple case of this, where the axes of F_2 are rotating with $\mathbf{r}$, so that $\dfrac{\partial\mathbf{r}}{\partial t}$ can be written instead of $\dot{r}\hat{\mathbf{r}}$. Then (2.7.1) can be written in the form

$$\frac{d\mathbf{r}}{dt} = \frac{\partial\mathbf{r}}{\partial t} + \boldsymbol{\omega} \times \mathbf{r}. \tag{2.7.2}$$

This is a general result, as we shall now show.

Let $\hat{\mathbf{i}}$, $\hat{\mathbf{j}}$, and $\hat{\mathbf{k}}$ form an orthogonal triad rigidly attached to F_2; then

$$\mathbf{r} = \sum (\mathbf{r}\cdot\hat{\mathbf{i}})\hat{\mathbf{i}},$$

where the summation is over $\hat{\mathbf{i}}$, $\hat{\mathbf{j}}$, and $\hat{\mathbf{k}}$. Then

$$\frac{d\mathbf{r}}{dt} = \sum \left\{\frac{d(\mathbf{r}\cdot\hat{\mathbf{i}})}{dt}\,\hat{\mathbf{i}}\right\} + \sum \left\{(\mathbf{r}\cdot\hat{\mathbf{i}})\,\frac{d\hat{\mathbf{i}}}{dt}\right\}.$$

But

$$\frac{d\hat{\mathbf{i}}}{dt} = \boldsymbol{\omega} \times \hat{\mathbf{i}},$$

so

$$\sum \left\{ (\mathbf{r} \cdot \hat{\mathbf{i}}) \frac{d\hat{\mathbf{i}}}{dt} \right\} = \boldsymbol{\omega} \times \sum (\mathbf{r} \cdot \hat{\mathbf{i}}) \hat{\mathbf{i}}$$

$$= \boldsymbol{\omega} \times \mathbf{r}.$$

To find $\dfrac{\partial \mathbf{r}}{\partial t}$ we treat $\hat{\mathbf{i}}$, $\hat{\mathbf{j}}$, and $\hat{\mathbf{k}}$ as constant vectors, so that

$$\frac{\partial \mathbf{r}}{\partial t} = \sum \left\{ \frac{d(\mathbf{r} \cdot \hat{\mathbf{i}})}{dt} \hat{\mathbf{i}} \right\}.$$

Hence (2.7.2) follows at once. It may be written in the notation of operators as

$$\frac{d}{dt} = \frac{\partial}{\partial t} + \boldsymbol{\omega} \times. \tag{2.7.3}$$

As an illustration of the use of this formula we shall find the components of velocity and acceleration in polar coordinates. Here $\mathbf{OP} = \mathbf{r}$ makes an angle θ with some fixed direction. Let $\hat{\mathbf{i}}$ point in the *radial* direction (along $\mathbf{OP}$) and $\hat{\mathbf{j}}$ in the *transverse* direction (i.e., in the direction of increasing θ), and let $\hat{\mathbf{i}} \times \hat{\mathbf{j}} = \hat{\mathbf{k}}$. (See Figure 2.10.) Then the angular velocity of $\mathbf{OP}$ is $\dot{\theta}\hat{\mathbf{k}}$, and

$$\frac{d\mathbf{r}}{dt} = \dot{r}\hat{\mathbf{i}} + r\dot{\theta}\hat{\mathbf{j}}. \tag{2.7.4}$$

This gives the radial and transverse components of velocity. Similarly,

$$\begin{aligned}
\frac{d^2\mathbf{r}}{dt^2} &= \left(\frac{d}{dt} \right) (\dot{r}\hat{\mathbf{i}} + r\dot{\theta}\hat{\mathbf{j}}) \\
&= \left(\frac{\partial}{\partial t} + \dot{\theta}\hat{\mathbf{k}} \times \right) (\dot{r}\hat{\mathbf{i}} + r\dot{\theta}\hat{\mathbf{j}}) \\
&= \ddot{r}\hat{\mathbf{i}} + (\dot{r}\dot{\theta} + r\ddot{\theta})\hat{\mathbf{j}} + \dot{\theta}\hat{\mathbf{k}} \times (\dot{r}\hat{\mathbf{i}} + r\dot{\theta}\hat{\mathbf{j}}) \\
&= (\ddot{r} - r\dot{\theta}^2)\hat{\mathbf{i}} + (r\ddot{\theta} + 2\dot{r}\dot{\theta})\hat{\mathbf{j}}. \tag{2.7.5}
\end{aligned}$$

This formula, which should be memorized, gives the radial and transverse components of acceleration. The transverse component can be written as

$$\frac{1}{r} \frac{d}{dt} (r^2 \dot{\theta}).$$

The term in the parentheses is easily verified to be twice the areal velocity of P.

Consider the situation when a particle travels in a circle with constant speed. Taking the center of the circle as origin, we have

$$\frac{d^2\mathbf{r}}{dt^2} = -r\dot{\theta}^2\hat{\mathbf{i}}.$$

This acceleration is a consequence of the kinematics of the particle. If an observer is moving round with the particle, and, through ignorance or prejudice or for convenience, he likes to work in terms of the kinematics with respect to his rotating axes, then he will be unable to account for what he observes unless he applies to every particle a "centrifugal acceleration" $r^2\dot{\theta}\hat{\imath}$. Alternatively he can introduce a fictitious force, the "centrifugal force", which would produce this acceleration.

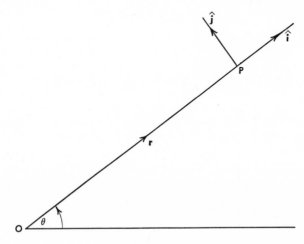

Figure 2.10

As an example of its application consider a conical pendulum consisting of a mass m at P suspended from O by a light string of length r, and traveling in a circle with constant angular velocity about the vertical, such that OP makes a constant angle ϕ with the vertical. The radius of the circle is $r \sin \phi$, so that the centrifugal force C, acting as shown in Figure 2.11 (see page 34) is equal to $mr \sin \phi \, \dot{\theta}^2$, where $\dot{\theta}$ is the angular velocity of P about the vertical. With this force included, the problem becomes one of statics. Resolving the forces at right angles to the string (to eliminate the tension), we have

$$mg \sin \phi = C \cos \phi = mr \sin \phi \cos \phi \, \dot{\theta}^2,$$

so

$$\dot{\theta}^2 = \frac{g}{r \cos \phi}.$$

As another illustration of the use of equation (2.7.3) consider the motion observed from a point fixed on the surface of the Earth. Let C be the center of the Earth, and let a man at O be observing the motion of a point P. Let $\mathbf{CO} = \mathbf{r}_0$ and $\mathbf{OP} = \mathbf{r}$; usually r is small compared with r_0. Let the angular velocity of the Earth be $\omega\hat{\mathbf{z}}$. The velocity of P with respect to nonrotating axes is

$$\frac{d\mathbf{P}}{dt} = \frac{d}{dt}(\mathbf{r}_0 + \mathbf{r})$$

$$= \frac{\partial \mathbf{r}}{\partial t} + \omega\hat{\mathbf{z}} \times \mathbf{r}_0 + \omega\hat{\mathbf{z}} \times \mathbf{r}.$$

The acceleration of P is

$$\frac{d^2\mathbf{P}}{dt^2} = \left(\frac{\partial}{\partial t} + \omega\hat{\mathbf{z}} \times\right)\frac{d\mathbf{P}}{dt}$$

$$= \frac{\partial^2\mathbf{r}}{\partial t^2} + 2\omega\hat{\mathbf{z}} \times \frac{\partial \mathbf{r}}{\partial t} + \omega^2\hat{\mathbf{z}} \times (\hat{\mathbf{z}} \times \mathbf{r}_0) + \omega^2\hat{\mathbf{z}} \times (\hat{\mathbf{z}} \times \mathbf{r}).$$

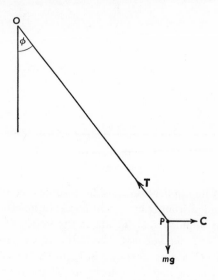

Figure 2.11

The usual equation of motion of P will contain $d^2\mathbf{P}/dt^2$ and terms dealing with the forces acting on P. If the equation is considered in terms of $\partial^2\mathbf{P}/\partial t^2$, or $\partial^2\mathbf{r}/\partial t^2$, or in terms of what the man at O observes, then we can replace $d^2\mathbf{P}/dt^2$ on one side of the equation by $\partial^2\mathbf{P}/\partial t^2$, provided we add the terms

$$-2\omega\hat{\mathbf{z}} \times \frac{\partial \mathbf{r}}{\partial t} - \omega^2\hat{\mathbf{z}} \times (\hat{\mathbf{z}} \times \mathbf{r}_0) - \omega^2\hat{\mathbf{z}} \times (\hat{\mathbf{z}} \times \mathbf{r}) \qquad (2.7.6)$$

to the other side, among the terms dealing with the forces acting on P. (Usually the last two terms can be neglected, since ω is small.) Again, the terms in

(2.7.6) can be interpreted as being due to fictitious forces: this time they are known as *Coriolis forces*. An example concerning them will be given in Section 3.5.

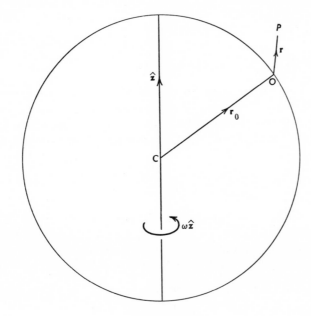

Figure 2.12

Problems

1. What conditions are necessary for $\ddot{r} = |\ddot{\mathbf{r}}|$?
2. If P moves in a plane and its areal velocity about O is constant, show that the transverse acceleration of P is zero.
3. Solve the simultaneous equations

$$\ddot{r} - r\dot{\theta}^2 = 0 \quad \text{and} \quad 2\dot{r}\dot{\theta} + r\ddot{\theta} = 0.$$

What can be deduced from these?

4. A particle moves in an ellipse with semiaxes a and b, with constant areal velocity A about the center of the ellipse. Find the components of its velocity and acceleration in Cartesian and polar coordinates. Find also the period of the orbit.

2.8 The Gradient of a Scalar

Consider a scalar function of position. This may be written $f(x,y,z)$ or $f(\mathbf{r})$. We shall suppose that it is defined and is continuous within the region of space with which we are concerned. If we move from (x,y,z) to $(x + \delta x, y, z)$, the change in f can be written $(\partial f/\partial x)\delta x$, where now $\partial/\partial x$ represents conventional partial differentiation with respect to x, so that for this differentiation, y and z are assumed to be constant. This could be written in the form

$$\frac{\partial f}{\partial x}\,\delta x = \left(\frac{\partial f}{\partial x}\,\hat{\mathbf{i}} + \frac{\partial f}{\partial y}\,\hat{\mathbf{j}} + \frac{\partial f}{\partial z}\,\hat{\mathbf{k}}\right)\cdot\hat{\mathbf{i}}\,\delta x$$

$$= \nabla f\cdot\hat{\mathbf{i}}\,\delta x, \quad\text{say.}$$

Similarly, a change from (x,y,z) to $(x, y + \delta y, z)$ produces a change in f of $\nabla f\cdot\hat{\mathbf{j}}\,\delta y$, and a change from $\mathbf{r}$ to $\mathbf{r} + \delta\mathbf{r}$ produces a change $\nabla f\cdot\delta\mathbf{r}$.

The vector with components $(\partial f/\partial x, \partial f/\partial y, \partial f/\partial z)$ is called the *gradient* of f. It is written as "grad f" or "∇f"; the symbol "∇" is called "Nabla" or "Del." Since

$$\frac{\partial}{\partial x}\,(f_1 + f_2) = \frac{\partial f_1}{\partial x} + \frac{\partial f_2}{\partial x}$$

there is no difficulty in establishing that ∇f obeys the vector law of addition; hence it is definitely a vector.

Consider a curve C and the values that f takes along this curve. The rate of change of f along C with respect to arc length s is

$$\frac{df}{ds} = \frac{\partial f}{\partial x}\cdot\frac{dx}{ds} + \frac{\partial f}{\partial y}\cdot\frac{dy}{ds} + \frac{\partial f}{\partial z}\cdot\frac{dz}{ds}$$

$$= \hat{\boldsymbol{\tau}}\cdot\nabla f, \tag{2.8.1}$$

from Section 2.5. Consider a surface with equation $f(x,y,z) = \text{constant}$. Along any line on the surface $df/ds = 0$, so that $\hat{\boldsymbol{\tau}}\cdot\nabla f = 0$. Therefore ∇f is perpendicular to the surface.

∇f is an example of a *field vector*; i.e., a vector that is a function of position.

Problems

1. Prove that $\nabla r^n = n\mathbf{r}r^{n-2}$.
2. Show that the components of ∇ in two-dimensional polar coordinates are

$$\frac{\partial}{\partial r} \quad\text{and}\quad \frac{1}{r}\cdot\frac{\partial}{\partial\theta}.$$

3. Find the components of ∇ in cylindrical coordinates (r,ϕ,z) and in spherical polar coordinates (r,θ,ϕ).
4. If f and g are scalar functions of $\mathbf{r}$, show that

$$\nabla\left(\frac{f}{g}\right) = \frac{g\nabla f - f\nabla g}{g^2}.$$

2.9 Spherical Trigonometry

We conclude this chapter with a short account of basic spherical trigonometry approached through vectors.

Spherical trigonometry is set on the surface of a sphere that is assumed to have unit radius. All lines with which we are concerned are portions of great circles. If two points are not at opposite ends of a diameter, then there is one and only one great circle passing through them. A spherical triangle ABC is defined by three points on the surface of the sphere, the sides of the triangle being the appropriate parts of the great circles through the points. If O is the center of the sphere,

$$\angle BOC = a, \qquad \angle COA = b \quad \text{and} \quad \angle AOB = c.$$

The angle between the planes AOB and AOC is A, and B and C are similarly defined.

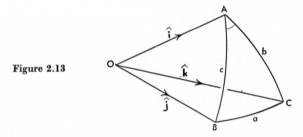

Figure 2.13

Let $\hat{\imath}$, $\hat{\jmath}$, and $\hat{k}$ be the unit vectors (not mutually perpendicular) along **OA**, **OB**, and **OC**. ($\hat{\imath} \times \hat{\jmath}$) is a vector with magnitude $\sin c$ and direction perpendicular to the plane AOB. Similarly, ($\hat{\imath} \times \hat{k}$) has magnitude $\sin b$ and direction perpendicular to the plane AOC. So the angle between these two vectors is A. Hence

$$(\hat{\imath} \times \hat{\jmath}) \cdot (\hat{\imath} \times \hat{k}) = \sin b \sin c \cos A.$$

But

$$(\hat{\imath} \times \hat{\jmath}) \cdot (\hat{\imath} \times \hat{k}) = \hat{\imath} \cdot [\hat{\jmath} \times (\hat{\imath} \times \hat{k})]$$

$$= \hat{\imath} \cdot [\hat{\imath}(\hat{\jmath} \cdot \hat{k}) - \hat{k}(\hat{\imath} \cdot \hat{\jmath})]$$

$$= (\hat{\jmath} \cdot \hat{k}) - (\hat{\imath} \cdot \hat{k})(\hat{\imath} \cdot \hat{\jmath})$$

$$= \cos a - \cos c \cos b.$$

Hence

$$\cos a = \cos b \cos c + \sin b \sin c \cos A. \qquad (2.9.1)$$

By the definition of the vector product,

$$\sin A = \frac{|(\hat{\imath} \times \hat{\jmath}) \times (\hat{\imath} \times \hat{k})|}{|\hat{\imath} \times \hat{\jmath}||\hat{\imath} \times \hat{k}|}$$

$$= \frac{|-\hat{\imath}[\hat{\jmath},\hat{\imath},\hat{k}] + \hat{\jmath}[\hat{\imath},\hat{\imath},\hat{k}]|}{\sin b \sin c}$$

$$= \frac{[\hat{\imath},\hat{\jmath},\hat{k}]}{\sin b \sin c}.$$

Hence

$$\frac{\sin A}{\sin a} = \frac{\sin B}{\sin b} = \frac{\sin C}{\sin c} = \frac{6 \text{ vol}(OABC)}{\sin a \sin b \sin c}. \tag{2.9.2}$$

These equations are the fundamental formulas of spherical trigonometry. Two other formulas are frequently used; they can be derived from (2.9.1) and (2.9.2) by elementary trigonometry. They are

$$\sin a \cos B = \cos b \sin c - \sin b \cos c \cos A \tag{2.9.3}$$

and

$$\cos a \cos C = \sin a \cot b - \sin C \cot B. \tag{2.9.4}$$

As an illustration of the use of these formulas, consider the problem of expressing right ascension and declination in terms of celestial longitude and latitude.

Let X be a star at (α,δ) or (λ,β). Let N and P be the celestial north pole and the north pole of the ecliptic, and let the great circles through these points and X meet the celestial equator and ecliptic in A and B, respectively, as shown in Figure 2.14, where the great circles through $P\Upsilon$ and $N\Upsilon$ are also drawn. Υ is the pole of the great circle PN, so the angles $PN\Upsilon$ and $NP\Upsilon$ are both equal to 90°

Now

$$\Upsilon A = \angle \Upsilon NA = \alpha$$

so

$$\angle PNX = 90° + \alpha.$$

Similarly,

$$\angle NPX = 90° - \lambda.$$

Also

$$PN = \epsilon,$$

$$NX = 90° - \delta,$$

and

$$PX = 90° - \beta.$$

Applying the formulas (2.9.1), (2.9.2), and (2.9.3) to the triangle PNX, we have

$$\cos PX = \cos NX \cos PN + \sin NX \cos PN \cos PNX,$$

$$\sin PX \sin NPX = \sin NX \sin PNX,$$

$$\sin PX \cos NPX = \cos NX \sin PN - \sin NX \cos PN \cos PNX,$$

or

$$\sin \beta = \sin \delta \cos \epsilon - \cos \delta \sin \epsilon \sin \alpha,$$

$$\cos \beta \cos \lambda = \cos \delta \cos \alpha, \qquad\qquad (2.9.5)$$

$$\cos \beta \sin \lambda = \sin \delta \sin \epsilon + \cos \delta \cos \epsilon \sin \alpha.$$

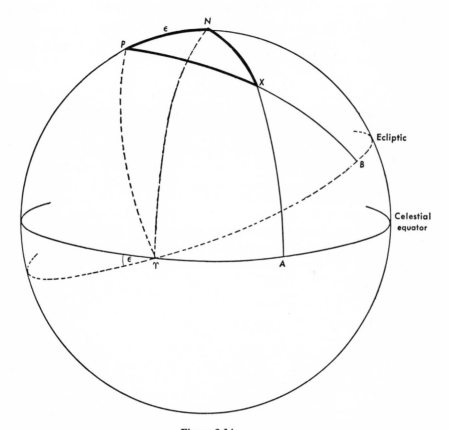

Figure 2.14

These expressions can also be found quickly without using spherical trigo-nometry. If we take axes $\hat{\imath}$, $\hat{\jmath}$, and $\hat{k}$, with $\hat{\imath}$ pointing toward ♈ and $\hat{k}$ toward N, and let these be changed to $\hat{l}$, $\hat{m}$, and $\hat{n}$ by a rotation about O♈ through the angle ϵ, so that $\hat{\mathbf{n}}$ points toward P, $\hat{\mathbf{m}}$ lies in the ecliptic (it is the summer solstice) and $\hat{\mathbf{i}} = \hat{\mathbf{I}}$, then

$$\hat{\mathbf{m}} = \hat{\mathbf{j}} \cos \epsilon - \hat{\mathbf{k}} \sin \epsilon,$$
$$\hat{\mathbf{n}} = \hat{\mathbf{j}} \sin \epsilon + \hat{\mathbf{k}} \cos \epsilon.$$

But the components of OX along these two sets of axes are

$$(\cos \delta \cos \alpha, \quad \cos \delta \sin \alpha, \quad \sin \delta)$$

and

$$(\cos \beta \cos \lambda, \quad \cos \beta \sin \lambda, \quad \sin \beta),$$

and equations (2.9.5) follow at once. So, although students must be familiar with the methods of spherical trigonometry, they should be on the lookout for methods that are quicker and perhaps safer. In particular, students familiar with matrix notation are advised to use the methods of Appendix B.

Problem

Using the triangle PNX, derive expressions for α and δ in terms of λ and β. Check these expressions, using the alternative method indicated above.

Chapter 3 ** INTRODUCTION TO VECTORIAL MECHANICS

3.1 Forces as Vectors

Mechanics deals with the effects of forces, and the first step in this chapter is to establish that forces are vectors. Certainly forces have magnitudes and directions, so we have to show that they can be added or resolved according to the vector law. It can be shown experimentally that a force P can be resolved in a direction making θ with its line of action, and that the resultant is $P \cos \theta$; so, forces can be resolved and therefore added as vectors. Alternatively we can accept the properties of the triangle of forces to be experimentally proved. That is, if three forces acting through a point are in equilibrium, then it is possible to construct a triangle with sides parallel to the lines of action of the forces and with lengths proportional to their magnitudes. This is precisely equivalent to the vector law of addition.

Forces are localized vectors, and they must always be treated as such. Expressions such as "resolving a force" or "the moment of a force" follow from their vector definitions.

3.2 Basic Definitions

The *mass* of a body is a measure of the amount of material in the body. A unit of mass can be defined in terms of a definite volume of some standard substance; for instance, the gram is the mass of a cubic centimeter of water. At some point on the Earth's surface the force exerted on a body of mass m is mg, where g is a constant for that place, due mostly to the Earth's gravity. mg is the *weight* of the body. On the Moon the body would weigh less, but its mass would remain the same; hence mass, and not weight, is the fundamental quantity. Two masses can be compared at some place by comparing their weights, so there is no difficulty in allotting a measure to any particular mass. Mass is, of course, a scalar quantity. In the work immediately following, it will

41

be convenient to assume that bodies are *point masses*; a point mass has its entire mass concentrated at a geometrical point.

The product $m\mathbf{v}$ of the mass and velocity of a body is the *linear momentum* of that body. This is a vector. (A discussion of the system of reference with respect to which $\mathbf{v}$ is measured is given in the following section.)

Let a mass m be at $\mathbf{r}$ with respect to some origin O. Then the product $\mathbf{r} \times m\mathbf{v}$ is the *angular momentum* about O of the mass. (This is sometimes called "moment of momentum.") Angular momentum is a vector of which the modulus is seen (from Section 2.5) to be $2m$ times the areal velocity with respect to O. Angular momentum will usually be used in preference to areal velocity.

The *kinetic energy* of m is $\tfrac{1}{2}m\mathbf{v}^2$, a scalar.

If a constant force $\mathbf{P}$ acts on a particle that suffers a displacement $\mathbf{r}$, then the *work* done by the force is $\mathbf{P}\cdot\mathbf{r}$, a scalar. If $\mathbf{P}$ is not constant, the work done in moving from A to B is compounded from the infinitesimal displacements $d\mathbf{r}$ along the curve AB, so that the total is

$$W_{AB} = \int_A^B \mathbf{P}\cdot d\mathbf{r} \tag{3.2.1}$$

integrated along the curve.

Power is the rate of doing work. The work done by $\mathbf{P}$ in a displacement $d\mathbf{r}$ is $\mathbf{P}\cdot d\mathbf{r}$, which can be written as $\mathbf{P}\cdot(d\mathbf{r}/dt)dt$, so that the rate of doing work is $\mathbf{P}\cdot\mathbf{v}$, a scalar.

These quantities can be measured in units of length, mass, and time. These units will often be taken in this text as the centimeter, the gram, and the second, or as "c.g.s." units. The unit of force is the *dyne*; it produces unit acceleration in unit mass. The unit of work is the *erg*, measured by one dyne moving its point of application through one centimeter; and so on. There is no ambiguity in denoting all these by "c.g.s. units."

It is always important to bear in mind the dimensions of these quantities. If L, M, and T stand for length, mass, and time, then speed has the dimensions L/T, kinetic energy has the dimensions ML^2/T^2, and so on. It is a useful check to make sure that all the terms in any equation have the same dimensions. For instance, it is all right to equate kinetic energy and work, but not work and power.

The force exerted by a body or system of bodies at some point is taken to mean the force that the system would exert on a particle of unit mass placed at that point. This is strictly "force per unit mass," and the dimensions must be altered accordingly. The phrase "per unit mass" ought, then, to be included also wherever quantities such as energy or momentum occur, but in practice there need be no ambiguity if it is not always used.

Let $\mathbf{P}$ be such a force, varying with $\mathbf{r}$; then it constitutes a *field of force*. An important type of field of force is one where $\mathbf{P}(\mathbf{r})$ is the gradient of a scalar function of **r**. This is expressed conventionally as

$$\mathbf{P} = -\nabla V \tag{3.2.2}$$

where $V(\mathbf{r})$ is the *potential* of the field. It should be noted that we get the same field of force if an arbitrary constant is added to V. If such a potential function exists, then the field is said to be *conservative*. In such a case it is often easier to work with V, a scalar, than with **P**. For a conservative field (3.2.1) becomes

$$
\begin{aligned}
W_{AB} &= -\int_A^B \nabla V \cdot d\mathbf{r} \\
&= -\int_A^B \nabla V \cdot \hat{\boldsymbol{\tau}}\, ds \\
&= -\int_A^B \frac{dV}{ds}\, ds \qquad \text{[by (2.8.1)]} \\
&= V(A) - V(B). \tag{3.2.3}
\end{aligned}
$$

So, the work done in going from A to B depends only on the positions of the ends of the path and not on the shape of the path itself. This is one of the most important properties of a conservative field, and it is possible to define it by this property.

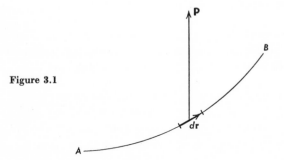

Figure 3.1

Consider a mass m on the Earth at A. If it is lifted to a point B, the work performed *by* the gravitational attraction of the Earth is negative, and equal to mW_{AB}. But the man who lifts it works *against* gravitational attraction of the Earth, and performs positive work of amount $-mW_{AB}$. Now, if the mass descends to A, energy equal to this amount of work is released and is available to be turned into any form of energy such as kinetic energy, heat, etc. Hence the mass has energy by virtue of its position, and this is known as *potential energy*. It should not be confused with "potential", since it has different dimensions.

Usually it is possible to choose the arbitrary constant in the potential such that V tends to zero at great distances. In this case the potential at A is equal to the work done by the attracting system in moving unit mass from A to infinity. The dimensions of potential are therefore work per unit mass.

In many texts students will find the potential defined as the negative value of that given by (3.2.2); usually when it is defined in this way it is called the *force function*. In practice it is easy to get the signs confused, and, regardless of the definition, when the potential finds its way into an actual equation, it is wise to check that its sign makes sense. For Newtonian attraction, V is negative and the force function is positive. An example of positive V is the potential of the field due to the repulsive force experienced by particles in the tail of a comet as a result of the radiation pressure from the Sun.

The potential function must be single-valued. For example, if $V = -k\theta$, in two-dimensional polar coordinates, then for any point V has an infinite number of values. The gradient of V gives a force that is k/r in the transverse direction, but if a point moves around the origin in a closed curve, the work done in one revolution is $2\pi k$ and not zero. If frictional forces, such as air resistance, are present, then the field will not be conservative. However, in nearly all the work in this text we shall be concerned with conservative fields.

The surfaces $V =$ constant are called *level surfaces*. No work is done in a displacement over a level surface. From Section 2.8 we see that the line of action of the force through any point is perpendicular to the level surface through that point.

3.3 Newton's Laws of Motion

The bridge between the kinematics of a particle and the forces acting on it is provided by Newton's three laws of motion. These are:

1. Every particle continues in a state of rest or uniform motion in a straight line unless it is compelled by some external force to change that state.

2. The rate of change of the linear momentum of a particle is proportional to the force applied to the particle and takes place in the same direction as that force.

3. The mutual actions of any two bodies are always equal and oppositely directed.

These laws can be introduced as fundamental laws, without proof, and followed up mathematically. To ignore possible laboratory verifications makes mechanics appear somewhat abstract; but all we shall say here is that the laws can be reasonably verified. A full discussion is given in most standard texts on mechanics.

Newton's first law demands some sort of reference system with respect to which the "uniform velocity" can be measured. If we have one such reference system, then any other that is not accelerated with respect to the first system will do equally well for the application of Newton's laws. Hence we have the usual stipulation that the axes must be "nonaccelerated." The trouble arises when we look for the first suitable reference system, and this involves discussion that is out of place in an elementary text. Here we shall adopt a common way out, working backwards and defining such a system as one with respect to which the first law holds. Axes rotating with the Earth are not suitable in principle (before Newton's laws can be applied to motion with respect to these, the Coriolis forces have to be imposed), although they are adequate for many laboratory experiments. Similarly, it may not be reasonable to assume that a suitable set of axes can be moving through space with the solar system, since such a set is undoubtedly accelerated with respect to the galaxy; but the effects of this are negligible and produce no practical difficulties.

Newton's first law clears the decks in showing whether a force is in action or not. If there is no net force acting on a body, its equation of motion must be of the form

$$\mathbf{r} = \mathbf{r}_0 + \mathbf{v}t,$$

and, conversely, if this is its equation of motion, then there is no net force acting on the body. For example, from Kepler's first law we can say that there must be *some* force acting on the planets. It is Newton's second law that enables us to investigate the force quantitatively.

The second law can be used as a proof that forces are vectors. But this makes the definition of a force unnecessarily abstract. If the mass of the body remains constant, the second law can be put in the familiar form:

$$\mathbf{P} = m\ddot{\mathbf{r}}. \tag{3.3.1}$$

Masses will be constant in the work in this text, but (3.3.1) would not be applicable, say, to the motion of a meteor burning up in the atmosphere. Some of the consequences of this law will be considered in the following section.

Newton's third law must always be borne in mind where forces are concerned. For instance, the Earth exerts a gravitational pull on the Moon; so, the Moon must exert a precisely equal and opposite pull on the Earth. It is only because the Earth is some eighty times more massive than the Moon that the kinematical effects on the Earth are less noticeable.

3.4   The Laws of Energy and Momentum

Consider Newton's second law in the form:

$$\mathbf{P} = \frac{d(m\mathbf{v})}{dt}. \tag{3.4.1}$$

This is equivalent to

$$\mathbf{P}\,dt = d(m\mathbf{v})$$

so that

$$\int \mathbf{P}\,dt = m\mathbf{v} + \mathbf{constant}. \tag{3.4.2}$$

This is the equation of linear momentum. In particular, if no net force is acting on a particle, then its linear momentum is constant.

Now consider $\mathbf{r} \times$ (3.4.1). We have

$$\mathbf{r} \times \mathbf{P} = \mathbf{r} \times \frac{d(m\mathbf{v})}{dt}$$

$$= \frac{d(\mathbf{r} \times m\mathbf{v})}{dt} \tag{3.4.3}$$

since $(d\mathbf{r}/dt) \times \mathbf{v} = \mathbf{v} \times \mathbf{v} = 0$. This means that the moment of the forces acting on a particle is equal to the rate of change of the angular momentum of the particle. In particular, if the moment is zero (when the line of action of the resultant of the forces passes through the origin), then the angular momentum is constant. Conversely, if the angular momentum is constant (so that the motion takes place in a plane and the law of areas is obeyed), then the resultant force passes through the origin. We have seen that some force must be acting on the planets to account for their curved paths; now we see that the force must be directed toward the Sun.

The work done in moving $\mathbf{P}$ through $d\mathbf{r}$ is

$$\mathbf{P} \cdot d\mathbf{r} = \frac{d(m\mathbf{v})}{dt} \cdot d\mathbf{r}$$

$$= \frac{d(m\mathbf{v})}{dt} \cdot \frac{d\mathbf{r}}{dt} \, dt$$

$$= \mathbf{v} \cdot \frac{d(m\mathbf{v})}{dt} \, dt.$$

If m is a constant, this integrates to give

$$W_{AB} = \int_A^B \mathbf{P} \cdot d\mathbf{r} = \tfrac{1}{2} m v_B{}^2 - \tfrac{1}{2} m v_A{}^2. \tag{3.4.4}$$

By (3.2.3) this can be written as

$$V(A) - V(B) = \tfrac{1}{2} v_B{}^2 - \tfrac{1}{2} v_A{}^2 \tag{3.4.5}$$

since V is derived from a function of force per unit mass. So the changes in kinetic and potential energy are equal. The energy integral, (3.4.5), can always be written down at once in any problem where V exists, without recourse to the equation of motion.

Any of these three equations may be more useful in a problem than the equation of motion (3.3.1), and it is always well to consider their merits before embarking on the solution to a problem. This applies in particular to the energy integral.

Consider motion with respect to axes that are rotating with constant angular velocity ω about the z-axis. If a mass m is acted on by a force $\mathbf{P}$, its motion with respect to the rotating axes will be given by

$$\mathbf{P} = m[\ddot{\mathbf{r}} + 2\omega\hat{\mathbf{z}} \times \dot{\mathbf{r}} + \omega^2\hat{\mathbf{z}} \times (\hat{\mathbf{z}} \times \mathbf{r})] \tag{3.4.6}$$

where equation (2.7.2) has been applied twice. Let $\mathbf{r}$ have components z along Oz, and $\boldsymbol{\rho}$ at right angles to Oz; then

$$\mathbf{r} = z\hat{\mathbf{z}} + \boldsymbol{\rho}$$

and

$$\mathbf{P} = m[\ddot{\mathbf{r}} + 2\omega\hat{\mathbf{z}} \times \dot{\mathbf{r}} - \omega^2\boldsymbol{\rho}]. \tag{3.4.7}$$

Multiply scalarly by $\dot{\mathbf{r}}$; then, since $\boldsymbol{\rho} \cdot \dot{\mathbf{r}} = \boldsymbol{\rho} \cdot \dot{\boldsymbol{\rho}}$,

$$\mathbf{P} \cdot \dot{\mathbf{r}} = m[\ddot{\mathbf{r}} \cdot \dot{\mathbf{r}} - \omega^2\boldsymbol{\rho} \cdot \dot{\boldsymbol{\rho}}].$$

If P arises from a potential V, described with respect to the rotating axes, then we get the *modified* energy integral

$$V - \tfrac{1}{2}\omega^2\rho^2 + \tfrac{1}{2}\dot{r}^2 = \text{constant}, \tag{3.4.8}$$

which is the same as the usual energy integral for the motion of a particle in a field of potential

$$V - \tfrac{1}{2}\omega^2\rho^2.$$

This is the *modified potential*. The term $-\tfrac{1}{2}\omega^2\rho^2$ is the *rotational potential*.

Some uses of the equations of motion will now be demonstrated by considering their application to five simple problems.

3.5 Simple Harmonic Motion

A particle moves in a straight line under the action of a force that varies directly with the distance from some fixed point. If this point is taken as origin and x is the distance measured from it, the force per unit mass can be written as $-k^2x$, and the equation of motion is

$$\ddot{x} = -k^2x. \tag{3.5.1}$$

The field is conservative, with potential $\tfrac{1}{2}k^2x^2$, so that the energy integral is

$$\tfrac{1}{2}\dot{x}^2 + \tfrac{1}{2}k^2x^2 = \text{constant}, \tag{3.5.2}$$

where the constant must be positive, so that it can be put equal to $\tfrac{1}{2}k^2a^2$. Writing (3.5.2) in the form:

$$\frac{dx}{(a^2 - x^2)^{1/2}} = k\,dt$$

we find the solution of the motion to be

$$x = a\cos(kt + b), \tag{3.5.3}$$

where a and b are arbitrary constants.

An inspection of the energy integral yields several properties of the motion. It is symmetrical about the origin; it is determined by the speed at the origin; and it represents finite oscillations whatever the initial speed may be.

3.6   Motion in a Uniform Field Subject to Resistance Proportional to the Velocity

Near the Earth's surface there is a uniform field of force, $-g\hat{z}$, where $\hat{z}$ is the unit vector pointing vertically upward. Between certain limits of speed the air resistance is proportional to the velocity. The equation of motion is then

$$m\ddot{r} = -mg\hat{z} - mk\mathbf{v}. \tag{3.6.1}$$

The forces are not conservative, so we cannot use the energy integral in the form of (3.4.5). The motion obviously takes place in a vertical plane (for there is no force to cause any deviation from such a plane) and there is no advantage in using vectors. Let position in the plane of motion be specified by (x,z), where the x-axis is horizontal; then the resolution of (3.6.1) gives

$$\ddot{x} = -k\dot{x}, \tag{3.6.2}$$

and

$$\ddot{z} = -g - k\dot{z}. \tag{3.6.3}$$

(3.6.2) can be put into the form:

$$\frac{d}{dt}(\dot{x}e^{kt}) = 0,$$

so

$$\dot{x} = Ae^{-kt}$$

and

$$x = -\frac{A}{k}e^{-kt} + B, \tag{3.6.4}$$

where A and B are arbitrary constants. Therefore the speed along the x-axis, which is the horizontal speed, tends to zero, and x, the horizontal range, tends to a finite limit as t tends to infinity.

A similar solution of (3.6.3) yields

$$\frac{d}{dt}(\dot{z}e^{kt}) = -ge^{kt},$$

so

$$\dot{z} = -\frac{g}{k} + Ce^{-kt}$$

and

$$z = -\frac{g}{k}t - \frac{C}{k}e^{-kt} + D. \tag{3.6.5}$$

If the particle is initially rising, $\dot{z}$ is positive; it will vanish when

$$e^{-kt} = \frac{g}{Ck},$$

or when

$$z = -\frac{g}{k^2} \log\left(\frac{kC}{g}\right) - \frac{g}{k^2} + D.$$

The particle will then start to descend and will have a limiting speed $-(g/k)$. The energy at any point is given by

$$\tfrac{1}{2}(\dot{x}^2 + \dot{z}^2) + gz,$$

and an evaluation of this will show how much energy is lost at any stage, owing to the air resistance.

3.7 Linear Motion in an Inverse Square Field

The approximation to a uniform field is valid only near the Earth's surface. Farther away we must use a force

$$-\frac{k^2}{r^2}\hat{z}$$

per unit mass, where r is the distance from the Earth's center. General motion in this field will be considered later; for the moment we shall only discuss motion in the z-direction. Since the motion is linear, it is pointless to use vectors.

The field is conservative with potential $-(k^2/r)$. The energy integral is therefore

$$\dot{z}^2 = \frac{2k^2}{z} - \frac{2k^2}{z_0} + v_0^2 \tag{3.7.1}$$

where z_0 and v_0 are the position and speed when $t = 0$. Important information can be found merely by applying the condition that the right-hand side of (3.7.1) must not be negative. There are three cases to be considered.

1. If $v_0^2 < 2k^2/z_0$, there will be some finite distance, z_1, at which $\dot{z}$ will vanish; at this distance the particle will turn and start to descend.

2. If $v_0^2 > 2k^2/z_0$, $\dot{z}$ will never vanish but will tend to some finite value as z tends to infinity; the particle will always continue to move away and will never return.

3. If $v_0^2 = 2k^2/z_0$, then $\dot{z} \to 0$ as $z \to \infty$. This critical value of v_0 is known as the *velocity of escape* (we should in this text write "speed of escape," but this use of the word "velocity" is too well established). It is of fundamental importance in many problems; one of the most topical is that of achieving the speed necessary for a rocket to escape completely from the Earth.

To calculate the velocity of escape from z_0, the value of k^2 must be known.

This is the product of the mass of the attracting body and the constant of gravitation. However, we can find the velocity of escape from the surface of the Earth from a knowledge of the Earth's radius (taken to be 6360 km) and the value of g at the surface of the Earth, for the latter is k^2 divided by the square of the Earth's radius. Taking $g = 981$ c.g.s. units, the velocity of escape is

$$(2 \times 981 \times 6360 \times 10^5)^{1/2} = 11.2 \times 10^5 \text{ cm/sec.}$$

From a point above the surface of the Earth, the velocity of escape would, of course, be less.

The velocity of escape is often referred to as the *velocity from infinity*, since it is the speed which a particle, starting from rest at infinity, would acquire on reaching z_0.

The full solution to the problem can be found by integrating (3.7.1). Cases 1, 2, and 3 must be treated separately. Here we shall consider only the first. Let $v = 0$ when $z = z_1$; then (3.7.1) can be written as

$$\frac{dz}{dt} = \pm \left\{ 2k^2 \left(\frac{1}{z} - \frac{1}{z_1} \right) \right\}^{1/2}$$

$$= \pm \left(\frac{2k^2}{z_1} \right)^{1/2} \left(\frac{z_1 - z}{z} \right)^{1/2}.$$

The $+$ or $-$ sign is to be taken when the particle is receding from or approaching the origin. Writing the equation as

$$\frac{z \, dz}{(zz_1 - z^2)^{1/2}} = \pm k \left(\frac{2}{z_1} \right)^{1/2} dt$$

we have, on integration,

$$-(zz_1 - z^2)^{1/2} + \frac{z_1}{2} \sin^{-1} \left(\frac{2z - z_1}{z_1} \right) = \pm kt \left(\frac{2}{z_1} \right)^{1/2} + \text{constant.}$$

Applying the condition $z = z_0$ when $t = 0$, we have

$$\frac{z_1}{2} \left\{ \sin^{-1} \left(\frac{2z - z_1}{z_1} \right) - \sin^{-1} \left(\frac{2z_0 - z_1}{z_1} \right) \right\} + (z_1 z_0 - z_0^2)^{1/2}$$

$$- (z_1 z - z^2)^{1/2} = \pm kt \left(\frac{2}{z_1} \right)^{1/2}. \quad (3.7.2)$$

3.8 Foucault's Pendulum

In 1851 the French scientist Foucault devised an experiment, which could be performed under laboratory conditions, to demonstrate the Earth's rotation. A simple pendulum was suspended from the dome of the Panthéon in Paris, and it was shown that the plane in which it swung was slowly rotating. This phenomenon is really due to the Earth's (and the observer's) rotating under the pendulum.

Let the point of suspension of the pendulum be O, and let the bob be at P. Let $\mathbf{OP} = \mathbf{r}$, where r is constant. Now let $\hat{\mathbf{k}}$ point along $\mathbf{CO}$, where C is the center of the Earth. Let us assume that r is very small compared with the radius of the Earth, r_0; then the forces acting on the bob, of mass m, are the tension in the string, acting along $\mathbf{PO}$, and gravity mg, acting along $-\hat{\mathbf{k}}$. These can be written

$$- T\hat{\mathbf{r}} - mg\hat{\mathbf{k}}.$$

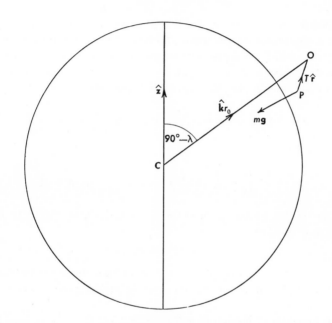

Figure 3.2

The equation of motion with respect to nonrotating axes fixed in space is found by equating $m(d^2\mathbf{r}/dt^2)$ with the above forces. But to write down the equation of motion observed with respect to axes moving with O, we must apply the Coriolis forces derived in (2.7.5). In this example ω^2 is so small compared with ω that it may be ignored. If d/dt now applies to the motion observed from O, we have

$$\frac{d^2\mathbf{r}}{dt^2} + 2\omega\hat{\mathbf{z}} \times \frac{d\mathbf{r}}{dt} = -g\hat{\mathbf{k}} - \frac{T}{m}\hat{\mathbf{r}}. \tag{3.8.1}$$

The normal equation of motion for the simple pendulum is found by putting $\omega = 0$. To solve (3.8.1), eliminate T by multiplying through vectorially by $\hat{\mathbf{r}} \times$. We get

$$\hat{\mathbf{r}} \times \frac{d^2\mathbf{r}}{dt^2} + 2\omega\hat{\mathbf{r}} \times \left(\hat{\mathbf{z}} \times \frac{d\mathbf{r}}{dt}\right) = -g\hat{\mathbf{r}} \times \hat{\mathbf{k}}.$$

Since $dr/dt = 0$, $\hat{\mathbf{r}} \cdot (dr/dt) = 0$, and the second term on the left-hand side reduces to

$$-2\omega \hat{\mathbf{r}} \cdot \hat{\mathbf{z}} \frac{d\mathbf{r}}{dt} = -2\omega \sin \lambda \frac{d\mathbf{r}}{dt},$$

where λ is the latitude of O. So we have

$$\hat{\mathbf{r}} \times \frac{d^2\mathbf{r}}{dt^2} - 2\omega \sin \lambda \frac{d\mathbf{r}}{dt} = -g\hat{\mathbf{r}} \times \hat{\mathbf{k}}. \tag{3.8.2}$$

From the known properties of the motion we are looking for a solution that includes a uniform rotation about $\hat{\mathbf{k}}$. Consider axes rotating with angular velocity $\omega'\hat{\mathbf{k}}$, and let $\partial/\partial t$ represent the rate of change with respect to these axes. ω' is constant, and is so small that ω'^2 and $\omega\omega'$ can be neglected (the justification for this will appear shortly). (3.8.2) becomes

$$\hat{\mathbf{r}} \times \left(\frac{\partial^2\mathbf{r}}{\partial t^2} + 2\omega'\hat{\mathbf{k}} \times \frac{\partial\mathbf{r}}{\partial t} \right) - 2\omega \sin \lambda \frac{\partial\mathbf{r}}{\partial t} = -g\hat{\mathbf{r}} \times \hat{\mathbf{k}}.$$

Rearranging this we get

$$\hat{\mathbf{r}} \times \frac{\partial^2\mathbf{r}}{\partial t^2} - 2(\hat{\mathbf{r}} \cdot \hat{\mathbf{k}}\omega' + \omega \sin \lambda) \frac{\partial\mathbf{r}}{\partial t} = -g\hat{\mathbf{r}} \times \hat{\mathbf{k}}.$$

During the motion we assume that the pendulum is never far from the vertical, so that $\hat{\mathbf{r}} \cdot \hat{\mathbf{k}} \simeq 1$. Then, if

$$\omega' = -\omega \sin \lambda,$$

the equation reduces to that of a simple pendulum. Hence the motion observed from O is that of a simple pendulum rotating with angular velocity $-\hat{\mathbf{k}}\omega \sin \lambda$.

3.9 The Equation of Motion of a Rocket, Subject Only to Its Own Propulsion

We include this section to illustrate the careful treatment required for problems that involve changing mass. A rocket traveling *in vacuo* is accelerated by the high-velocity expulsion of a small part of its mass. With respect to axes fixed in space, we have the situations before and after the expulsion that are shown in Figure 3.3.

The relative speed at which the expelled matter leaves the rocket is $U + V$; and for a time dt, a thrust $dM(U + V)$ is exerted on the rocket so that the force propelling it forward is

$$(U + V) \frac{dM}{dt}.$$

Since linear momentum is conserved, we have

$$MU = (M - dM)(U + dU) - V\,dM$$

or

$$M\,dU - U\,dM - V\,dM = 0.$$

Rearranging and dividing by dt, we find

$$M \frac{dU}{dt} = (U + V) \frac{dM}{dt}.$$

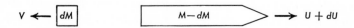

Figure 3.3

Problems

1. Under what conditions will both the linear and angular momenta of a moving particle be constant?

2. Show that the following fields of force are conservative, and find the potential functions:

$$\mathbf{P} = \mathbf{g} \text{ (a constant)}; \quad \mathbf{P} = c\mathbf{r}; \quad \mathbf{P} = -\mu \frac{\mathbf{r}}{r^2}; \quad \mathbf{P} = -\mu \frac{\mathbf{r}}{r^n}.$$

3. A particle is whirled around at the end of a light, inextensible string of length a, with constant speed v. If the particle has mass m, find the tension in the string and the angular momentum about the point of rotation. If the string breaks, describe the path of the particle (neglecting gravity) and show that the angular and linear momenta are conserved.

4. Show that when $\mathbf{P} = \mathbf{g}$, the motion of a particle takes place in a plane, and that the path is a parabola.

5. A mass m is suspended from a point O by a light inextensible string of length r. The string makes a constant angle with the vertical. By taking moments about O and using the equation for the angular momentum, show that m moves around the vertical with constant angular velocity; find this velocity.

6. Show that the equation $\ddot{x} + k^2x = 0$ describes the projection of uniform circular motion on the x-axis, and find the angular velocity of this motion. Hence deduce the general solution to the equation.

7. By trying a solution of the form $x = e^{mt}$, solve the equation $\ddot{x} - k^2x = 0$, and show that the same method can be used to solve $\ddot{x} + k^2x = 0$.

8. A particle describing simple harmonic motion coalesces with a similar particle at rest at the origin. Describe the subsequent motion.

9. Show that if a particle starting from rest moves subject to an attractive force varying directly as the *initial* distance of the particle from the origin, then the time of traveling from any point to the origin is independent of the initial distance.

10. Discuss linear motion in a constant field of force with air resistance proportional to the square of the velocity. Investigate the limiting velocities, if any.

11. A particle, subject to a constant field of force g, falls from a height h, encountering air resistance proportional to its velocity. Find an expression for the kinetic energy at any point of its descent. How much energy is lost to the frictional force during the total fall?

12. A particle moving initially in simple harmonic motion becomes subject to an air resistance varying with its speed. Investigate the subsequent motion.

13. Write down the equations of motion for a freely falling body in a constant field as observed from a point on the surface of the rotating Earth. Investigate any deviations of its path from the vertical; do these depend on the latitude?

14. For the examples given in the text, find out whether the motion is reversible (i.e., whether the path would be retraced if the velocity were to be suddenly reversed). Discuss the reasons in the cases where the motion is not reversible.

For the remaining problems an inverse square field is assumed.

15. A particle is projected vertically upward from a height s_0 with speed v_0 (less than the velocity of escape). What is the maximum height attained? How long will it take to reach this height?

16. Prove that the time taken for a particle to fall from rest at the height s_1 to the origin is

$$\frac{\pi}{k}\left(\frac{s_1}{2}\right)^{3/2}.$$

17. Solve the problem of linear motion in an inverse square field when the initial speed is equal to the velocity of escape.

18. Solve the problem of linear motion in an inverse square field when the initial speed is greater than the velocity of escape.

19. Compare the velocity of escape from the surface of the Earth with that from a point 500 km above the surface. What initial speed must a particle be given when launched from the Earth's surface so that it will just reach the Moon (380,000 km away)? If the actual speed is 0.1 per cent less than this, how close will the particle get to the Moon? (Neglect the Moon's gravitational pull.)

20. A minor planet has radius 2 km, and average density 3.0. What is the velocity of escape from its surface? If a particle on the Earth's surface

were given this (vertical) velocity, how far would it rise? Discuss the possibility of a man jumping off the minor planet and escaping from it altogether.

21. A meteor, mass one gram, falls from rest at infinity and burns up in the Earth's atmosphere (neglect the height above the surface of the Earth). Given that a body weighing one kilogram, falling 4.25×10^4 cm near the surface of the Earth, generates one calorie, find the number of calories generated by the meteor, assuming that all its energy is turned into heat (but neglecting the energy from any chemical changes).

22. Find the surface gravity (in terms of g for the Earth) and the velocity of escape for each of the following objects (masses and radii are given in terms of the terrestrial values).

The Sun, $M = 333{,}000$, $R = 109$ Mercury, $M = 0.056$, $R = 0.39$
The Moon, $M = 0.0123$, $R = 0.272$ Mars, $M = 0.108$, $R = 0.53$
Venus, $M = 0.817$, $R = 0.97$ Saturn, $M = 95.2$, $R = 9.5$
Jupiter, $M = 318$, $R = 11.2$ Neptune, $M = 17.3$, $R = 4.2$.
Uranus, $M = 14.6$, $R = 3.9$

23. In a gas containing molecules of mass M grams, at a temperature $T°K$, the "most probable speed" of a molecule is v, where

$$Mv^2 = 2kT.$$

k is Boltzmann's constant and has the value 1.38×10^{-16}. Jeans has shown that if this speed is greater than about one-fifth of the velocity of escape of a planet, then the gas will almost entirely have escaped from the planet after a few million years. Bearing in mind that the solar system has existed for several billions of years and that at some time the planets may have been much hotter than they are now, investigate the likelihood that each planet and the Moon has retained its initial supply of hydrogen ($M = 1.67 \times 10^{-24}$), nitrogen ($M = 28 \times 1.66 \times 10^{-24}$), and argon ($M = 39.9 \times 1.66 \times 10^{-24}$).

Chapter 4 ** CENTRAL ORBITS

4.1 General Properties

A central orbit is an orbit described by a particle acted on by forces, the resultant of which always passes through a fixed point. In practice only a single force, the resultant, is considered. Take the fixed point as origin and let the force, per unit mass, be

$$-f\hat{\mathbf{r}},$$

where f is a scalar function that could depend not only on position but also on time, velocity, etc. f is the law of attraction toward the origin.

The equation of motion is

$$\ddot{\mathbf{r}} = -f\hat{\mathbf{r}}. \tag{4.1.1}$$

Multiplying by $\mathbf{r} \times$ we get

$$\mathbf{r} \times \ddot{\mathbf{r}} = 0,$$

which can be integrated at once to give

$$\mathbf{r} \times \dot{\mathbf{r}} = \mathbf{h}, \tag{4.1.2}$$

where $\mathbf{h}$, the angular momentum per unit mass, is a constant vector. Hence Kepler's second law holds for all central orbits. (We have also seen that, should Kepler's second law be obeyed, the orbit is a central orbit.) Multiplying (4.1.2) by $\mathbf{r} \cdot$, we get

$$\mathbf{r} \cdot \mathbf{h} = 0, \tag{4.1.3}$$

the equation of a plane through the origin. So, the motion takes place in this plane. Since central orbits are two-dimensional, the vector notation has no advantage and therefore will not be used.

A linear orbit is possible only if it passes through the origin. Often f has a singularity at the origin, and students are frequently worried about the meaning of such an orbit. In practical cases the center of force is occupied by matter that prevents too close an approach; should the moving particle penetrate this matter, then the physical circumstances become obscure, but we should expect the law of force to change. A few orbits passing through the origin will be considered here from a mathematical angle; but such orbits are not realistic.

We shall assume that f varies with position only, and we shall consider only conservative fields. This means that there must be a scalar function $V(\mathbf{r})$ such that the radial component of ∇V is equal to $f(\mathbf{r})$, and the transverse component is zero; i.e.,

$$\frac{\partial V}{\partial r} = f(\mathbf{r}) \quad \text{and} \quad \frac{1}{r}\frac{\partial V}{\partial \theta} = 0.$$

The latter condition means that f is a function of r only and so can be written $f(r)$. In this case we can find a V for *any* f from

$$V = \int^r f(r)\, dr. \tag{4.1.4}$$

Hence the necessary and sufficient condition for the field to be conservative is that f should not vary with θ.

The equation of motion is now

$$\ddot{\mathbf{r}} = -f(r)\hat{\mathbf{r}}. \tag{4.1.5}$$

The energy integral is

$$\tfrac{1}{2}\dot{\mathbf{r}}^2 + V(r) = C. \tag{4.1.6}$$

This and (4.1.2) are the fundamental equations for central orbits. If V is chosen such that it tends to zero when r tends to infinity, C is defined as the *energy of the orbit*. From (4.1.6) $C - V(r)$ must be nonnegative, so that the circles given by the solutions, if any, of

$$C - V(r) = 0$$

represent in general important boundaries that cannot be crossed during the motion. In particular, if C is negative, there must be an upper limit to the possible values of r, so that the motion is finite. If C is positive and dV/dr (or f) always has the same sign, the velocity will tend to a finite limit when r tends to infinity; the particle will never return, and the motion is infinite.

Resolving (4.1.5) along the radial and transverse directions, we have

$$\ddot{r} - r\dot{\theta}^2 = -f(r) \tag{4.1.7}$$

and

$$r\ddot{\theta} + 2\dot{r}\dot{\theta} = 0. \tag{4.1.8}$$

(4.1.8) integrates at once to give

$$r^2\dot{\theta} = h, \tag{4.1.9}$$

which is equivalent to (4.1.2). The energy equation in polar coordinates is

$$\tfrac{1}{2}(\dot{r}^2 + r^2\dot{\theta}^2) + V(r) = C. \tag{4.1.10}$$

The equations are not altered if $-t$ replaces t and h has its sign reversed; so the motion is reversible. This means that if **v** were to change its sign at some point, the path would be retraced. From (4.1.9) it is clear that $\dot\theta$ must have the same sign throughout the motion; it will usually be taken as positive. Also from (4.1.9) we see that if C is positive, $\dot\theta$ tends to zero as r tends to infinity; then, since $\dot r$ tends to a finite limit, the motion must be asymptotic, such as hyperbolic motion. This will not be the case if $C = 0$ (corresponding to a parabolic orbit for Newtonian motion), since $\dot r$ tends to zero.

Eliminating $\dot\theta$ from (4.1.9) and (4.1.10), we get

$$\frac{1}{2}\dot r^2 = C - V(r) - \frac{h^2}{2r^2},\qquad(4.1.11)$$

which relates r and t. The condition that the right-hand side must be non-negative provides more stringent limits for the motion than $C - V(r) = 0$. A point where $\dot r = 0$ is called an *apsis* (plural *apsides*). Not all orbits have apsides; a spiral orbit may have none; a branch of a hyperbola has one and an elliptic orbit has two. The existence of apsides depends on the equation

$$0 = C - V(r) - \frac{h^2}{2r^2}.\qquad(4.1.12)$$

In particular, if r lies between two single roots, r_1 and r_2, of this equation, then the motion must always take place within the ring bounded by the circles with radii r_1 and r_2. An apsis at the shorter distance is called *pericentron*, and at the longer one, *apocentron* (with variations according to context, as explained in Section 1.3). The angle between two successive apsidal lines (which must be pericentron and apocentron) is called the *apsidal angle*. Since the orbits are reversible, they must be symmetrical about any apsis.

4.2 The Stability of Circular Orbits

The simplest central orbit is a circle with center at the origin; it can be described under any force of attraction $f(r)$. If the radius of the circle is a, we have $r = a$ and $\dot r = \ddot r = 0$, so that

$$a\dot\theta^2 = f(a),\qquad(4.2.1)$$

$$h = [a^3 f(a)]^{1/2},\qquad(4.2.2)$$

and $$\tfrac{1}{2}a^2\dot\theta^2 + V(a) = C.\qquad(4.2.3)$$

Now suppose that the particle receives a small impulse. The impulse can be resolved along and perpendicular to **h**. The impulse along **h** will slightly alter the value of h and the plane of the orbit (or $\hat{\mathbf{h}}$). The impulse along $\hat{\mathbf{r}}$ will leave **h** unchanged, while the transverse impulse will change h but not $\hat{\mathbf{h}}$. The resulting orbit will remain in one plane, which cannot be very different from the original plane; then, since the change in $\hat{h}$ is always small, there is no loss of generality, in considering the stability of the orbit, if we neglect it. Therefore we shall consider only the effects of the component of the impulse that is perpendicular to **h**. For the new orbit we can write

$$r^2\dot\theta = [a^3 f(a) + \delta]^{1/2}, \tag{4.2.4}$$

where δ, giving the change in h, is small. Eliminating $\dot\theta$ from (4.2.4) and (4.1.7), we get

$$\ddot r - \frac{1}{r^3}[a^3 f(a) + \delta] = -f(r). \tag{4.2.5}$$

Let us assume that the subsequent motion is very nearly circular, so that we can put

$$r = a + x,$$

where x remains small; then $f(a + x)$ can be expanded in a Taylor series in powers of x. (4.2.5) becomes

$$\ddot x - \frac{1}{a^3}\left(1 - 3\frac{x}{a}\right)[a^3 f(a) + \delta] = -f(a) - xf'(a) + O(x^2).$$

Simplifying, and ignoring terms of order x^2, we get

$$\ddot x + x\left[3\frac{f(a)}{a} + f'(a)\right] - \frac{\delta}{a^3} = 0. \tag{4.2.6}$$

The constant term on the left-hand side can be absorbed by changing the variable; this will leave an equation of the form

$$\ddot x + kx = 0.$$

If k is positive, the solution is the well-known one for simple harmonic motion. If k is negative, the solution involves hyperbolic functions and x no longer remains small; in this case the orbit deviates entirely from a circle and is said to be unstable. The condition for stability is, then,

$$3\frac{f(a)}{a} + f'(a) > 0. \tag{4.2.7}$$

We notice that if equality occurs, the δ term in (4.2.6) is enough to tip the balance and insure instability. When the inequality is reversed, the orbit is unstable.

Let us consider orbits with constant energy C, but variable angular momentum h, and assume that one such circular orbit is possible. From (4.1.11) we find

$$h^2 = 2r^2 C - 2r^2 V(r) - r^2\dot r^2. \tag{4.2.8}$$

So, for some C, if r and $\dot r$ are known, h can be found. As r and $\dot r$ vary, h will vary. We shall now investigate when h has a maximum.

Writing

$$h^2 = g(r, \dot{r})$$

and using the notation

$$g_r = \frac{\partial g}{\partial r}, \qquad g_{rr} = \frac{\partial^2 g}{\partial r^2}, \qquad g_{r\dot{r}} = \frac{\partial^2 g}{\partial r \partial \dot{r}}, \text{ etc.}$$

we have

$$d(h^2) = g_r \, dr + g_{\dot{r}} \, d\dot{r}$$

and

$$d^2(h^2) = g_{rr}(dr)^2 + 2g_{r\dot{r}} \, dr \, d\dot{r} + g_{\dot{r}\dot{r}}(d\dot{r})^2.$$

For h^2 to have a stationary value, $d(h^2) = 0$; so,

$$g_r = 0 = g_{\dot{r}}. \tag{4.2.9}$$

For that value to be a maximum, $d^2(h^2)$ must be negative for all dr and $d\dot{r}$, so that

$$g_{rr}g_{\dot{r}\dot{r}} - g_{r\dot{r}}^2 > 0. \tag{4.2.10}$$

(4.2.9) gives

$$r\left(4C - 4V(r) - 2r\frac{dV(r)}{dr} - 2\dot{r}^2\right) = 0 = -2r^2\dot{r}. \tag{4.2.11}$$

So, $\dot{r} = 0$ and therefore the orbit must be a circle; the energy is C and the circular velocity is given by the square root of $r^2(dV/dr)$. (4.2.10) gives

$$-2r^2\left[4C - 4V - 8r\frac{dV}{dr} - 2r^2\frac{d^2V}{dr^2}\right] > 0$$

or, simplifying by means of (4.2.11),

$$-2r^2\left[-6r\frac{dV}{dr} - 2r^2\frac{d^2V}{dr^2}\right] > 0.$$

But $dV/dr = f(r)$, and r^2 must be positive; so, we have

$$3f(r) + rf'(r) < 0$$

as the condition for h to have a maximum. Hence, if the circular orbit is stable, h has a maximum. Similarly, if the circular orbit is unstable, h has a minimum value.

4.3 Further Basic Formulas

Two other formulas are often used where only the form of the orbit (as opposed to its description in time) is important. We have

$$\frac{dr}{d\theta} = \frac{\dot{r}}{\dot{\theta}},$$

so, using this to eliminate $\dot{r}$ and $\dot{\theta}$ from the equations of energy and angular momentum (4.1.10) and (4.1.9), we get

$$\left(\frac{dr}{d\theta}\right)^2 = \frac{2r^4}{h^2}\left[C - V(r) - \frac{h^2}{2r^2}\right]. \tag{4.3.1}$$

Another equation that does not involve the time can be found as follows: Let $1/r = u$. Then

$$\begin{aligned}
\frac{du}{d\theta} &= -\frac{1}{r^2}\frac{dr}{d\theta} \\[2mm]
&= -\frac{1}{r^2}\cdot\frac{dr}{dt}\cdot\frac{dt}{d\theta} \\[2mm]
&= -\frac{\dot{r}}{h}.
\end{aligned}$$

Also

$$\begin{aligned}
\frac{d^2u}{d\theta^2} &= -\frac{d}{d\theta}\left(\frac{\dot{r}}{h}\right) \\[2mm]
&= -\frac{dt}{d\theta}\cdot\frac{d}{dt}\left(\frac{\dot{r}}{h}\right) \\[2mm]
&= -\frac{1}{h^2u^2}\cdot\frac{d^2r}{dt^2}.
\end{aligned}$$

Substituting into (4.1.7) and putting $r\dot{\theta}^2 = h^2u^3$, we get

$$\frac{d^2u}{d\theta^2} + u = \frac{1}{h^2u^2}f\left(\frac{1}{u}\right). \tag{4.3.2}$$

In general (and as long as we have a conservative field), (4.3.2) is not so useful as (4.3.1), since the latter is only a first-order differential equation. In fact (4.3.2) can be recovered (rather laboriously) by differentiating (4.3.1), and its only advantage occurs when $f(1/u)$ has such a form that the solution can be written down directly; this is the case when

$$f\left(\frac{1}{u}\right) = au^2 + bu^3.$$

Equations (4.1.7) and (4.1.8) require four arbitrary constants for their complete solution; so far we have discussed two, h and C. Since θ does not occur explicitly in the equations of motion, but only $\dot{\theta}$ and $\ddot{\theta}$, an arbitrary constant can be added to θ in the final answer. Once the equation of the orbit is known, as a function $g(r,\theta) = 0$, say, (4.1.9) can be used to find a first-order differential equation for r or θ in terms of t; the solution to this supplies the fourth arbitrary constant in the form $r = r(t - t_0)$, $\theta = \theta(t - t_0)$. Alternatively we can use the expression for the areal velocity,

$$\frac{dA}{dt} = \frac{1}{2}r^2\dot{\theta} = \frac{1}{2}h.$$

Then

$$A = \tfrac{1}{2}ht + \text{constant.} \tag{4.3.3}$$

This is useful when the area A can be conveniently calculated as a function of r or θ. In particular, if the area swept out between two points r_1 and r_2 is known, then the time in the orbit between these points is

$$t_{21} = \frac{2}{h} A_{21}.$$

The uses of these equations will be illustrated by some examples in the following four sections.

4.4 Newtonian Attraction

(The student is advised to review his knowledge of conics at this stage and to refer to Appendix A.)

If a massive body is at the origin, it will give rise to a field of force

$$- \frac{\mu}{r^2} \hat{\mathbf{r}}$$

according to Newton's law of gravitation. So

$$f = \frac{\mu}{r^2} \quad \text{and} \quad V = -\frac{\mu}{r}.$$

Here we assume that the attracting body is at rest; a different and more general treatment will be given in Chapter Six. (4.3.2) gives

$$\frac{d^2u}{d\theta^2} + u = \frac{\mu}{h^2}$$

and the solution to this may be written down at once as

$$u - \frac{\mu}{h^2} = A \cos(\theta - \theta_0).$$

This can be put into the form

$$\frac{p}{r} = 1 + e \cos(\theta - \theta_0), \tag{4.4.1}$$

where

$$p = \frac{h^2}{\mu} \tag{4.4.2}$$

and e and θ_0 are arbitrary constants. But (4.4.1) is the polar equation of a conic with a focus at the origin, eccentricity e, and *semilatus rectum* (or *parameter*) p.

We could now use (4.4.1) and (4.1.9) to find an equation for r or θ in terms of t, and the solution of this would provide another arbitrary constant which, together with h, e, and θ_0, completes the solution. This solution does not include C, and since the energy integral is often very convenient to work with, C will now be found in terms of the other constants of integration.

The energy integral is

$$\frac{v^2}{2} - \frac{\mu}{r} = C.$$

Now

$$v^2 = \dot{r}^2 + r^2\dot{\theta}^2.$$

Differentiating (4.4.1) with respect to t, we have

$$-\frac{p}{r^2}\dot{r} = -e\sin(\theta - \theta_0)\dot{\theta},$$

so

$$\dot{r} = \frac{eh}{p}\sin(\theta - \theta_0) \qquad \text{(since } r^2\dot{\theta} = h)$$

$$= \frac{e\mu}{h}\sin(\theta - \theta_0). \tag{4.4.3}$$

Also

$$r\dot{\theta} = \frac{h}{r}$$

$$= \frac{\mu}{h}[1 + e\cos(\theta - \theta_0)].$$

So

$$v^2 = \left(\frac{\mu}{h}\right)^2[1 + 2e\cos(\theta - \theta_0) + e^2]$$

$$= \mu\left[\frac{2}{r} - \frac{1 - e^2}{p}\right]. \tag{4.4.4}$$

Hence

$$C = -\mu\frac{1 - e^2}{2p}. \tag{4.4.5}$$

For the ellipse, parabola, and hyperbola we have $C = -\mu/2a$, 0, and $+\mu/2a$, respectively. Hence the energy of the orbit depends only on the major axis.

Now consider equation (4.3.3) and apply it to an elliptic orbit. Let us start to measure A, the area swept out by the radius vector, when $t = 0$, and continue until the particle has returned to its starting point in the ellipse; then A will be equal to the area of the ellipse, πab, and we find that the time taken over one complete orbit is

$$P = \frac{2}{h}\pi ab.$$

Since $b = a\sqrt{1 - e^2}$, and $h^2/\mu = p = a(1 - e^2)$, we have

$$P = 2\pi \frac{a^{3/2}}{\mu^{1/2}}. \tag{4.4.6}$$

P is the period of the elliptic orbit; this also depends only on the major axis of the ellipse.

The energy equation for an elliptic orbit is

$$v^2 = \mu\left(\frac{2}{r} - \frac{1}{a}\right)$$

so that the energy of the orbit is equal to the energy of a particle at rest on the circumference of a circle with center the origin and radius $2a$. Hence the speed at any point in the orbit is equal to the speed that would be acquired in falling from rest on the circumference of the circle to that point.

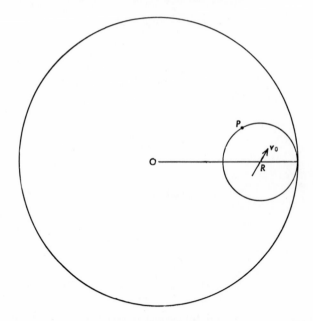

Figure 4.1

If a particle is projected from a point R, distant c from the center of force O, with speed v_0, then it will move in an ellipse, parabola, or hyperbola according as v_0^2 is less than, equal to, or greater than $2\mu/c$. Let the first condition hold; then the major axis of the ellipse is given by

$$v_0^2 = \mu\left(\frac{2}{c} - \frac{1}{a}\right).$$

Let P be the other focus of the ellipse; this will vary, depending on the direction of projection. But since $OR + RP = 2a$, then $RP = 2a - c$, so that P must lie on the circumference of a circle with center R and radius $(2a - c)$. If the orbit passes through a point S, then similar reasoning shows that P must lie on the circumference of a circle with center S and radius $(2a - OS)$.

Consider the problem of projecting the particle from R with initial speed v_0 so that it later passes through S. If the two circles intersect each other in two real points, there are two possible foci P, and two possible routes from R to S with initial speed v_0. If the circles do not intersect, then S cannot be reached from R with this speed. The limit of accessibility occurs when the two circles touch, as shown in Figure 4.2; in this case there is a unique orbit from R to S.

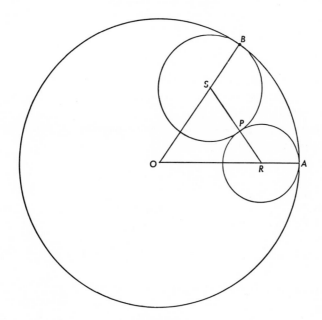

Figure 4.2

Consider the locus of points S which are just accessible from R. In the notation of Figure 4.2 we have

$$OS + SR = OS + SP + PR$$
$$= OS + SB + RA$$
$$= OB + RA$$
$$= OA + RA,$$

which is constant. So the locus of S is an ellipse, with foci O and R and major axis $OA + RA$, touching at A the circle with center O and radius OA. The tangent to this ellipse at S is the bisector of the angle BSR; since this must also be the tangent to the orbit from R to S (the bisector of the angle BSP), the ellipses touch at S. Therefore the locus of S is the envelope of all the possible orbits from R. This ellipse defines the region of accessibility from R corresponding to the initial speed of projection v_0.

4.5 Einstein's Modification of the Equation of the Orbit

As a consequence of the theory of relativity, Newton's law is modified so that the equation of the orbit becomes

$$\frac{d^2u}{d\theta^2} + u = \frac{\mu}{h^2} + \alpha u^2 \tag{4.5.1}$$

where

$$\alpha = 3\frac{\mu}{c^2}. \tag{4.5.2}$$

c is the speed of light, so α is a small quantity, the square of which will be neglected. The ratio of αu^2 to μ/h^2 is equal to three times the square of the transverse velocity in units of c.

Equation (4.5.1) is to be solved by approximations. A first approximation, found by neglecting α altogether, is

$$u = \frac{\mu}{h^2}[1 + e \cos(\theta - \theta_0)].$$

To find a better approximation, we substitute this value of u into the right-hand side of (4.5.1); this gives

$$\frac{d^2u}{d\theta^2} + u = \frac{\mu}{h^2} + \alpha\frac{\mu^2}{h^4} + 2\alpha\frac{\mu^2}{h_4} e \cos(\theta - \theta_0) + \frac{1}{2}\alpha\frac{\mu^2}{h^4} e^2[1 + \cos 2(\theta - \theta_0)]. \tag{4.5.3}$$

Now it is easily verified that a particular integral of

$$\frac{d^2u}{d\theta^2} + u = \alpha\frac{\mu^2}{h^4}\left\{1 + 2e \cos(\theta - \theta_0) + \frac{1}{2} e^2[1 + \cos 2(\theta - \theta_0]\right\}$$

is

$$u = \alpha\frac{\mu^2}{h^4}\left\{\left(1 + \frac{1}{2} e^2\right) + e\theta \sin(\theta - \theta_0) - \frac{1}{6} e^2 \cos 2(\theta - \theta_0)\right\}.$$

The complete solution of (4.5.3) is, then,

$$u - \frac{1}{p}[1 + e \cos(\theta - \theta_0)] = \frac{\alpha}{p^2}\left\{\left(1 + \frac{1}{2} e^2\right) + e\theta \sin(\theta - \theta_0)\right.$$
$$\left. - \frac{1}{6} e^2 \cos 2(\theta - \theta_0)\right\}, \tag{4.5.4}$$

where $p = h^2/\mu$.

Consider the modification to Keplerian motion described by (4.5.4); this is due to the terms on the right-hand side. The first of these has the effect of slightly increasing u by a constant quantity; this amount will be imperceptible. The third term is small and periodic and its effects will also be imperceptible. But the other term, while fluctuating, has a steadily increasing amplitude, so that after a long enough time it is sure to have a perceptible effect. Ignoring the other terms, we have, so far as observable effects are concerned,

$$u = \frac{1}{p}[1 + e \cos(\theta - \theta_0)] + \frac{\alpha e}{p} \theta \sin(\theta - \theta_0). \tag{4.5.5}$$

Let

$$k\theta = \frac{\alpha\theta}{p},$$

then, neglecting α^2, (4.5.5) can be written

$$u = \frac{1}{p}[1 + e \cos(\theta - \theta_0 - k\theta)]. \tag{4.5.6,}$$

Now at any instant $(\theta_0 + k\theta)$ is the angular coordinate of perihelion, and from (4.5.6) we see that at any instant the planet may be considered to be moving in an ellipse. But the coordinate that defines the line of apsides is continually changing, so that the ellipse can be considered as rotating slowly in space. The rate of angular change of the line of apsides is

$$\Delta\omega = \frac{2\pi\alpha}{p} \text{ per period.} \tag{4.5.7}$$

Now, if we substitute the values for the orbit of Mercury, we find that the change, $\Delta\omega$, in a century is 43″. This may seem to be a very small quantity, but its effects can be observed, and until the advent of the theory of relativity this 43″ remained as a serious discrepancy between observation and prediction based on Newton's law.

4.6   The Case $f(r) = n^2 r$

Here it is simplest to resolve the equation of motion along the x- and y-axes to get

$$\ddot{x} + n^2 x = 0 \quad \text{and} \quad \ddot{y} + n^2 y = 0.$$

The solution is

$$x = A \cos(nt + a), \quad y = B \cos(nt + b).$$

This motion is always finite and must possess apsides. Let the axes be directed so that one apsis lies on the y-axis, and let $t = 0$ correspond to this apsis. Then at $t = 0$, $x = 0$, and $\dot{y} = 0$, so that $a = \pm(\pi/2)$ and $b = 0$. Hence the solution can be put in the form

$$x = A \sin nt, \quad y = B \cos nt,$$

so that the orbit is an ellipse with the origin at its center.

4.7 The Case $f(r) = \mu/r^3$: Cotes' Spirals

This case can be discussed rather simply for two reasons; (4.3.2) takes an elementary form, and f is such that the equations of motion can be integrated easily. We have

$$V(r) = -\frac{\mu}{2r^2},$$

so

$$\ddot{r} - r\dot{\theta}^2 = -\frac{\mu}{r^3}, \tag{4.7.1}$$

$$r^2\dot{\theta} = h, \tag{4.7.2}$$

and

$$\dot{r}^2 + r^2\dot{\theta}^2 - \frac{\mu}{r^2} = 2C. \tag{4.7.3}$$

Multiplying (4.7.1) by r and adding (4.7.3), we get

$$r\ddot{r} + \dot{r}^2 = 2C.$$

This can be integrated at once to give

$$r\dot{r} = 2Ct + A \tag{4.7.4}$$

and

$$r^2 = 2Ct^2 + 2At + B, \tag{4.7.5}$$

where A and B are arbitrary constants.

If (4.7.5) is valid for all t, then the right-hand side must be positive for all t, or

$$C > 0 \quad \text{and} \quad 2BC - A^2 > 0. \tag{4.7.6}$$

In this case the motion will never terminate (we assume that it would terminate if the particle fell into the origin); r has one minimum value, an apsis, and the orbit branches off asymptotically on either side.

If the conditions (4.7.6) do not hold, the motion must involve the particle's falling into (or starting from) the origin, so that the motion must begin or end. If C is negative, the motion will begin and end, and the orbit will possess one apsis. Otherwise r will vary monatonically between zero and infinity, and there will be no apsis; the motion is asymptotic unless $C = 0$.

The solution can be continued as follows: From (4.2.8) we have

$$\begin{aligned}
h^2 &= 2Cr^2 + \mu - (r\dot{r})^2 \\
&= 2C(2Ct^2 + 2At + B) + \mu - (2Ct + A)^2 \\
&= \mu + 2BC - A^2.
\end{aligned}$$

Now

$$\dot{\theta} = \frac{h}{r^2}$$

so

$$\theta = (\mu + 2BC - A^2)^{1/2} \int \frac{dt}{2Ct^2 + 2At + B} + D.$$

The various cases depending on the signs of C and $(2BC - A^2)$ are reflected in the behavior of the integral. A full discussion is left to the student; there are six separate cases to be considered. These curves are known as *Cotes' spirals*.

The form of the orbit can also be investigated by using (4.3.2). We have

$$\frac{d^2u}{d\theta^2} + u = \frac{\mu}{h^2} u$$

or

$$\frac{d^2u}{d\theta^2} + u\left(1 - \frac{\mu}{h^2}\right) = 0$$

or, substituting for h^2,

$$\frac{d^2u}{d\theta^2} + \frac{u}{h^2}(2BC - A^2) = 0.$$

Again, we are concerned with the sign of $(2BC - A^2)$.

An interesting situation occurs when a force ν/r^3 is superimposed onto another field, $f(r)$. The equations of motion for the field $f(r)$ alone can be written

$$\frac{1}{2}\dot{r}^2 = \frac{h^2}{2r^4}\left(\frac{dr}{d\theta}\right)^2 = C - V(r) - \frac{h^2}{2r^2}. \tag{4.7.7}$$

With the added attraction ν/r^3, the equations of motion become

$$\frac{1}{2}\dot{r}^2 = \frac{h_1^2}{2r^4}\left(\frac{dr}{d\theta}\right)^2 = C_1 - V(r) - \frac{h_1^2 - \nu}{2r^2}. \tag{4.7.8}$$

h_1 and C_1 are constants for the new motion; if they are chosen such that

$$h_1^2 = h^2 + \nu \quad \text{and} \quad C_1 = C, \tag{4.7.9}$$

then the equations (4.7.8) become

$$\frac{1}{2}\dot{r}^2 = \frac{h^2}{2r^4}\left[\frac{dr}{d(k\theta)}\right]^2 = C - V(r) - \frac{h^2}{2r^2}$$

where $k = h/h_1$.

Now suppose that the original equations have the solution

$$r = r_1(t), \quad r = r_2(\theta).$$

Then in the new motion,

$$r = r_1(t - t_0), \quad r = r_2[k(\theta - \theta_0)].$$

So, the new orbit resembles the old except that the latter is continuously rotating. Apsidal angles are increased by the factor $1/k$. This result was known to Newton.

4.8   To Find the Law of Force, Given the Orbit

So far we have started with a law of force and have investigated possible orbits. The reverse problem of finding the law of force that may be responsible for a given orbit is also important.

Consider the case of a circular orbit of radius a, passing through the origin. If the direction $\theta = 0$ passes through the center of the circle, the polar equation is

$$r = 2a \cos \theta. \tag{4.8.1}$$

Then

$$u = \frac{1}{2a \cos \theta},$$

$$2a \frac{du}{d\theta} = \frac{\sin \theta}{\cos^2 \theta},$$

$$2a \frac{d^2u}{d\theta^2} = \frac{1 + \sin^2 \theta}{\cos^3 \theta},$$

and

$$\frac{d^2u}{d\theta^2} + u = \frac{1}{a \cos^3 \theta}.$$

So, by (4.3.2), we have

$$f(r) = \frac{h^2}{ar^2 \cos^3 \theta}.$$

This field of force is not conservative, nor is it unique, for we can substitute from (4.8.1) to get laws of force such as

$$f(r) = \frac{h^2}{2a^2r \cos^4 \theta},$$

or

$$f(r) = \frac{h^2}{4a^3 \cos^5 \theta},$$

or infinitely many others. But if we want a conservative field, we must use (4.8.1) to eliminate θ. In this case the solution is unique, and we have

$$f(r) = \frac{8a^2h^2}{r^5}. \tag{4.8.2}$$

If we are interested only in conservative fields, it is usually simpler to use equation (4.3.1). This avoids the use of u and involves only one differentiation. Here the equation of the orbit must be used to eliminate θ from $dr/d\theta$. For the case considered above we have

$$\left(\frac{dr}{d\theta}\right)^2 = 4a^2 \sin^2 \theta = 4a^2 - r^2,$$

so

$$V(r) = C - \frac{h^2}{2r^2} - \frac{h^2}{2r^4}(4a^2 - r^2)$$

$$= C - \frac{2a^2h^2}{r^4},$$

leading immediately to (4.8.2).

Now consider the case of a circular orbit of radius a, where the center of force O is inside the circle and at a distance c from its center C. Let P be a point on the circumference of the circle, and let $\angle POC = \theta$. From the triangle OPC we have

$$a^2 = c^2 + r^2 - 2cr \cos \theta,$$

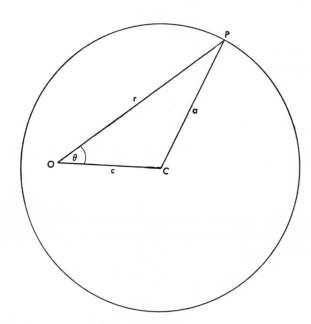

Figure 4.3

which is the polar equation of the circle. Differentiating this we have

$$0 = (2r - 2c \cos \theta)dr + 2cr \sin \theta \, d\theta,$$

so that

$$\left(\frac{dr}{d\theta}\right)^2 = \frac{4c^2 r^2 \sin^2 \theta}{4(r - c \cos \theta)^2}$$

$$= \frac{r^2[4c^2 r^2 - (a^2 - c^2 - r^2)^2]}{(a^2 - c^2 + r^2)^2}.$$

But

$$\left(\frac{dr}{d\theta}\right)^2 = \frac{2r^4}{h^2}(C - V(r)) - r^2$$

so

$$\frac{2r^4}{h^2}(C - V(r)) = \frac{4a^2 r^4}{(a^2 - c^2 + r^2)^2}$$

and

$$C - V(r) = \frac{2a^2h^2}{(a^2 - c^2 + r^2)^2}.$$ (4.8.3)

Then

$$f(r) = \frac{8a^2h^2r}{(a^2 - c^2 + r^2)^3}.$$ (4.8.4)

This solution is unique, provided $c \neq 0$.

It should be remembered that if we start off with the law of force (4.8.4), then there are infinitely many possible orbits, of which the circular orbit is only one. Also, if we wanted a law of force to account for *any* circular orbit with the center of force *anywhere* inside the circle, then (4.8.4) would be no good, since it specifies $a^2 - c^2$.

Consider the Keplerian orbit. From Kepler's first two laws it is established that the orbit of a planet is central and that its equation can be expressed as

$$\frac{p}{r} = 1 + e \cos \theta.$$

Here p and e are not specified; in fact we can give e any positive value. From the equation of the orbit,

$$\left(\frac{dr}{d\theta}\right)^2 = \left(\frac{e}{p} r^2 \sin \theta\right)^2$$

$$= \frac{r^4}{p^2}\left[e^2 - \left(\frac{p}{r} - 1\right)^2\right].$$

So, from (4.3.1),

$$\frac{h^2}{2p^2}\left[e^2 - \left(\frac{p}{r} - 1\right)^2\right] + \frac{h^2}{2r^2} = C - V(r)$$

or

$$\frac{h^2}{pr} + \frac{h^2(e^2 - 1)}{2p^2} = C - V(r).$$

Then, with the proviso that V tends to zero as r tends to infinity, the constant terms go out, and we have

$$V(r) = -\frac{h^2/p}{r} = -\frac{\mu}{r}.$$

This is the inverse square law of attraction. It will account for any conic orbit as long as the origin is at one focus.

In writing down (4.1.1) we considered $-f\hat{r}$ to be the force per unit mass. Assuming the form $f(r) = \mu/r^2$, it follows that the force acting on a planet of mass m is $-(\mu m/r^2)\hat{r}$. Now, from Newton's third law, the planet must be exerting an equal and opposite force on the Sun; but this force should be predicted by the same inverse square law and must be of the form $-(\mu' M/r^2)\hat{r}$, where M is the mass of the Sun. Hence both forces must be equal in magnitude to

$$G \frac{Mm}{r^2}.$$

This embodies Newton's law of gravitation. G is the Newtonian gravitational constant, and its value is found experimentally to be 6.670×10^{-8} c.g.s. units. The motion observed in the solar system confirms that G is a constant which is independent of physical conditions such as temperature or chemical composition, and it is reasonable to expect that it is a universal constant of nature.

Since M is much greater than m for any planet, the effects of the attraction of that planet on the Sun are small compared with the effects of the attraction of the Sun on the planet; so the situation in the solar system corresponds approximately to a model with a fixed center of attraction. The general problem, in which two masses move in one another's fields, is considered in Chapter Six.

4.9 The "Universality" of Newton's Law

Newton's law of gravitation is described as being "universal." It is applied in many contexts, and it is important to see what justification there may be for applying it to situations outside the solar system. We have seen that Newton's law follows from Kepler's first two laws of planetary motion (the third cannot be invoked because it is not accurate), so if we can find two bodies traveling around each other in accord with Kepler's first two laws, we know that they are subject to Newton's law.

Fortunately there are many such systems, where two stars are observed to be moving around each other; these are called *visual binaries* (as opposed to other types of binary, which reveal their duplicity by showing two spectra, or one spectrum with regularly shifting lines, or by eclipsing each other). Where two such stars are observed, the motion of the fainter star, or *companion*, is plotted with respect to the brighter or *primary* star. These observed, or *apparent*, orbits are found to be ellipses, and the law of areas about the primary is obeyed; but the primaries are not at the foci of the ellipses. This is not necessarily a contradiction of Kepler's first law, since we are not observing the *true* orbit, but a projection of it. The true orbit, S, will lie in a plane that is unlikely to be at right angles to the line of sight. The apparent orbit S' is the projection of S onto the plane (sometimes called the *plane of the sky*) which is at right angles to the line of sight.

Now an ellipse will always project into another ellipse, and therefore since S' is observed to be an ellipse, S is an ellipse also. The law of areas depends on ratios; but ratios are not altered by projection, and since the law of areas holds for the apparent orbit, it must also hold for the true orbit. Hence we can apply the theory of central orbits to the true orbit. We assume that the stars are spheres, so that their fields depend on the distance from their centers and not on orientation, and we assume conservative fields.

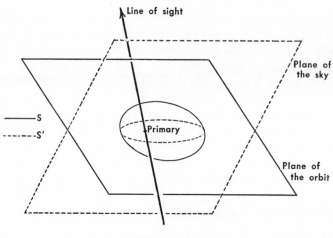

Figure 4.4

Now, with a suitable projection, a focus of S can be made to project into any desired point of S' (although the shape of S' will naturally be affected by the projection), so whatever the position of the primary in S', there is always a possible ellipse S with the primary at one focus. Thus it is possible, by geometrical reasoning, to argue that Kepler's first two laws *could* hold for the motion of double stars so that Newton's law would follow. But we want to show that Newton's law is the *only* plausible one, and to do this we must show that there is no reasonable law to account for elliptic motion unless the center of attraction is at one focus of the ellipse.

Consider an elliptic orbit described under the action of a force directed toward an arbitrary point inside the ellipse. If this point is taken as origin, the equation of the ellipse must be taken in its general form:

$$g(x,y) \equiv ax^2 + 2nxy + by^2 + 2mx + 2ly + c = 0. \qquad (4.9.1)$$

To find a law of force that is responsible for this orbit, we can change to polar coordinates and use (4.3.2). But it is more straightforward to derive an expression for the force in terms of cartesian coordinates.

The equations of motion are

$$\ddot{x} = -f(r)\frac{x}{r}, \qquad \ddot{y} = -f(r)\frac{y}{r}, \qquad (4.9.2)$$

and the angular momentum integral can be written

$$x\dot{y} - y\dot{x} = h. \qquad (4.9.3)$$

The equation of the orbit is $g(x,y) = 0$. Differentiating this with respect to t, we find

$$\frac{\partial g}{\partial x}\cdot\frac{dx}{dt} + \frac{\partial g}{\partial y}\cdot\frac{dy}{dt} = 0$$

which can be written

$$g_x\dot{x} + g_y\dot{y} = 0.$$

Eliminating $\dot{y}$ by means of (4.9.3), we have

$$\dot{x} = -\frac{hg_y}{xg_x + yg_y}.$$

Similarly,

$$\dot{y} = \frac{hg_x}{xg_x + yg_y}.$$

Differentiating again, we have

$$\ddot{x} = \frac{\partial \dot{x}}{\partial x}\dot{x} + \frac{\partial \dot{x}}{\partial y}\dot{y}.$$

Substituting for x and performing the differentiations, we get, eventually,

$$\ddot{x} = \frac{h^2x(-g_y^2g_{xx} + 2g_xg_yg_{xy} - g_x^2g_{yy})}{(xg_x + yg_y)^3}.$$

Then, from (4.9.2), we have

$$f(r) = h^2r\frac{(g_y^2g_{xx} - 2g_xg_yg_{xy} + g_x^2g_{yy})}{(xg_x + yg_y)^3}. \qquad (4.9.4)$$

This law of force will account for any orbit, $g(x,y) = 0$. Now substituting from (4.9.1), differentiating, and using (4.9.1) to eliminate quadratic terms, we get

$$f(r) = h^2r\frac{(abc + 2lmn - al^2 - bm^2 - cn^2)}{(mx + ly + c)^3}. \qquad (4.9.5)$$

Now the line $mx + ly + c = 0$ is called the *polar* of the origin with respect to the conic, and the distance of the point (x,y) from this line is the positive value of

$$\frac{mx + ly + c}{(l^2 + m^2)^{1/2}}.$$

Hence (4.9.5) can be expressed verbally in the following form, due to Hamilton:

For a particle at P to describe an elliptic orbit under the action of a central force directed toward the point O, the force acting on P varies directly as the radius from O and inversely as the cube of the perpendicular distance from P to the polar of O with respect to the ellipse.

This is not valid if O is at the center of the ellipse, since then the polar of O is at infinity. A proof of this theorem, using projective geometry, is given in *Introduction to Dynamics* by L. A. Pars, p. 299 (Ref. 13).

In general the law of force given by Hamilton's theorem is not conservative. If it is conservative, then for points (x,y) on the ellipse, $(mx + ly + c)$ must be a function of r. To investigate this condition, rotate the axes so that the polar of the origin is parallel to the y-axis, when $l = 0$. Then, for points on the ellipse, x must be a function of r. This can be written

$$x = q(r), \tag{4.9.6}$$

an expression that must be identical with the equation of the ellipse. It follows that (4.9.6) must be a quadratic in x and y, and this means that the function q is confined to the following two forms: (1) $q(r) \equiv a + br^2$, and (2) $q(r) \equiv a + br$. [The form $q(r) \equiv a + br + cr^2$ does not make (4.9.6) a quadratic in x and y.]

Form (1) gives a circular orbit with the center of force somewhere inside the circle. This is not acceptable for various reasons. The force exerted by the primary would at first increase and later decrease with increasing distance from the star, which seems unlikely. It is strange that *only* circular orbits occur. That there are other orbits close to the circular orbits can be seen as follows: Consider the apsidal equation, (4.1.12). For the circular orbit this has two positive roots, $r = (a + c)$ and $(a - c)$. Then, provided c is not zero, *small* changes in the energy and angular momentum will still leave the apsidal equation with two positive roots (which will differ only slightly from those of the circular orbit), and the motion will be confined to values of r lying between these roots; but it will no longer be circular, so that the observed orbit will no longer be elliptic. Hence this case can be disregarded. (In some cases spectroscopic observations yield the component of orbital velocity in the line of sight; this is of such a nature as to rule out these circular orbits.)

Form (2) gives the orbit

$$r \cos \theta = a + br,$$

since $x = r \cos \theta$. But this is the Keplerian orbit which we are trying to justify.

One other case must be discussed. If the primary is at the center of the ellipse S, then we have the law of force $f = n^2 r$. But from the properties of projection the primary will still be at the center of the apparent ellipse, S', and this is not observed.

We have established that Newton's law is the only plausible law governing the Keplerian motion within the solar system, and, where they are sufficiently observed, the motions of exterior systems. In addition this law has successfully predicted or accounted for nearly every other observed motion that involves deviations from Keplerian motion caused by perturbations. It has also led to an accurate modification of Kepler's third law. The remainder of the text will be devoted to a discussion of some of its consequences.

4.10 Worked Examples

The problems below are intended to get the student thoroughly accustomed to working with central orbits. In many cases the solution is halfway achieved when the energy and angular momentum integrals have been written down, and the values of h and C found from the initial conditions. The student should have these equations at his fingertips; he should also be able to use all the properties of Keplerian motion discussed above. Facility with these formulas can only be achieved through practice. Some of the methods that are useful in solving these problems are illustrated in the examples worked below.

1. *A particle moves in a circular orbit of radius a under an attraction to a point inside the circle. The greatest and least speeds of the particle in its orbit are v_1 and v_2. (See Figure 4.5, page 78.) Prove that the period is*

$$\frac{\pi a(v_1 + v_2)}{v_1 v_2}.$$

Since the angular momentum about the center of force is constant, the greatest and least speeds must be achieved at the ends of a diameter that passes through the center of force. Let the pericentron distance be x; then the angular momenta at the ends of this diameter are $x v_1$ and $(2a - x)v_2$. But these are both equal to h, so

$$h = x v_1 = (2a - x)v_2.$$

Eliminating x and solving for h, we find

$$h = 2a \frac{v_1 v_2}{v_1 + v_2}.$$

The areal velocity is $\tfrac{1}{2}h$, and the product of the areal velocity and the period is equal to the total area of the circle, πa^2. Hence

$$P \cdot a \frac{v_1 v_2}{v_1 + v_2} = \pi a^2$$

and the answer follows at once.

[N.B. A student who set about this problem by finding the law of force and working from that would find himself in difficulties.]

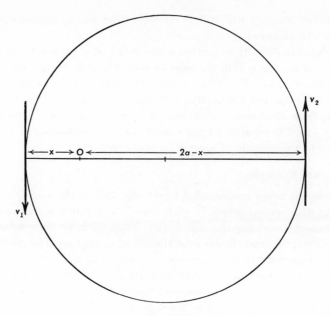

Figure 4.5

2. *A particle is projected with velocity* $\sqrt{2\mu/3a^3}$ *at right angles to the radius vector at a distance* a *from the center of an attracting force* μ/r^4 *per unit mass. Find the path of the particle and show that the time it takes to reach the center is*

$$\frac{3\pi}{8}\sqrt{\frac{3a^5}{2\mu}}.$$

From the initial conditions the angular momentum is

$$h = a\sqrt{\frac{2\mu}{3a^3}} = \sqrt{\frac{2\mu}{3a}}.$$

The potential function is $V = -\mu/3r^3$, so the energy of the orbit is

$$C = \frac{1}{2}\left(\frac{2\mu}{3a^3}\right) - \frac{\mu}{3a^3} = 0.$$

Then, from equation (4.3.1), we have

$$\left(\frac{dr}{d\theta}\right)^2 = \frac{2r^4}{h^2}\left(\frac{\mu}{3r^3} - \frac{h^2}{2r^2}\right)$$

and substituting for h and simplifying, we get

$$\left(\frac{dr}{d\theta}\right)^2 = ar - r^2$$

$$= \tfrac{1}{4}[a^2 - (2r - a)^2].$$

Then

$$\frac{2dr}{[a^2 - (2r - a)^2]^{1/2}} = d\theta$$

which integrates to give

$$\cos^{-1}\left(\frac{2r - a}{a}\right) = \theta - \theta_0$$

or

$$2r = a[1 + \cos(\theta - \theta_0)].$$

Let us measure θ such that $\theta = 0$ when $r = a$; then $\theta_0 = 0$.

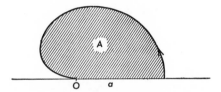

Figure 4.6

As θ goes from 0 to π, r goes from a to 0. The area swept out by the radius vector is

$$A = \frac{1}{2}\int_0^\pi r^2\, d\theta = \frac{a^2}{8}\int_0^\pi (1 + \cos\theta)^2 d\theta$$

$$= \frac{a^2}{8}\left[\theta + 2\sin\theta + \frac{1}{2}\theta + \frac{1}{4}\sin 2\theta\right]_0^\pi$$

$$= \frac{3a^2\pi}{16}.$$

The time taken is this area divided by the areal velocity, or

$$\frac{2A}{h} = \frac{3\pi}{8}\sqrt{\frac{3a^5}{2\mu}}.$$

3. *A particle moving under the action of a central force of attraction μ/r^2 is projected from infinity with velocity V so as to pass the center of force at a distance c if the force did not exist. Show that the equation of the orbit is*

$$\frac{1}{r} = \frac{\mu}{V^2 c^2} + \frac{1}{c}\cos\theta\sqrt{1 + \frac{\mu^2}{c^2 V^4}}$$

where θ is measured from an apsis.

From the properties of motion under the inverse square law of attraction, we know that the orbit is a conic, and since the particle has finite velocity at infinity, it is a hyperbola. Then if θ is measured from the apsis, the polar equation of the orbit is

$$\frac{p}{r} = 1 + e \cos \theta,$$

where

$$p = a(e^2 - 1) = \frac{h^2}{\mu}, \tag{1}$$

h being the angular momentum.

The energy equation is

$$v^2 = \mu \left(\frac{2}{r} + \frac{1}{a} \right),$$

and from the initial conditions, this gives

$$a = \frac{\mu}{V^2}.$$

Also from the initial conditions,

$$h = cV.$$

Substituting for a and h into equation (1) and solving for e^2, we find

$$e^2 = 1 + \frac{c^2 V^4}{\mu^2}$$

so that the equation of the orbit becomes

$$\frac{(c^2 V^2/\mu)}{r} = 1 + \cos \theta \sqrt{1 + \frac{c^2 V^4}{\mu}},$$

from which the result follows at once.

4. *A particle is projected from a point A at right angles to SA and is acted on by a force varying inversely as the square of the distance toward S. If the intensity of the force is unity at unit distance, SA, and the speed of projection is $\frac{1}{2}$, prove that the eccentricity of the orbit is $\frac{3}{4}$ and find the periodic time.*

With the dimensions given in the question, the law of attraction is $1/r^2$, and the potential function is $-(1/r)$. The energy of the orbit is

$$C = \frac{1}{2} v^2 - \frac{1}{r} = \frac{1}{8} - 1$$

which is negative; hence the orbit is an ellipse. Using the energy integral in the form

$$v^2 = \frac{2}{r} - \frac{1}{a},$$

we find $a = 4/7$.

The angular momentum of the orbit is $\frac{1}{2}$, and since

$$a(1 - e^2) = h^2,$$

we have

$$\tfrac{4}{7}(1 - e^2) = \tfrac{1}{4}$$

so that $$e = \tfrac{3}{4}.$$

To find the period, we use the formula

$$P = 2\pi \sqrt{\frac{a^3}{\mu}}, \qquad \text{where } \mu = 1$$

so that $P = 16\pi/7\sqrt{7}$ units of time.

Problems

1. Find the condition for the law of force to result in finite motion for all values of C.

2. A particle moves in a field of force μ/r^2 toward the origin. Prove that its orbit is a conic. If the maximum and minimum speeds in an elliptical orbit are v_1 and v_2, find the values of a, e, the period and the angular momentum, in terms of v_1, v_2, and μ.

3. A particle moves in a field of force μ/r^2 toward the origin. It is projected with velocity V from a point at distance R, at an angle β to the radius vector. Prove that in the subsequent motion

$$\dot{r}^2 = V^2 - \frac{2\mu}{R} + \frac{2\mu}{r} - \frac{R^2 V^2 \sin^2 \beta}{r^2}.$$

Hence find conditions satisfied by R, V, and β, that r may (a) increase steadily to infinity, (b) decrease to a minimum and then increase to infinity, (c) oscillate between two fixed values.

4. Show that in elliptic motion about a focus under attraction μ/r^2, the radial velocity is given by the equation

$$r^2 \dot{r}^2 = \frac{\mu}{a} \{a(1 + e) - r\} \{r - a(1 - e)\}.$$

5. Show that for a central orbit described under the law of force μ/r^2, the apsidal distances are given by the roots of the quadratic

$$2Cr^2 + 2\mu r - h^2 = 0.$$

Hence, or otherwise, show that for an elliptic orbit $C = -(\mu/2a)$ and $h^2 = \mu p$, where p is the length of the semilatus rectum.

6. Find the condition for a circular orbit, described under the law of force

$f(r) = \mu/r^n$, to be stable. Investigate the stability of circular motion under the following laws of force:

$$\frac{\mu}{r^2}, \qquad \frac{\nu}{r^3}, \qquad \frac{\mu}{r^2} + \frac{\nu}{r^3}, \qquad \frac{\mu}{r^2} + \frac{\nu}{r^4}.$$

7. A particle moves subject to a repulsive force μ/r^2 away from the origin. Show that the orbit is the branch of a hyperbola that does not contain the origin, the origin being at a focus. If the particle is projected with velocity $\sqrt{\mu/c}$ from a point distant c from the origin, at right angles to the radius vector, prove that the orbit is a branch of a rectangular hyperbola.

8. A particle describes an ellipse under the action of a central force directed toward a focus. Find, in terms of the eccentricity of the ellipse, the ratio of the time spent near pericentron between the ends of the latus rectum to the total period of the orbit.

9. A particle acted on by a central force μ/r^2 is projected with velocity u at right angles to the radius vector at a distance c from the center of force. Investigate the limits of u that yield the various types of conic orbit, and in the case of the elliptic orbit find the eccentricity and major axis, and also find the condition as to whether the projection point is at the end of the major axis at pericentron or apocentron.

10. A body is describing an ellipse of eccentricity e under the action of a force tending toward a focus, and when it is at the near apsis the center of force is transferred to the other focus. Prove that the eccentricity of the new orbit is

$$\frac{e(3+e)}{1-e}.$$

11. If the apsidal distances are a and b, where a is greater than b, prove that the velocity at the former is given by

$$v_a^2 = \frac{2b^2}{b^2 - a^2} \int_a^b F\, dr$$

and the velocity at any distance r is given by

$$v^2 = \frac{2a^2}{b^2 - a^2} \int_a^r F\, dr + \frac{2b^2}{b^2 - a^2} \int_r^b F\, dr,$$

where F is the central force.

12. If (C) is a closed orbit described under the action of a central force, S the center of force, O the center of gravity of the area enclosed by the curve (C), and G the center of gravity of the curve (C), on the supposition that the density at each point varies inversely as the speed, show that the points S, O, and G are collinear and that $2SG = 3SO$. Show also that the

center of gravity of the curve (C), assuming constant density, also lies on the line SOG.

13. Find the condition for the stability of a circular orbit, described under the law of force $f(r)$ toward the center of the circle, by considering the equation (4.1.11).

14. A particle moving in a circular orbit with speed v_c under the action of a force directed toward its center is given a small radial impulse resulting in an initial radial velocity δv_c. If the resulting motion is stable, show that the mean of the apsidal distances is approximately a, the radius of the original circle. Solve the equations of motion for r and θ, and show that the apsidal angle is π/p, where

$$p^2 = 3 + \frac{af'(a)}{f(a)}.$$

15. A particle describes a circle, of radius a, steadily under a central attraction $\phi(r)/r^3$ to the center of the circle, where $\phi'(a) > 0$. Prove that the period of a small oscillation about the steady motion is

$$2\pi\sqrt{\frac{a^3}{\phi'(a)}}.$$

16. A body is describing an ellipse under the action of a force to a focus. When the body is at one extremity of the minor axis, the law of force is changed without instantaneous change of the magnitude of the force or of the velocity. If the force now varies as the distance, prove that the periodic time is the same as before.

17. A particle, acted on by a central force of attraction toward a point O, varying as the distance, is projected from a point P so as to pass through a point Q such that $OP = OQ$. Show that the least possible speed of projection is

$$OP\sqrt{\mu}\sin \angle POQ$$

where μOP is the force per unit mass, and find its direction.

18. Two particles are describing the same ellipse about a center of force in the center in opposite directions, the mass of one being double that of the other. If the particles meet and coalesce at the end of the minor axis, show that the new orbit trisects the major axis of the old.

19. If two particles P, Q describe the same ellipse under the same central force to the center C, prove that the area of the triangle CPQ is invariable.

20. If a particle is describing an ellipse about a center of force in the center, show that the sum of the reciprocals of its angular velocities about the foci is constant.

21. A particle is moving in a circular orbit under the action of a central force μ/r^3 when it receives a small tangential impulse. Trace the future

orbit for the two cases of the impulse increasing and decreasing the speed.

22. A particle is subject to a central attraction μ/r^3 per unit mass toward a fixed point O. It is projected from a point P, with speed $\sqrt{\mu}/OP$, in a direction making an angle α with the radius vector OP. Prove that the tangent to the path at every point makes a fixed angle with the radius vector.

23. Using the theorem on revolving orbits, and letting the initial force tend to zero, deduce some of the possible orbits under the law of force μ/r^3. Why cannot all the possible orbits be found in this way?

24. When the law of force is $(\mu/r^2) + (\nu/r^3)$, show that the orbit is a conic whose major axis is revolving around the focus, and find its mean angular velocity in terms of the period if the conic is an ellipse.

25. Discuss the possible orbits under an inverse cube law of attraction. Show that there are six possible cases, and describe each one, sketching specimen curves.

26. A particle moves under an attraction μ/r^5 per unit mass toward a fixed point O. It is projected from a point A, distant a from O, with velocity v at right angles to OA. Prove that the differential equation of the orbit is

$$\left(\frac{dr}{d\theta}\right)^2 = \frac{r^2 - a^2}{a^2 v^2}\left[\left(v^2 - \frac{\mu}{2a^4}\right)r^2 - \frac{\mu}{2a^2}\right].$$

Prove that in the special case when $v^2 = \mu/2a^4$, the orbit is the circle on OA as diameter, and that the time from A to O is

$$\frac{a^3}{\sqrt{8\mu}}.$$

27. By considering the energy equation, investigate some possible orbits when the law of force is μ/r^5.

28. A particle moves under the central force $-\mu(\dot{r}^2/r)\hat{\mathbf{r}}$. Solve the motion for position and time.

29. Show that if the central force is $\mu(r/x^3)$, the orbit is a conic; and show further that if the particle is projected at right angles to the radius vector at $(a,0)$ with speed given by $2v^2a = \mu$, the orbit is a circle.

30. A particle of mass m is projected from an apsis with the velocity from infinity under the attraction of a force

$$\frac{m}{r^3}\log\frac{r}{a}$$

directed to a center at a distance a; find the equation of the orbit described.

31. A particle is projected at a distance a from the center of force with velocity $2(\sqrt{\mu}/a)$ at an angle $\pi/4$ with the radius vector, the force being

$\mu[(3/r^3) + (a^2/r^5)]$ per unit mass. Determine the orbit, and show that the time to the center of force is

$$\frac{a^2}{\sqrt{2\mu}}\left(2 - \frac{\pi}{2}\right).$$

32. A particle under the action of a central force $\mu[(r + a)/r^3]$ is projected from an apsis at distance a with a speed that is proportionate to that in a circle at the same distance as $1 : \sqrt{2}$. Show that the equation of the orbit is $r(2 + \theta^2) = 2a$ and that the particle will arrive at the origin in time

$$\pi\sqrt{\frac{a^3}{8\mu}}.$$

33. Find the conservative law of force to the origin when the path is the cardioid $r = a(1 - \cos\theta)$; and prove that if F is the force at the apsis and v the speed, then $3v^2 = 4aF$.

34. Find the conservative laws of force under which a particle can describe the orbits (a) $r = 1/c\theta$ and (b) $r = e^\theta$.

35. Find the conservative law of force under which a particle can describe the orbit $r^2 = a^2 \cos 2\theta$.

36. Prove that in order that it may be possible for a particle to describe a circular orbit under the attraction of a center of force situated at a given point within the circle, the law of force must be of the form

$$\mu\frac{r}{(r^2 + b^2)^3}.$$

Prove that the group of possible circles in a field of this form consists of the orbits described when the particle is projected from any point distant b from the center of force in any direction with the velocity from infinity, and that the periods vary as the cubes of the radii of the circles.

37. Find expressions for the central force when the orbit is an ellipse with the origin lying at the ends of the major and minor axes, respectively. What do they reduce to when the orbit becomes a circle?

38. Show that the curves

$$ax + by + c = xf\left(\frac{y}{x}\right),$$

where a, b, and c are arbitrary constants and f is a given function, can be described under the same law of central force to the origin.

39. If a conic is described under the central force $\mu(r/p^3)$ given by Hamilton's theorem, show that the periodic time is

$$2\pi\sqrt{\frac{p_0^3}{\mu}},$$

where p_0 is the perpendicular from the center of the conic on the polar of the center of force.

Chapter 5 ** SOME PROPERTIES OF SOLID BODIES

5.1 Center of Mass and Center of Gravity

Consider a system of point masses of which the ith has mass m_i and position vector $\mathbf{r}_i$ with respect to any origin. The *center of mass* of the system is defined to be at the point $\bar{\mathbf{r}}$ where

$$\bar{\mathbf{r}} = \frac{\sum m_i \mathbf{r}_i}{\sum m_i}, \tag{5.1.1}$$

and the summation extends over all members of the system. By the vector definition this point is independent of the orientation of the axes; we have to show that it is also independent of the position of the origin. Let the origin be transferred to $\mathbf{r}'$, then the position vectors with respect to the new origin are $\mathbf{r}_i' = \mathbf{r}_i - \mathbf{r}'$, so that the center of mass with respect to this new origin is at

$$\bar{\mathbf{r}}' = \frac{\sum m_i (\mathbf{r}_i - \mathbf{r}')}{\sum m_i}$$
$$= \bar{\mathbf{r}} - \mathbf{r}',$$

which is the same point as that found with respect to the first origin. This means that the center of mass is independent of the reference system and depends only on the configuration of the masses.

The *center of gravity*, $\mathbf{r}_g$, is defined such that the sum of the moments of the forces $m_i \mathbf{g}$ acting at $\mathbf{r}_i$ is equal to the moment of the combined masses, $\sum m_i$, acting at $\mathbf{r}_g$; i.e.,

$$\mathbf{r}_g \times \mathbf{g} \sum m_i = \sum (\mathbf{r}_i \times g m_i).$$

The general solution of this equation for $\mathbf{r}_g$ is

$$\mathbf{r}_g = \frac{\sum \mathbf{r}_i m_i}{\sum m_i} + k\mathbf{g} = \bar{\mathbf{r}} + k\mathbf{g},$$

where k is an arbitrary scalar. To be useful, this point must depend only on the configuration of the masses and not on the direction of $\mathbf{g}$, so that $k = 0$ and

$$\mathbf{r}_g = \bar{\mathbf{r}}. \tag{5.1.2}$$

These definitions are for systems of point masses. One purpose of this chapter is to break away from the use of abstract point masses so that we can apply the laws of mechanics to solid bodies. The generalization here is simple: we replace the summation signs by integral signs, to give

$$\bar{\mathbf{r}} = \frac{\int \mathbf{r}\, dm}{\int dm} \qquad (5.1.3)$$

integrated over the whole body. If ρ is the density and dv is an element of volume, then we have $dm = \rho\, dv$. Provided the density is finite everywhere, there is no difficulty over the convergence of the integral.

If a solid is symmetrical about some plane (for instance if the plane is the x–y plane, the distribution of mass would be independent of the sign of z), then that plane is called a *plane of symmetry*. By symmetry the center of mass of the body must lie in that plane. In general, three planes meet in a point, so that if a body has three planes of symmetry, the center of mass is found. It may be that the three planes meet in a line; in this case there is still some ambiguity and integration must be used. But all the bodies considered here will be spheres or, at worst, ellipsoids, for which the center of mass is immediately seen to be the geometrical center.

5.2 The Moments and Products of Inertia: The Inertia Tensor

In order to discuss the angular momentum of a solid body, we need some quantities known as the moments and products of inertia. In considering these, we shall, for convenience, introduce the inertia tensor. Tensor notation will be used only in this section and will, with regret, be developed only as far as is needed for the purpose in hand.

Consider coordinates (x_1, x_2, x_3) instead of (x, y, z). We shall use the *dummy suffix* notation where, if a suffix appears twice in a term, then the term is summed over the (three) possible values of the suffix. Thus $a_i x_j$ means precisely what it says, but $a_i x_i$ stands for

$$\sum_{i=1,2,3} a_i x_i \quad \text{or} \quad (a_1 x_1 + a_2 x_2 + a_3 x_3).$$

Although the results will be applied to continuous solids, we shall, for convenience, continue to use summations over mass elements. These can easily be replaced by integrals.

Define the six quantities I_{ij} by

$$\left.\begin{aligned}
I_{11} &= \sum m x_i x_i - \sum m x_1^2 = A, \\
I_{22} &= \sum m x_i x_i - \sum m x_2^2 = B, \\
I_{33} &= \sum m x_i x_i - \sum m x_3^2 = C, \\
I_{23} &= -\sum m x_2 x_3 \qquad\quad = -F, \\
I_{31} &= -\sum m x_3 x_1 \qquad\quad = -G, \\
I_{12} &= -\sum m x_1 x_2 \qquad\quad = -H.
\end{aligned}\right\} \qquad (5.2.1)$$

A, B, and C are the *moments of inertia* and F, G, and H are the *products of inertia* of the system of masses. They can all be given by the one equation

$$I_{\alpha\beta} = \sum m x_i x_i \delta_{\alpha\beta} - \sum m x_\alpha x_\beta, \qquad (5.2.2)$$

where $\delta_{\alpha\beta}$, called the *Kronecker delta*, is zero if α and β are unequal and is one if they are equal.

Let the system have angular velocity $\boldsymbol{\omega}$ so that the velocity of the mass element m at $\mathbf{r}$ is $\boldsymbol{\omega} \times \mathbf{r}$, and its angular momentum about the origin is $m\mathbf{r} \times (\boldsymbol{\omega} \times \mathbf{r})$. The total angular momentum of the system about the origin is, then,

$$\begin{aligned}
\mathbf{H} &= \sum m\mathbf{r} \times (\boldsymbol{\omega} \times \mathbf{r}) \\
&= \sum m[r^2\boldsymbol{\omega} - (\mathbf{r}\cdot\boldsymbol{\omega})\mathbf{r}] \\
&= \sum m[x_i x_i \boldsymbol{\omega} - (x_i \omega_i)\mathbf{r}].
\end{aligned}$$

Resolving along the component directions, we see that the x_1 component is

$$H_1 = I_{11}\omega_1 + I_{12}\omega_2 + I_{13}\omega_3 = I_{1i}\omega_i.$$

Then, using matrix notation, we have

$$[H_1\ H_2\ H_3] = [\omega_1\ \omega_2\ \omega_3] \begin{bmatrix} I_{11} & I_{12} & I_{13} \\ I_{21} & I_{22} & I_{23} \\ I_{31} & I_{32} & I_{33} \end{bmatrix} \qquad (5.2.3)$$

where $I_{\alpha\beta} = I_{\beta\alpha}$.

The matrix $[I]$ has been defined with respect to a particular set of axes, but from (5.2.3) we might expect it to have some existence, similar to that of a vector, that is independent of the system of reference. This is the case. $[I]$ is an example of a *tensor* of rank two. The operative definition (from Milne's *Vectorial Mechanics*, Ref. 15) is as follows:

With each set of orthogonal triads of unit vectors associate a set of nine numbers, $t_{\mu\nu}$. Then the sets are said to describe a tensor, $\boldsymbol{T}$, provided that if $t_{\mu\nu}$ is associated with the triad $(\hat{\mathbf{i}}_1, \hat{\mathbf{i}}_2, \hat{\mathbf{i}}_3)$ and $t'_{\mu\nu}$ is the set associated with $(\hat{\mathbf{i}}'_1, \hat{\mathbf{i}}'_2, \hat{\mathbf{i}}'_3)$, then

$$t'_{\mu\nu} = l_{\mu\alpha} l_{\nu\beta} t_{\alpha\beta},$$

where

$$l_{\rho\sigma} = \hat{\mathbf{i}}'_\rho \cdot \hat{\mathbf{i}}_\sigma.$$

[The l's are the direction cosines of the new set of axes with respect to the old set.] According to this definition we cannot describe a tensor without reference to some triad, but the tensor itself is to be distinguished from any one of its descriptions. Just as a vector may be considered as the class of all its representations with respect to different triads, so a tensor is the class of all its descriptions.

To prove that $[I]$ is a tensor, use (5.2.3), written in the form

$$H_\beta = \omega_\alpha I_{\alpha\beta}.$$

With respect to the new triad we have

$$H'_\beta = \omega'_\alpha I'_{\alpha\beta}.$$

Now **H** and **ω** are vectors.

$$\mathbf{H} = H_1\hat{\mathbf{i}}_1 + H_2\hat{\mathbf{i}}_2 + H_3\hat{\mathbf{i}}_3 = H_\alpha\hat{\mathbf{i}}_\alpha$$

and

$$\mathbf{H}' = H'_\alpha\hat{\mathbf{i}}'_\alpha.$$

Also

$$\hat{\mathbf{i}}'_1 = l_{11}\hat{\mathbf{i}}_1 + l_{12}\hat{\mathbf{i}}_2 + l_{13}\hat{\mathbf{i}}_3, \quad \text{etc.}$$

so we have

$$H'_\beta = l_{\beta i}H_i$$

and similarly,

$$\omega'_\alpha = l_{\alpha i}\omega_i.$$

Therefore

$$\omega'_\alpha I'_{\alpha\beta} = H'_\beta$$
$$= l_{\beta i}H_i$$
$$= l_{\beta i}\omega_j I_{ji}$$
$$= l_{\beta i}l_{jk}I_{ji}\omega'_k.$$

By changing the dummy suffixes, this can be put into the form

$$\omega'_\alpha(I'_{\alpha\beta} - l_{\beta i}l_{i\alpha}I_{j\beta}) = 0,$$

and since this holds for any ω'_α, the result is established.

It would be profitable but, unfortunately, not to the point, to devote much more space to a discussion of tensors. As it is, the student is urged to find out more about them elsewhere. It is important to realize that tensors are quantities obeying certain laws of transformation when the reference system is changed; these are such that a tensor equation which is true in one reference system is true in *any* reference system.

The product $x_i I_{ij}$ will be denoted by $\mathbf{x} \cdot \mathbf{I}$; it is an *inner product* of the vector and the tensor. Since $I_{\alpha\beta} = I_{\beta\alpha}$, **I** is said to be a *self-conjugate* tensor.

When considering the rotation of a body about some axis, it is necessary to know the moment of inertia of the body about that axis. Let OS, the axis of rotation, pass through the origin, and let P be a mass element m. (See Figure 5.1, page 90.) Then the angular momentum about OS is

$$\sum \omega m P R^2,$$

where PR is the perpendicular distance of P from OS and ω is the angular velocity. The moment of inertia about OS is $\sum m P R^2$.

Let us return for a moment to more familiar notation, such that the direction of OS is (l,m,n) and the coordinates of P are (x,y,z). Then

$$PR^2 = OP^2 - OR^2$$
$$= (x^2 + y^2 + z^2) - (lx + my + nz)^2$$
$$= (x^2 + y^2 + z^2)(l^2 + m^2 + n^2) - (lx + my + nz)^2,$$

so

$$\sum mPR^2 = Al^2 + Bm^2 + Cn^2 - 2Fmn - 2Gnl - 2Hlm. \quad (5.2.4)$$

Consider the quadric

$$Ax^2 + By^2 + Cz^2 - 2Fyz - 2Gzx - 2Hxy = \text{constant}. \quad (5.2.5)$$

If P is a point on the quadric, the moment of inertia about the axis OP is inversely proportional to the square of the distance OP. Since there is a real moment of inertia in any direction, the quadric must be an ellipsoid; it is called

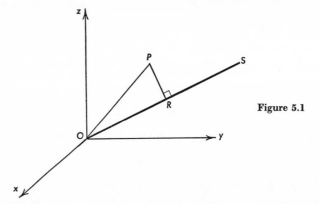

Figure 5.1

the *momental ellipsoid*, and its axes are the *principal axes of inertia*. If the student does not like the abstraction of the inertia tensor, it may help if he thinks instead of the momental ellipsoid; this is something that is obviously independent of its description with respect to any particular triad. (But not all tensors are amenable to this sort of parallel.)

As the body moves, the description of I with respect to a fixed reference system will vary, but it will remain constant with respect to axes fixed in the body itself. If the body is rotating about a line through the origin and is subject to external forces of moment $\mathbf{\Gamma}$, then the angular momentum equation is

$$\mathbf{\Gamma} = \frac{d}{dt}(\mathbf{\omega} \cdot I)$$

$$= \frac{\partial}{\partial t}(\mathbf{\omega} \cdot I) + \mathbf{\omega} \times (\mathbf{\omega} \cdot I) \qquad \text{(from Section 2.7)}$$

$$= \dot{\mathbf{\omega}} \cdot I + \mathbf{\omega} \times (\mathbf{\omega} \cdot I). \quad (5.2.6)$$

If the axes of reference fixed in the body are chosen as the principal axes of inertia, (5.2.6) can be written as

$$
\left.
\begin{aligned}
\Gamma_1 &= A\,\frac{d\omega_1}{dt} - (B - C)\omega_2\omega_3, \\[2mm]
\Gamma_2 &= B\,\frac{d\omega_2}{dt} - (C - A)\omega_3\omega_1, \\[2mm]
\Gamma_3 &= C\,\frac{d\omega_3}{dt} - (A - B)\,\omega_1\omega_2.
\end{aligned}
\right\}
\tag{5.2.7}
$$

These are Euler's equations of motion.

We complete this section by finding the moments of inertia of two homogeneous solids, the sphere, and the ellipsoid about its axes. For the sphere, we have, by symmetry, $A = B = C$. But

$$
A + B + C = 2 \int (x^2 + y^2 + z^2)dm = 2\rho \int r^2 \, dv
$$

integrated over the volume of the sphere, where ρ is the density and dv is the element of volume. Dividing the sphere up into thin concentric shells, we find

$$
A + B + C = 2\rho\, 4\pi \int_0^a r^4 \, dr
$$

$$
= \frac{8\pi}{5}\,\rho a^5,
$$

where a is the radius of the sphere. Hence

$$
A = \frac{8\pi}{15}\,\rho a^5 = \frac{2}{5}\,Ma^2,
\tag{5.2.8}
$$

where M is the mass of the sphere.

For the ellipsoid, the axes are the principal axes of inertia, and

$$
A = \int (y^2 + z^2)dm = \rho \int (y^2 + z^2) \, dx\, dy\, dz,
$$

integrated throughout the ellipsoid

$$
\frac{x^2}{a^2} + \frac{y^2}{b^2} + \frac{z^2}{c^2} = 1.
$$

If the variables are changed to $x' = x/a$, $y' = y/b$, $z' = z/c$, then the integration reduces to an integration throughout a sphere and is performed without difficulty. The result is

$$
A = \tfrac{1}{5}\, M(b^2 + c^2),
\tag{5.2.9}
$$

with similar expressions for B and C, where M is the mass of the ellipsoid.

(The moments of inertia about the principal axes of simple bodies are given by a mnemonic known as *Routh's rule*. This states that they are Ms^2/n, where s^2 is the sum of the squares of the lengths of the semiaxes of the body at right angles to the given axis, and n has the values 3, 4, or 5, according as the body is rectangular, elliptical, or ellipsoidal.)

Problems

1. Prove that the moment of inertia of a body with center of gravity G about any axis is equal to the moment of inertia about a parallel axis through G plus Mp^2, where M is the mass of the body and p is the perpendicular distance from G to the axis.

2. A body has angular velocity $\boldsymbol{\omega}$ about an axis passing through the origin. Show that twice its kinetic energy is $I_{ij}\omega_i\omega_j$.

3. A body has symmetry about an axis $\hat{\imath}$ such that $A = B$. Show that the angular velocity of the body can be expressed as

$$n\hat{\imath} + \hat{\imath} \times \frac{d\hat{\imath}}{dt}$$

and that its angular momentum is

$$Cn\hat{\imath} + A\hat{\imath} \times \frac{d\hat{\imath}}{dt}.$$

Interpret n.

4. Assuming them to be homogeneous bodies with constant angular rotations throughout, find the angular momenta due to axial rotation of the Sun, the Earth, the Moon, and Jupiter.

5. Find the angular momentum of each planet due to its revolution round the Sun. Hence investigate the distribution of angular momentum in the solar system.

5.3 The Potential of a Sphere

The potential at O of a solid body is

$$V = -G \int \frac{dm}{r} = -G \int \rho \frac{dv}{r} \tag{5.3.1}$$

where the integral is taken throughout the body. If O lies outside the body, the integrand is finite everywhere (as long as the density has no singularity), so that there is no trouble over convergence. If O lies inside the body, the integrand has a singularity at O; but if we use spherical polar coordinates, the element of volume is

$$dv = r^2 \sin \theta \, dr \, d\theta \, d\phi$$

and

$$V = -G \iiint \rho r \sin \theta \, dr \, d\theta \, d\phi$$

and the integral converges.

Consider the attraction experienced at an internal point O of a uniform spherical shell, bounded by concentric spheres. Let a cone with vertex O and small solid angle $d\omega$* cut the shell, as shown in Figure 5.2, in two frustra $PQQ'P'$ and $RSS'R'$. If ρ is the density, the mass of a thin slice of the cone of thickness dr is $\rho r^2 \, d\omega \, dr$, and its attraction at O is $G\rho \, d\omega \, dr$. So, the attractions of the two frustra are $G\rho \, d\omega \, PQ$ and $G\rho \, d\omega \, RS$. But, since the bounding spheres are concentric, they make equal intercepts on any chord; hence $PQ = RS$ and the attractions at O are equal and opposite. By taking cones in all directions round O, we see that the resultant attraction is zero. In integrating $G\rho \, d\omega \, dr$

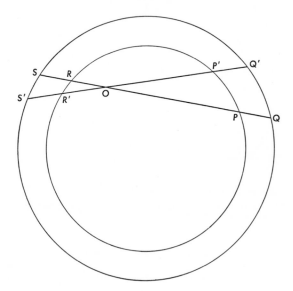

Figure 5.2

with respect to r, we appear to have neglected wedge-shaped elements at P and Q, but the further integration with respect to ω implies that $d\omega$ tends to zero, so that these wedge-shaped elements contribute nothing.

At this stage it is convenient to consider the internal attraction of a uniform shell bounded by two similar ellipsoids, called a *homoid*. (Two ellipsoids are *similar* if their axes are in a constant ratio.) The same method is used, the relevant figure being Figure 5.3. Now this figure can be regarded as the projection of Figure 5.2, so that we still have $PQ = RS$. Hence the attraction of a homoid at an internal point is zero.

---

* Consider a sphere of unit radius; then unit area on its surface subtends unit solid angle at the center. The element of solid angle in spherical polar coordinates is

$$d\omega = \sin \theta \, d\theta \, d\phi.$$

Now consider the potential of a uniform, thin spherical shell at a point O outside the shell. Let the shell have center C, radius a and thickness da, and let $OC = r$. If P is a point on the shell, let the angle $OCP = \theta$. Divide the shell

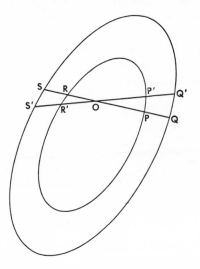

Figure 5.3

into thin rings perpendicular to OC and defined by θ lying within the limits θ and $\theta + d\theta$. The radius of the ring is $a \sin \theta$, and its mass is

$$\rho \times 2\pi a \sin \theta \times a \, d\theta \times da$$

where ρ is the density of the shell. Any element of the ring is at the distance

$$(r^2 + a^2 - 2ar \cos \theta)^{1/2}$$

from O, so that the potential of the ring at O is

$$-G\rho 2\pi a^2 \, da \, \frac{\sin \theta \, d\theta}{(r^2 + a^2 - 2ar \cos \theta)^{1/2}}$$

and the total potential at O is

$$V = -G\rho 2\pi a^2 \, da \int_0^\pi \frac{\sin \theta \, d\theta}{(r^2 + a^2 - 2ar \cos \theta)^{1/2}}$$

where the square root must always be positive. This can be integrated at once to give

$$V = -\frac{1}{2} G \, dm \left[\frac{1}{ra} (r^2 + a^2 - 2ar \cos \theta)^{1/2} \right]_{\theta=0}^\pi$$

$$= -G \frac{dm}{a},$$

where $dm = 4\pi a^2 \rho \, da$ is the mass of the shell. This means that, as far as O is concerned, the shell could just as well have all its mass concentrated at C. This must also apply to a shell of finite thickness, since the result is not affected by integration over a, and it applies in particular to a solid sphere constructed out of shells of equal density, with total radius less than r.

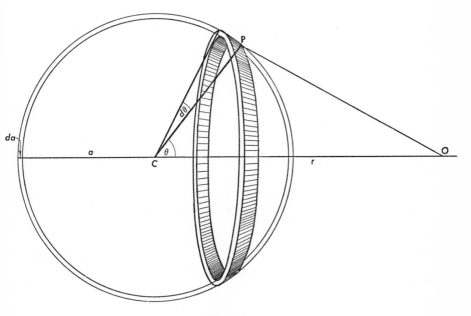

Figure 5.4

If a sphere has total mass M, center C, and density that is a function only of distance from C, then for gravitational purposes we can treat it as a point mass M at C, as long as we remain outside it. So, there is no difficulty in generalizing particle motion under Newton's law to apply to the motion of spheres. For much of the dynamics in the solar system it is sufficient to assume that the Sun and planets are constructed in spherical shells, so that they can be treated as point masses.

Problems

1. A sphere of 150 kg, placed with its center 30 cm vertically below that of another sphere, is found to cause an apparent increase of the latter's weight by the 1.14×10^{-8} part. What value does this imply for the constant of gravitation?

2. The density of a sphere varies as the depth below the surface. Show that the resultant attraction is greatest at a depth equal to one-third of the radius, and that the value here is four thirds of the value at the surface.

3. A solid sphere of radius a is such that its density at any point is proportional to the nth power of the distance of that point from the center of the sphere. Find the potential at any external point and show that the potential at an internal point at a distance r from the center is

$$\frac{GM}{n+2} \left[\frac{n+3}{a} - \frac{r^{n+2}}{a^{n+3}} \right],$$

where M is the total mass of the sphere.

4. Show that the initial rate of increase of g in descending a mine shaft would be equal to g/a if the density ρ of the Earth (of radius a) were uniform. But if the Earth had a spherical nucleus of different density and radius b, the density of this nucleus must be

$$1 + \frac{a^3(1 - \lambda)}{b^3(2 + \lambda)},$$

where $\lambda(g/a)$ is the initial rate of increase of g in descending the shaft.

5. Assuming the Earth to be a homogeneous sphere of density σ and radius a, surrounded by a spherical shell of density ρ and thickness $(b - a)$, show that the weight of a body given by a spring balance is unaltered at first on descending vertically if

$$\rho = \sigma \frac{2a^3}{2a^3 + b^3}.$$

The rotation of the Earth may be neglected.

6. A solid sphere of radius a and uniform density is surrounded by a concentric shell of internal radius a and external radius b in which the density is a function of the distance from the center. Find the law of density if the force of attraction is constant in the substance of the shell, and prove that the mass of the shell to the mass of the sphere is as $(b^2 - a^2)$ is to a^2.

7. The density of a sphere of radius a and *mean* density $\bar{\rho}$ is a function of distance from the center, such that the attraction at any point inside the sphere is proportional to the square of the distance from the center. Express the density at distance r from the center in terms of $\bar{\rho}$, a, and r, and prove that the potential of an internal point at a distance r from the center is

$$\frac{4}{9} \pi G \bar{\rho} \frac{4a^3 - r^3}{a}.$$

8. A system of particles, m_i, is assembled from a state of infinite diffusion. Show that the potential energy lost in the process of assembly is $\frac{1}{2} \sum m_i V_i$, where V_i is the potential at the ultimate position of m_i.

Assuming that the Sun remains a homogeneous sphere, find the change in potential energy if it contracts by x per cent of its radius. If the amount of heat emitted annually by the Sun would raise the temperature of a mass of water equal to the mass of the Sun by 1.44°C, and this heat were produced by a contraction of x per cent per million years, find x.

5.4   The Potential of a Distant Body: MacCullagh's Formula

When we leave simple figures such as the sphere, expressions for their potentials become somewhat tiresome; this will become patently clear in the following section on the ellipsoid. However, if the point that we are considering is at a distance from the attracting body which is large compared with the body's over-all dimensions (as is often the case in astronomy), there is a simple approximate formula for the potential, due to MacCullagh.

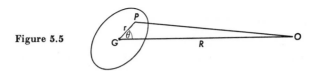

Figure 5.5

Let G be the center of gravity of the attracting body and O a point distant R from G, where R is large compared with the dimensions of the body. If dm is the mass of an element at P, such that $GP = r$ and $\angle OGP = \theta$, the potential at O is

$$V = -G \int \frac{dm}{OP}$$

$$= -G \int \frac{dm}{(R^2 + r^2 - 2Rr \cos \theta)^{1/2}}$$

$$= -\frac{G}{R} \int dm \left(1 - 2\frac{r}{R} \cos \theta + \frac{r^2}{R^2}\right)^{-1/2}$$

$$= -\frac{G}{R} \int dm \left\{1 + \frac{r}{R} \cos \theta - \frac{1}{2}\cdot\frac{r^2}{R^2} + \frac{3}{2}\cdot\frac{r^2}{R^2} \cos^2 \theta + O\left(\frac{r}{R}\right)^3\right\}$$

$$= -\frac{G}{R} \left\{\int dm + \frac{1}{R} \int r \cos \theta \, dm + \frac{1}{2R^2} \int (2r^2 - 3r^2 \sin^2 \theta) \, dm + O\left(\frac{r}{R}\right)^3\right\}.$$

The first integral on the right-hand side gives M, the total mass of the body. Since G is at the center of gravity of the body, the second integral is zero. Let I be the moment of inertia of the body about GO; then

$$I = \int r^2 \sin^2 \theta \, dm.$$

Also, if A, B, and C are the principal moments of inertia,

$$A + B + C = 2 \int r^2 \, dm.$$

Hence

$$V = -\frac{GM}{R} - \frac{G}{2R^3} (A + B + C - 3I), \qquad (5.4.1)$$

where terms of the order $(r/R)^3$ have been neglected. This is MacCullagh's formula.

Most celestial bodies are only slightly distorted from spherical figures, and the second term on the right-hand side of (5.4.1) is small, not only by virtue of the smallness of r/R but also because the quantity $A + B + C - 3I$ is small. Hence (5.4.1) can be applied even for moderately small r/R.

5.5   The Field of a Homogeneous Ellipsoid

There are several ways of arriving at the formulas for the field of a homogeneous ellipsoid, and all depend at some stage on somewhat brutal integration. The approach given here is based on that used by Ramsey in his text *Newtonian Attraction* (Ref. 19). It falls into several stages.

First we shall find the internal potential of a homoid. Since there is no net force inside the homoid, the potential is constant and equal to the value at the center O. Let the boundaries of the homoid have axes a, b, c, and pa, pb, pc, where p is less than one. With the center as apex, construct a cone with solid angle $d\omega$, intercepting the homoid at distances r and pr from O. The potential at O due to the frustrum contained in this cone is

$$-G \int_{pr}^{r} \rho r^2 \, d\omega \, \frac{dr}{r} = -\frac{1}{2} G\rho(1 - p^2) r^2 \, d\omega,$$

so the total potential at O is

$$V_0 = -\tfrac{1}{2} G\rho(1 - p^2) \int r^2 \, d\omega$$

integrated over the outer boundary.

Now the equation of the outer boundary is

$$\frac{x^2}{a^2} + \frac{y^2}{b^2} + \frac{z^2}{c^2} = 1.$$

Let a point on the boundary have coordinates (rl, rm, rn), where l, m, and n are direction cosines. Then

$$r^2\left(\frac{l^2}{a^2} + \frac{m^2}{b^2} + \frac{n^2}{c^2}\right) = 1.$$

If r, θ, and ϕ are taken as spherical polar coordinates, we have $l = \sin\theta\cos\phi$, $m = \sin\theta\sin\phi$, $n = \cos\theta$. Also, the element of solid angle is $d\omega = \sin\theta \, d\theta \, d\phi$.

Since the integrand in the expression for V_0 is symmetrical about each axis, its integrated value is eight times the value when integrated over one quadrant. Hence

$$V_0 = -\frac{1}{2} G\rho(1 - p^2) \int \frac{d\omega}{\left(\dfrac{l^2}{a^2} + \dfrac{m^2}{b^2} + \dfrac{n^2}{c^2}\right)}$$

$$= -4G\rho(1 - p^2) \int_0^{\pi/2} \int_0^{\pi/2} \frac{\sin\theta \, d\theta \, d\phi}{\sin^2\theta\left(\dfrac{\cos^2\phi}{a^2} + \dfrac{\sin^2\phi}{b^2}\right) + \dfrac{\cos^2\theta}{c^2}}.$$

Let $\tan\phi = t$. Then

$$V_0 = -4G\rho(1 - p^2) \int_0^{\pi/2} \int_0^{\infty} \frac{\sin\theta \, d\theta \, dt}{\dfrac{\sin^2\theta}{a^2} + \dfrac{\cos^2\theta}{b^2} + \left(\dfrac{\sin^2\theta}{b^2} + \dfrac{\cos^2\theta}{c^2}\right)t^2}.$$

Now

$$\int_0^{\infty} \frac{dt}{A^2 + B^2 t^2} = \left[\frac{1}{AB}\tan^{-1}\left(\frac{Bt}{A}\right)\right]_0^{\infty} = \frac{1}{2} \cdot \frac{\pi}{AB},$$

so

$$V_0 = -2\pi G\rho(1 - p^2) \int_0^{\pi/2} \frac{\sin\theta \, d\theta}{\left\{\left(\dfrac{\sin^2\theta}{a^2} + \dfrac{\cos^2\theta}{c^2}\right)\left(\dfrac{\sin^2\theta}{b^2} + \dfrac{\cos^2\theta}{c^2}\right)\right\}^{1/2}}.$$

Put $u = c^2 \tan\theta$; then substituting and rearranging, we eventually get

$$V_0 = -\pi G\rho(1 - p^2)abcI, \tag{5.5.1}$$

where

$$I = \int_0^{\infty} \frac{du}{\Delta} \quad \text{and} \quad \Delta^2 = (a^2 + u)(b^2 + u)(c^2 + u). \tag{5.5.2}$$

If we put $p = 0$, we have the potential at the center of a solid homogeneous ellipsoid.

Next we shall find the components of attraction at a point P, (x,y,z), inside a solid ellipsoid. Since the homoid outside the similar ellipsoid passing through P exerts no force at P, it is sufficient to find the force exerted by an ellipsoid at a point on its surface.

From P let a line in the direction (l,m,n) meet the ellipsoid again at Q, where $PQ = r$; then the coordinates of Q are

$$(x + lr, \quad y + mr, \quad z + nr).$$

Writing down the conditions for P and Q to lie on the ellipsoid with semiaxes

a, b, and c, and subtracting them, we get

$$r^2\left(\frac{l^2}{a^2} + \frac{m^2}{b^2} + \frac{n^2}{c^2}\right) + 2r\left(\frac{lx}{a^2} + \frac{my}{b^2} + \frac{nz}{c^2}\right) = 0. \tag{5.5.3}$$

$r = 0$ gives P; the other value gives Q.

Construct a cone with vertex P, solid angle $d\omega$, and axis lying along PQ. The force at P due to the matter in this cone is

$$-G\rho \, d\omega \int_0^r dr = -G\rho r \, d\omega.$$

So, the components of this force at P are

$$(-G\rho lr \, d\omega, \quad -G\rho mr \, d\omega, \quad -G\rho nr \, d\omega),$$

and to get the total components of force, we integrate over all possible values of ω. But, since every line through P has a real intersection with the ellipsoid, an integration over all ω will cover the ellipsoid twice. So the x-component of force is

$$X = -\frac{1}{2} G\rho \int lr \, d\omega$$

$$= -\frac{1}{2} G\rho \int \frac{2l\left(\dfrac{lx}{a^2} + \dfrac{my}{b^2} + \dfrac{nz}{c^2}\right)}{\dfrac{l^2}{a^2} + \dfrac{m^2}{b^2} + \dfrac{n^2}{c^2}} \, d\omega.$$

The terms in mn, nl, and lm contribute nothing to the integral, since terms in lm and $l(-m)$, for instance, occur equally and cancel one another. So we get

$$X = -G\rho x \int \frac{\dfrac{l^2}{a^2} \, d\omega}{\dfrac{l^2}{a^2} + \dfrac{m^2}{b^2} + \dfrac{n^2}{c^2}} \tag{5.5.4}$$

$$= -G\rho Ax. \tag{5.5.5}$$

There are similar expressions for Y and Z, functions B and C being similarly defined. (The notation is confusing; A, B, and C must not be confused with the moments of inertia.)

To simplify the expression for A, we use the same substitutions as were used to find (5.5.1) and (5.5.2). In this case we get, eventually,

$$A = 2\pi abc \int_0^\infty \frac{du}{\Delta(a^2 + u)} \tag{5.5.6}$$

and similar expressions for B and C.

Now we are able to find the potential V at any point inside an ellipsoid. From the relation between the potential function and the field of force, V

must be of the form

$$V = -\tfrac{1}{2}G\rho(D - Ax^2 - By^2 - Cz^2). \qquad (5.5.7)$$

From (5.5.1) and (5.5.2) the value of D is known, and we have

$$V = -G\pi\rho abc \int_0^\infty \left\{1 - \frac{x^2}{a^2 + u} - \frac{y^2}{b^2 + u} - \frac{z^2}{c^2 + u}\right\}\frac{du}{\Delta}. \qquad (5.5.8)$$

This can also be written in the form

$$V = -G\pi\rho abc\left\{1 + \frac{x^2}{a}\cdot\frac{\partial I}{\partial a} + \frac{y^2}{b}\cdot\frac{\partial I}{\partial b} + \frac{z^2}{c}\cdot\frac{\partial I}{\partial c}\right\}. \qquad (5.5.9)$$

From (5.5.4) we see that

$$A + B + C = \int d\omega = 4\pi. \qquad (5.5.10)$$

Also

$$Aa^2 + Bb^2 + Cc^2 = \int \frac{d\omega}{\dfrac{l^2}{a^2} + \dfrac{m^2}{b^2} + \dfrac{n^2}{c^2}}. \qquad (5.5.11)$$

It should be noted that the values of A, B, and C depend only on the ratios of the axes.

In general the integrals can be evaluated only in terms of elliptic functions. But, for spheroids, two axes are equal, and elementary functions can be used. Let $a = b$, so that $A = B$. From (5.5.11) we have

$$2Aa^2 + Cc^2 = \int \frac{d\omega}{\dfrac{l^2 + m^2}{a^2} + \dfrac{n^2}{c^2}}$$

$$= \int_0^\pi \int_0^{2\pi} \frac{\sin\theta\, d\theta\, d\phi}{\dfrac{\sin^2\theta}{a^2} + \dfrac{\cos^2\theta}{c^2}}$$

$$= 2\pi \int_{-1}^{+1} \frac{du}{\dfrac{1}{a^2} + \left(\dfrac{1}{c^2} - \dfrac{1}{a^2}\right)u^2}$$

where $u = \cos\theta$.

There are two cases:

1. OBLATE SPHEROID, $a > c$.

$$2Aa^2 + Cc^2 = \frac{4\pi a^2 c}{\sqrt{a^2 - c^2}}\tan^{-1}\sqrt{\frac{a^2}{c^2} - 1}$$

$$= 4\pi a^2 \frac{\sqrt{1 - e^2}}{e}\tan^{-1}\left(\frac{e}{\sqrt{1 - e^2}}\right) \qquad (5.5.12)$$

where $a^2(1 - e^2) = c^2$.

2. PROLATE SPHEROID, $a < c$.

$$2Aa^2 + Cc^2 = \frac{2\pi a^2 c}{\sqrt{c^2 - a^2}} \log \left\{ \frac{c + \sqrt{c^2 - a^2}}{c - \sqrt{c^2 - a^2}} \right\}$$

$$= 2\pi c^2 \frac{1 - e^2}{e} \log \frac{1 + e}{1 - e}, \qquad (5.5.13)$$

where $a^2 = c^2(1 - e^2)$.

In each case e is the eccentricity of the generating ellipse. The separate values of A and C can be found by (5.5.10).

Consider the case of a prolate spheroid that is only slightly distorted from a sphere. Then

$$c = a(1 + \epsilon),$$

where ϵ, called the *ellipticity*, is small. Approximately,

$$e^2 = 2\epsilon.$$

Expanding (5.5.13) in powers of e, we have

$$2Ac^2(1 - e^2) + Cc^2 = 2\pi c^2 \frac{1 - e^2}{e} \left(2e + \frac{2}{3} e^3 + \frac{2}{5} e^5 + \cdots \right)$$

$$= 4\pi c^2 (1 - \tfrac{2}{3} e^2 - \tfrac{2}{15} e^4 + \cdots).$$

Then, since $2A + C = 4\pi$, we find

$$2A = 4\pi(\tfrac{2}{3} + \tfrac{2}{15} e^2 + \cdots).$$

Then, neglecting powers of ϵ, we have

$$\left. \begin{array}{l} A = \tfrac{4}{3}\pi(1 + \tfrac{2}{5}\epsilon). \\[2ex] C = \tfrac{4}{3}\pi(1 - \tfrac{4}{5}\epsilon). \end{array} \right\} \qquad (5.5.14)$$

Then

These expressions will be needed later when we consider the tidal distortion of a liquid sphere. Similar expressions for the slightly distorted oblate spheroid are

$$\left. \begin{array}{l} A = \tfrac{4}{3}\pi(1 - \tfrac{2}{5}\epsilon), \\ C = \tfrac{4}{3}\pi(1 + \tfrac{4}{5}\epsilon), \end{array} \right\} \qquad (5.5.15)$$

where $c = a(1 - \epsilon)$.

Now suppose we have a nearly spherical ellipsoid with axes a, $a(1 - \eta)$ and $a(1 - \epsilon)$. Since we are neglecting powers of ϵ and η, the expressions for A, B, and C will be linear in ϵ and η. When $\eta = 0$, we have, from the results above,

$$A = \tfrac{4}{3}\pi(1 - \tfrac{2}{5}\epsilon),$$
$$B = \tfrac{4}{3}\pi(1 - \tfrac{2}{5}\epsilon),$$
$$C = \tfrac{4}{3}\pi(1 + \tfrac{4}{5}\epsilon).$$

Similarly, if $\epsilon = 0$, b becomes the unequal axis of a spheroid, and we have

$$A = \tfrac{4}{3}\pi(1 - \tfrac{2}{5}\eta),$$
$$B = \tfrac{4}{3}\pi(1 + \tfrac{4}{5}\eta),$$
$$C = \tfrac{4}{3}\pi(1 - \tfrac{2}{5}\eta).$$

These two cases must be particular cases of a general formula for the potential; since this is linear in ϵ and η, we must have

$$\begin{rcases} A = \tfrac{4}{3}\pi(1 - \tfrac{2}{5}\epsilon - \tfrac{2}{5}\eta), \\ B = \tfrac{4}{3}\pi(1 - \tfrac{2}{5}\epsilon + \tfrac{4}{5}\eta), \\ C = \tfrac{4}{3}\pi(1 + \tfrac{4}{5}\epsilon - \tfrac{2}{5}\eta). \end{rcases} \qquad (5.5.16)$$

These results can be put into a symmetrical form if we take k to be the mean radius so that

$$3k = a + b + c.$$

Then

$$\begin{rcases} A = \frac{4}{3}\pi \left(1 - \frac{6}{5}\cdot\frac{a-k}{k}\right), \\[2mm] B = \frac{4}{3}\pi \left(1 - \frac{6}{5}\cdot\frac{b-k}{k}\right), \\[2mm] C = \frac{4}{3}\pi \left(1 - \frac{6}{5}\cdot\frac{c-k}{k}\right). \end{rcases} \qquad (5.5.17)$$

No direct way to find the field outside an ellipsoid is known; this must be done in two stages, using a theorem due to Ivory.

Let the boundary S of the ellipsoid have equation

$$\frac{x^2}{a^2} + \frac{y^2}{b^2} + \frac{z^2}{c^2} = 1.$$

Then an ellipsoid $S(\lambda)$ with equation

$$\frac{x^2}{a^2 + \lambda} + \frac{y^2}{b^2 + \lambda} + \frac{z^2}{c^2 + \lambda} = 1 \qquad (5.5.18)$$

has the same foci as S and is said to be *confocal* with S. If we consider (x,y,z) as any fixed point, there are three quadrics passing through it which are confocal to S, since (5.5.18) can be considered as a cubic in λ. It is easy to show that all the roots are real; for consider

$$\phi(\lambda) \equiv \frac{x^2}{a^2 + \lambda} + \frac{y^2}{b^2 + \lambda} + \frac{z^2}{c^2 + \lambda} - 1.$$

Let (x,y,z) lie outside S; then taking a and c to represent the largest and smallest axes, respectively, we see that for

λ large and positive, $\phi(\lambda)$ is nearly equal to -1;
$\lambda = 0$, $\phi(\lambda) > 0$ [since (x,y,z) lies outside S];
$\lambda = -c^2 + \epsilon$, ($\epsilon$ small and positive), $\phi(\lambda)$ is large and positive;
$\lambda = -c^2 - \epsilon$, $\phi(\lambda)$ is large and negative;

and so on. The graph of $\phi(\lambda)$ is of the form:

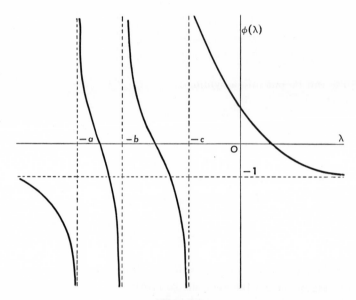

Figure 5.6

The only root that interests us here is the one which keeps all the denominators in (5.5.18) positive, so that we still have an ellipsoid. There is clearly one and only one such root, and it is the largest of the three. Where λ is mentioned, it is this root that is meant.

Let P', (x',y',z'), be a point on $S(\lambda)$, and let P, (x,y,z), be defined so that

$$\frac{x}{a} = \frac{x'}{a'}, \qquad \frac{y}{b} = \frac{y'}{b'}, \qquad \frac{z}{c} = \frac{z'}{c'}, \tag{5.5.19}$$

where $a'^2 = a^2 + \lambda$, etc. Then P must lie on S. The points P and P' are called *corresponding points*, and there is a one-to-one correspondence between them.

Let QR be an elementary strip of S with cross-section $dy\,dz$, parallel to the x-axis, and let $Q'R'$ be the corresponding strip of $S(\lambda)$, with cross-section $dy'\,dz'$, so that

$$\frac{dy\,dz}{dy'\,dz'} = \frac{bc}{b'c'}. \tag{5.5.20}$$

Then if $df(r)/dr$ denotes the law of force for distance r (an inverse square law for Newtonian attraction) and ρ is the density of each ellipsoid, the attraction

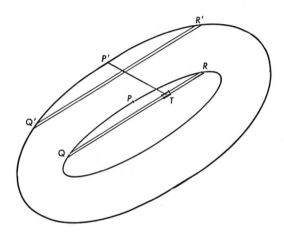

Figure 5.7

at P' due to the strip QR has as its x-component:

$$\Delta X = -G\rho\, dy\, dz \int \frac{df}{dr} \cos \angle P'TR\, dx$$

where T is the position of an element $dx\, dy\, dz$. Now

$$x^2 + y^2 + z^2 = r^2;$$

if y and z are constant (as they are along the strip) then

$$x\, dx = r\, dr$$

so

$$\cos \angle P'TR = \frac{x}{r} = \frac{dr}{dx}$$

and we have

$$\Delta X = -G\rho\, dy\, dz \int \frac{df}{dr} \frac{dr}{dx}\, dx$$

$$= G\rho\, dy\, dz\, [f'(P'Q) - f(P'R)],$$

since the limits of integration are the ends, Q and R, of the strip.

In the same way, the x-component of the attraction at P due to the strip $Q'R'$ is

$$\Delta X' = G\rho\, dy'\, dz'[f(PQ') - f(PR')].$$

Now, from (5.5.19), we see that for any pair of corresponding points, $PQ' = P'Q$ and $PR' = P'R$. So, using (5.5.20) we find

$$\frac{\Delta X}{\Delta X'} = \frac{bc}{b'c'}.$$

Taking all strips such as QR of S and $Q'R'$ of $S(\lambda)$, we finally have

$$\frac{X}{X'} = \frac{bc}{b'c'},$$

where X is the x-component of the attraction due to the ellipsoid S at P', and X' is the similar component of $S(\lambda)$ at P. This result is Ivory's theorem and is true for any conservative law of force. For Newton's law we have, since P is inside $S(\lambda)$,

$$X' = -A'G\rho x,$$

where A' is the same function of a', b', and c' as A is of a, b, and c. So,

$$X = -\frac{bc}{b'c'} A'G\rho x = -\frac{abc}{a'b'c'} A'G\rho x', \tag{5.5.21}$$

with similar expressions for Y and Z.

To calculate the components of force at P, it is necessary first to find the appropriate value of λ, then a', b', and c', and then A', B', and C'. It is easy, if not practically useful, to find analytical expressions for the components. We have

$$X = -\frac{abc}{a'b'c'} G\rho x' \int_0^\infty \frac{2\pi a'b'c'\, du}{(a'^2 + u)\sqrt{(a'^2 + u)(b'^2 + u)(c'^2 + u)}}.$$

Putting $u + \lambda = v$,

$$X = -2\pi G\rho abc x' \int_\lambda^\infty \frac{dv}{(a^2 + v)\sqrt{(a^2 + v)(b^2 + v)(c^2 + v)}}$$

$$= -2\pi G\rho abc x' \int_\lambda^\infty \frac{dv}{(a^2 + v)\,\Delta(v)}, \tag{5.5.22}$$

with similar expressions for Y and Z.

This suggests that the exterior potential should be

$$V = -\pi G\rho abc \int_\lambda^\infty \left(1 - \frac{x'^2}{a^2 + v} - \frac{y'^2}{b^2 + v} - \frac{z'^2}{c^2 + v}\right) \frac{dv}{\Delta(v)}. \tag{5.5.23}$$

To establish this, it is sufficient to show that $\partial V/\partial x = -X$. Differentiating

(5.5.23) partially with respect to x, we find

$$-\frac{\partial V}{\partial x} = -2\pi G\rho abcx' \int_\lambda^\infty \frac{dv}{(a^2 + v)\Delta(v)}$$

$$-\pi G\rho abc\, \frac{\partial \lambda}{\partial x}\left\{1 - \frac{x'^2}{a^2 + \lambda} - \frac{y'^2}{b^2 + \lambda} - \frac{z'^2}{c^2 + \lambda}\right\}\frac{1}{\Delta(\lambda)}.$$

Since (x',y',z') lies on $S(\lambda)$, the second term on the right-hand side vanishes, and we are left with the first, which is X; so, (5.5.23) is established.

Problems

1. Show that if $a > b > c$, then $A < B < C$ and $Aa^2 > Bb^2 > Cc^2$. Show also that for points on the surface of the ellipsoid, the potential is greatest at the ends of the c-axis.

2. Prove that for a prolate spheroid where $a = b = c\sqrt{1 - e^2}$,

$$C = 4\pi\left\{\frac{1}{3} - 2\sum_{n=1}^\infty \frac{e^{2n}}{(2n + 1)(2n + 3)}\right\}.$$

3. Prove that a spheroid of uniform density cannot have its boundary surface as one of its equipotential surfaces.

4. Find the external potential of a uniform shell bounded by two confocal ellipsoids (a *focaloid*).

5. Prove that if a solid uniform ellipsoid of mass M is nearly spherical and has axes a, $\sqrt{a^2 - h}$ and $\sqrt{a^2 - k}$, the potential at an external point is

$$-\frac{GM}{r} - \frac{GM}{10r^5}\{x^2(h + k) + y^2(-2h + k) + z^2(h - 2k)\}$$

to the first order of small quantities. Investigate the relation between this and the approximation of MacCullagh's formula.

6. A solid of uniform density ρ is in the form of the spheroid obtained by rotating an ellipse, of latus rectum $2p$ and eccentricity e, about the major axis. Prove that the potential and intensity of the attracting force at a focus of the generating ellipse are

$$2\pi G\rho\, \frac{p^2}{1 - e^2}$$

and

$$2\pi G\rho\, \frac{p}{e^2}\left\{\log\frac{1 + e}{1 - e} - 2e\right\}.$$

5.6 Laplace's Equation, Legendre Polynomials, and the Potential of the Earth

Celestial bodies are not homogeneous; their internal densities are increased, owing to pressure, so that we cannot apply the results for homogeneous bodies when investigating their fields. Should some law of density be assumed, the potential can, of course, be calculated by integration. But regardless of the nature of the attracting bodies, the potential must satisfy one of the following two differential equations. For regions *away* from attracting matter,

$$\nabla^2 V = 0, \tag{5.6.1}$$

which is Laplace's equation.

For regions *within* attracting matter,

$$\nabla^2 V = 4\pi G\rho, \tag{5.6.2}$$

where ρ is the density; this is Poisson's equation. These equations, it has been remarked, make mathematics much easier for anyone who does not have to solve them; but there are times when the solution can be expressed relatively simply. This is notably so in the investigation of the external field of a body with axial symmetry and which is only slightly distorted from spherical symmetry—assumptions that can reasonably be made about many celestial bodies. We shall not discuss Poisson's equation further, but shall consider some of the properties of solutions of Laplace's equation, which are relevant to the expression for the external potential of the Earth.

To derive Laplace's equation, consider first a system of point masses, m_i at (ξ_i, η_i, ζ_i). At a point (x,y,z), not in contact with a particle, the potential is

$$V = -G \sum_i \frac{m_i}{r_i},$$

where

$$r_i^2 = (x - \xi_i)^2 + (y - \eta_i)^2 + (z - \zeta_i)^2.$$

Then

$$\frac{\partial V}{\partial x} = G \sum_i \frac{m_i}{r_i^2} \frac{\partial r_i}{\partial x}$$

$$= G \sum_i m_i \frac{(x - \xi_i)}{r_i^3},$$

and

$$\frac{\partial^2 V}{\partial x^2} = G \sum_i \left\{ \frac{m_i}{r_i^3} - 3m_i \frac{(x - \xi_i)^2}{r_i^5} \right\}.$$

There are similar expressions for $\partial^2 V/\partial y^2$ and $\partial^2 V/\partial z^2$, and by addition we find that

$$\frac{\partial^2 V}{\partial x^2} + \frac{\partial^2 V}{\partial y^2} + \frac{\partial^2 V}{\partial z^2} = 0,$$

which is Laplace's equation. The generalization for continuous attracting bodies is made by replacing the summations by integrals.

A solution of (5.6.1) that is homogeneous in x, y, and z is called a *harmonic function*, or a *spherical harmonic*. We say that $f(x,y,z)$ is a *homogeneous* function of degree n if

$$f(\lambda x, \lambda y, \lambda z) = \lambda^n f(x,y,z).$$

Should f be harmonic, n is its *degree*. Harmonic functions are immensely important, and accounts of them are given in standard works on analysis and applied mathematics; a useful introduction is given in Ramsey's *Newtonian Attraction* (Ref. 19). In this section we consider integral values of n and shall merely note some properties of immediate concern.

In spherical polar coordinates, Laplace's equation can be written

$$\frac{\partial}{\partial r}\left(r^2 \frac{\partial V}{\partial r}\right) + \frac{1}{\sin\theta}\cdot\frac{\partial}{\partial\theta}\left(\sin\theta \frac{\partial V}{\partial\theta}\right) + \frac{1}{\sin^2\theta}\cdot\frac{\partial^2 V}{\partial\phi^2} = 0. \qquad (5.6.3)$$

A harmonic function of degree n will have the form

$$r^n S_n(\theta,\phi),$$

where S_n is called a *surface harmonic* of order n. Substituting

$$V = r^n S_n(\theta,\phi)$$

into (5.6.3), we find that r^n divides out, and that

$$\frac{\partial^2 S_n}{\partial\theta^2} + \cot\theta \frac{\partial S_n}{\partial\theta} + \frac{1}{\sin^2\theta}\frac{\partial^2 S_n}{\partial\phi^2} + n(n+1)S_n = 0. \qquad (5.6.4)$$

Now let

$$\cos\theta = \mu.$$

(5.6.4) becomes

$$\frac{\partial}{\partial\mu}\left\{(1-\mu^2)\frac{\partial S_n}{\partial\mu}\right\} + \frac{1}{1-\mu^2}\frac{\partial^2 S_n}{\partial\phi^2} + n(n+1)S_n = 0. \qquad (5.6.5)$$

Suppose now that the distribution of attracting matter has axial symmetry and that θ is measured from the axis of symmetry. ϕ no longer appears, and if

$$r^n P_n(\mu)$$

is harmonic, then P_n satisfies the differential equation

$$\frac{d}{d\mu}\left\{(1-\mu^2)\frac{dP_n}{d\mu}\right\} + n(n+1)P_n = 0, \qquad (5.6.6)$$

known as *Legendre's equation*.

If (5.6.6) is solved in series, the solution takes the form

$$P_n = (a_0 + a_2\mu^2 + a_4\mu^4 + \cdots) + (a_1\mu + a_3\mu^3 + a_5\mu^5 + \cdots)$$

where the first series terminates if n is even, and the second if n is odd. In each case the infinite series fails to converge in the entire range $|\mu| \leqslant 1$, and so is of no use to us here. Hence the relevant solution for P_n is a polynomial in μ, known as the *Legendre polynomial* of order n. The series giving P_n is found to be

$$P_n = A_n \frac{(2n)!}{2^n(n!)^2} \left\{ \mu^n - \frac{n(n-1)}{2(2n-1)} \mu^{n-2} + \frac{n(n-1)(n-2)(n-3)}{2 \cdot 4 \cdot (2n-1)(2n-3)} \mu^{n-4} - \cdots \right\}$$

$$(5.6.7)$$

where A_n, the arbitrary constant, is taken as one, for reasons which will appear shortly. The series ends in a constant if n is even, and a term in μ if n is odd.

There are many ways in which these polynomials can be considered. One, in particular, is often used for their original definition and is useful when calculating the polynomials in the absence of a reference. Consider Figure 5.8. The potential at P due to a mass m at Q is

$$-\frac{mG}{PQ},$$

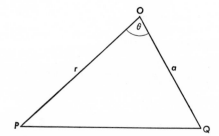

Figure 5.8

and clearly the function

$$\frac{1}{PQ}$$

is harmonic. Let O be any origin; then since

$$PQ^2 = r^2 - 2ra \cos \theta + a^2$$
$$= r^2 - 2ra\mu + a^2,$$

the function

$$V = \frac{1}{(r^2 - 2ra\mu + a^2)^{1/2}}$$

satisfies Laplace's equation. It can be expanded in powers of a/r for $r > a$, and r/a for $r < a$. Denoting the coefficient of r^n/a^{n+1} or a^n/r^{n+1} by P_n, we have

$$V = \frac{1}{a} \left\{ 1 + \frac{r}{a} P_1 + \left(\frac{r}{a}\right)^2 P_2 + \cdots + \left(\frac{r}{a}\right)^n P_n + \cdots \right\}, \quad r < a,$$

and

$$(5.6.8)$$

$$V = \frac{1}{r} \left\{ 1 + \frac{a}{r} P_1 + \left(\frac{a}{r}\right)^2 P_2 + \cdots + \left(\frac{a}{r}\right)^n P_n + \cdots \right\}, \quad r > a.$$

The P_n are polynomials in μ, and they satisfy Legendre's equations; they must therefore be given by (5.6.7) for some A_n. P_n is the coefficient of h^n in the expansion of

$$(1 - 2\mu h + h^2)^{-1/2}$$

or

$$(1 - [2\mu h - h^2])^{-1/2}$$

or

$$1 + \frac{1}{2}(2\mu h - h^2) + \frac{1 \cdot 3}{2 \cdot 4}(2\mu h - h^2)^2 + \cdots$$

We find that

$$P_1 = \mu$$
$$P_2 = \tfrac{1}{2}(3\mu^2 - 1)$$
$$P_3 = \tfrac{1}{2}(5\mu^3 - 3\mu)$$
$$P_4 = \tfrac{1}{8}(35\mu^4 - 30\mu^2 + 3), \text{ etc.}$$

and in general P_n is given by (5.6.7) where $A_n = 1$.

Let us assume that the Earth has symmetry about the north-south axis, and that θ is measured from the north pole. The external potential must be of the form

$$V = -\frac{MG}{r}\left\{1 - \frac{1}{r^2}J_2P_2 - \frac{1}{r^3}J_3P_3 - \cdots\right\} \tag{5.6.9}$$

where the J's are constants. Here we have neglected the term in P_1 altogether, since it can be removed by a change of origin north or south so that it coincides with the center of gravity of the Earth. In the same way the term in $1/R^2$ in the derivation of MacCullagh's formula (Section 5.4) vanishes by virtue of the choice of the centre of gravity as origin.

An advantage of (5.6.9) is that it can immediately be written down, once axial symmetry has been assumed, and any suitable experiment (such as the study of the orbit of an artificial satellite) can be used to determine the J's. For a spherical Earth all the J's would be zero; in fact J_2 is of the order of 10^{-3} (the unit of length being the Earth's equatorial radius), J_4 is of the order of J_2^2, and the others are smaller. The inclusion of the odd P's allows for a lack of symmetry about the equator. Certainly the odd J's are very small, but it has now been established that J_3 is perceptible and that the Earth is slightly "pear-shaped."

Considering (5.6.9) as a series expansion in a_E/r where a_E is the equatorial radius of the Earth, we might expect that it would be necessary to consider many terms when r is only slightly greater than a_E. But because the J's are so small, this is not the case, and only the first few terms (and for many purposes only J_2) need to be considered. Very close to the Earth's surface there are additional gravitational anomalies to be taken into account; these should be considered, for instance, in the launching or descent of a missile.

Problems

1. If V is a harmonic function of degree n, prove that

$$\frac{\partial^a}{\partial x^a} \frac{\partial^b}{\partial y^b} \frac{\partial^c}{\partial z^c} V$$

is also harmonic, of degree $(n - a - b - c)$.

2. If $r^n S_n$ is harmonic, prove that $r^{-n-1} S_n$ is also harmonic.

3. Solve Legendre's equation in series, justifying the comments made in the text.

4. Account for the absence of terms in r, r^2, etc., and of the term in P_1 from the series in (5.6.9).

5. Prove that

$$\int_{-1}^{+1} P_n P_m \, d\mu = 0$$

if $n \neq m$, and

$$\int_{-1}^{+1} (P_n)^2 \, d\mu = \frac{2}{2n + 1}.$$

6. Compare the first two terms of (5.6.9) with MacCullagh's formula.

7. A circular ring of radius a has line density ρ. Taking the origin as the center of the ring and measuring θ from the axis perpendicular to its plane, write down the potential of the ring at points along the axis, and hence, or otherwise, prove that the potential at (r,θ) is given by

$$V_1 = -2\pi G\rho \left\{ 1 - \frac{1}{2} \left(\frac{r}{a}\right)^2 P_2 + \frac{1\cdot 3}{2\cdot 4} \left(\frac{r}{a}\right)^4 P_4 - \cdots \right\}$$

for $r < a$, and

$$V_2 = -2\pi G\rho \left\{ \frac{a}{r} - \frac{1}{2} \left(\frac{a}{r}\right)^3 P_2 + \frac{1\cdot 3}{2\cdot 4} \left(\frac{a}{r}\right)^5 P_4 - \cdots \right\}$$

for $r > a$.

8. A circular disc has radius a and density ρ per unit area. Prove that its potential at (r,θ) is given by

$$V_1 = -2\pi a G\rho \left\{ 1 - \frac{r}{a} P_1 + \frac{1}{2} \left(\frac{r}{a}\right)^2 P_2 - \frac{1\cdot 1}{2\cdot 4} \left(\frac{r}{a}\right)^4 P_4 + \frac{1\cdot 1\cdot 3}{2\cdot 4\cdot 6} \left(\frac{r}{a}\right)^6 P_6 - \cdots \right\}$$

for $r < a$ and $0 \leqslant \theta \leqslant \pi/2$, the sign of the term in P_1 being changed if $\pi/2 < \theta \leqslant \pi$, and

$$V_2 = -2\pi a G\rho \left\{ \frac{1}{2} \cdot \frac{a}{r} - \frac{1\cdot 1}{2\cdot 4} \left(\frac{a}{r}\right)^3 P_2 + \frac{1\cdot 1\cdot 3}{2\cdot 4\cdot 6} \left(\frac{a}{r}\right)^5 P_4 - \cdots \right\}$$

for $r > a$. The coordinate system is similar to that of problem 7.

9. Find, in the form of an infinite series, the potential due to a flat circular annulus (e.g., Saturn's ring) at points moderately near the center of the ring.

    If a small but massive planet occupies the center of the ring, show that the maximum deflection of the plumb line on its surface (on account of the attraction of the ring) will occur in latitude 45°, approximately.

5.7   The Tidal Distortion of a Liquid Sphere Under the Action of a Distant Point Mass

The theory of this chapter will be illustrated by its application to two problems of astronomical interest; these concern the tides and possible figures of rotating fluid masses.

Consider a spherical mass M of incompressible fluid of density ρ, called *the primary*. Suppose that this is made subject to the tidal influence of a second body which is at a great distance from the primary compared with the radius of the latter, and which is such that for gravitational purposes it can be treated as a point mass M'. Let the origin be at the center of mass of the primary, and take coordinates (r,θ,ϕ) in spherical polars. The potential at (r,θ,ϕ) due to M' at the point $(R,0,\phi)$, where $r \ll R$, is

$$V = -\frac{M'G}{(R^2 + r^2 - 2Rr\cos\theta)^{1/2}}$$

$$= -\frac{M'G}{R}\left(1 - 2\frac{r}{R}\cos\theta + \frac{r^2}{R^2}\right)^{-1/2}$$

$$= -\frac{M'G}{R} - \frac{M'Gr\cos\theta}{R^2} - \frac{M'Gr^2(3\cos^2\theta - 1)}{2R^3} + \cdots$$

The first term is constant if R is constant, and so gives rise to no force on M. The second gives rise to a uniform force with intensity $-(M'G/R^2)$. This can be neutralized if the axes of reference are rotating with an acceleration $M'G/R^2$ while the center of mass of M always remains at the origin. This condition is fulfilled in the case of the Earth-Moon system if we suppose that the Moon remains at a constant distance from the Earth; the x-axis will then always point toward the Moon. We are left with the remaining terms, which constitute the *tide raising potential* V_T. Since $r \ll R$, only the first term will be considered, and expressing this in cartesian coordinates, where the x-axis points toward M', we have

$$V_T = -\mu(x^2 - \tfrac{1}{2}y^2 - \tfrac{1}{2}z^2), \tag{5.7.1}$$

where

$$\mu = \frac{M'G}{R^3}.$$

We have to find out what effect this will have on the shape of the primary. The condition to apply is that the free surface of M must be an equipotential surface in the combined fields of M and M'. This is reasonable, since, if possible, matter tends to move from places of higher to lower potential energy, and on the free surface of a liquid there is nothing to prevent such an adjustment.

Alternatively, consider the pressure in the liquid. Pressure is "force per unit area." Consider an element of mass δm with volume $\delta x\,\delta y\,\delta z$ and density ρ. If p_x is the pressure acting on the face $\delta y\,\delta z$, the force acting on that face must be $p_x\,\delta y\,\delta z$. The difference between this force and the force acting on the opposite face is

$$\left(\frac{\partial p_x}{\partial x}\,\delta y\,\delta z\right)\delta x.$$

But this must be equal to the net force in the x-direction which is acting on the element. This force is $X\,\delta m$, or $X\rho\,\delta x\,\delta y\,\delta z$. Hence

$$\frac{\partial p_x}{\partial x}\,\delta x = X\rho\,\delta x.$$

This leads at once to the equation for the general change of pressure:

$$\frac{dp}{\rho} = \nabla V\cdot d\mathbf{r}.$$

Now, over a free surface the pressure must be constant, so that V must be constant and the surface is an equipotential.

Let us assume that M takes up the figure of an ellipsoid; then the potential at (x,y,z) is

$$\tfrac{1}{2}G\rho(Ax^2 + By^2 + Cz^2) - \mu(x^2 - \tfrac{1}{2}y^2 - \tfrac{1}{2}z^2) + \text{constant}.$$

This must be constant over the surface

$$\frac{x^2}{a^2} + \frac{y^2}{b^2} + \frac{z^2}{c^2} = 1,$$

and the condition for this is that the coefficients of x^2, y^2, and z^2 must be proportional; i.e.,

$$a^2\left(A - 2\frac{\mu}{G\rho}\right) = b^2\left(B + \frac{\mu}{G\rho}\right) = c^2\left(C + \frac{\mu}{G\rho}\right). \tag{5.7.2}$$

This provides two equations for the ratios of the axes, and (5.5.10) is a third; they can be solved, and the solutions are considered in more detail in the following section on rotating fluid masses. As in the case of the rotating fluid, there are solutions with three unequal axes, but we are concerned with small distortions from spherical figures, and for these two axes are equal. This means that there are two symmetrical bulges pointing toward and away from M'.

Let $b = c$; then if $c = a(1 - \epsilon)$, we have

$$\frac{4}{3}\pi\left(1 - \frac{4}{5}\epsilon\right) - 2\frac{\mu}{G\rho} = (1 - \epsilon)^2\left\{\frac{4}{3}\pi\left(1 + \frac{2}{5}\epsilon\right) + \frac{\mu}{G\rho}\right\}$$

$$= \frac{4}{3}\pi\left(1 - \frac{8}{5}\epsilon\right) + \frac{\mu}{G\rho} + \cdots$$

We may neglect terms of the order ϵ^2 and $\mu\epsilon$, and solve this equation to find

$$\epsilon = \frac{45}{16\pi}\frac{\mu}{G\rho}. \tag{5.7.3}$$

If this is applied to the Earth-Moon system, and we assume that the Earth is a fluid mass with density 5.52, then we have $M' = 7.38 \times 10^{25}$ gm and $R = 3.84 \times 10^{10}$ cm. Then

$$\epsilon = 0.84 \times 10^{-5}.$$

Taking the Earth's radius as 6.4×10^8 cm, the difference between the axes is 5.4×10^3 cm.

Comparison with actuality is not profitable here. The Earth is not a fluid mass, nor is it even entirely covered with water. Also, there are complicating factors such as the friction between the water and the sea beds, which delays the tides at any place. (This friction is believed to be partly responsible for the slowing down of the Earth's rotation, mentioned in Section 1.11.) In practice the forecasting of tides is largely empirical.

5.8   Ellipsoidal Figures of Rotating Fluid Masses

We shall consider only homogeneous fluid masses rotating uniformly as solid bodies. Then from Section 3.4 we can treat the problem as one of statics, provided we include the term

$$-\tfrac{1}{2}\omega^2(x^2 + y^2)$$

per unit mass in the potential function, where the angular velocity is ω about Oz. Here we shall consider only possible ellipsoidal forms; but it has been shown by Poincaré that there are infinitely many other possibilities.

For an ellipsoid a surface of constant pressure is given by

$$(\omega^2 - AG\rho)x^2 + (\omega^2 - BG\rho)y^2 - CG\rho z^2 = \text{constant}.$$

Assuming the free surface to be

$$\frac{x^2}{a^2} + \frac{y^2}{b^2} + \frac{z^2}{c^2} = 1,$$

the condition for this also to be a surface of constant pressure is

$$a^2(\omega^2 - AG\rho) = b^2(\omega^2 - BG\rho) = -c^2CG\rho. \tag{5.8.1}$$

Eliminating ω we get

$$a^2b^2(B - A) = (a^2 - b^2)c^2C. \tag{5.8.2}$$

So, we can have $a = b$, when the figure is an oblate spheroid, known as a *Maclaurin spheroid*. The nearly spherical case will be discussed later in this section. If $a \neq b$, the substitution for A, B, and C, according to the formulas of Section 5.5, into (5.8.2) gives

$$\int_0^\infty \left\{\frac{1}{a^2} + \frac{1}{b^2} - \frac{1}{c^2} + \frac{u}{a^2b^2}\right\} \frac{u\,du}{\Delta^3} = 0. \tag{5.8.3}$$

If a and b are known, this can be regarded as an equation for finding c; and since the left-hand side is negative for small c and positive for large c, there must be a real root.

From (5.8.1) the value of ω^2 is found to be

$$\omega^2 = \frac{(Aa^2 - Bb^2)G\rho}{(a^2 - b^2)}$$
$$= 2\pi G\rho abc \int_0^\infty \frac{u\,du}{(a^2 + u)(b^2 + u)\Delta}. \tag{5.8.4}$$

Since the right-hand side is positive, the corresponding value of ω is real.

Also from (5.8.1) we have

$$a^2\omega^2 = G\rho(Aa^2 - Cc^2)$$
$$= 2\pi G\rho abc(a^2 - c^2) \int_0^\infty \frac{u\,du}{(a^2 + u)(c^2 + u)\Delta},$$

so that $c < a$. Similarly, $c < b$, so that the ellipsoid rotates about its shortest axis. An ellipsoid of this type is known as a *Jacobi ellipsoid*. There are no nearly spherical Jacobi ellipsoids, but they form a one-parameter family, branching off from the Maclaurin spheroids. The sequence of models depends on the ratio ω^2/ρ and not only on ω. Numerical values have been found by Darwin, and have been discussed, in particular, by Jeans (Refs. 20, 21).

Returning to the Maclaurin spheroids, consider the case of a slightly distorted sphere. Using the formulas (5.5.15) and following the method of the preceding section, we find

$$\epsilon = \frac{15}{16\pi} \cdot \frac{\omega^2}{G\rho}. \tag{5.8.5}$$

Taking $\rho = 5.52$ and $\omega = 2\pi/86{,}164$ (since there are 86,164 seconds in a sidereal day), we find $\epsilon = 4.3 \times 10^{-3}$. This leads to a predicted difference of about $43\frac{1}{4}$ miles between the polar and equatorial diameters. This is more than the actual flattening, but the discrepancy is hardly surprising in view of the assumptions that we have made.

Problems

1. Prove that there are no Jacobi ellipsoids which are only slightly distorted spheres.

2. The polar and equatorial diameters of Jupiter are observed to be 133,200 and 142,700 km, respectively, and its mean density is 1.34. Assuming that it is a homogeneous fluid and that its distortion is the result of a solid body rotation, find the predicted period of rotation. The observed period is of the order of ten hours; what conclusions can be drawn from this?

3. The period of rotation of the Sun is of the order of 25.4 days, and its mean density is 1.41. Assuming that it is a homogeneous fluid mass and rotates as a solid body, what distortion from a spherical figure is predicted?

4. Prove that for a Maclaurin spheroid:

$$\frac{\omega^2}{2\pi G\rho} = \frac{3 - 2e^2}{e^3}\sqrt{1 - e^2}\sin^{-1}e - 3\left(\frac{1}{e^2} - 1\right),$$

where $c^2 = a^2(1 - e^2)$. By expanding this for the cases e small and e nearly equal to one, show that the left-hand side is small at each extreme. Find the maximum possible value for the left-hand side.

5. Assuming that the Moon is composed of a homogeneous fluid of density 3.34 and total mass 7.36×10^{25} gm, and that it is at a constant distance 3.84×10^{10} cm from the Earth, find the predicted tidal distortion of its figure.

6. A homogeneous fluid body has a slow uniform rotation; it is subject to the tidal influence of a distant body which lies in the plane of its equator. Investigate the total distortion of the body.

   Apply this theory to the predicted figure of the Moon, using the data above, given that the period of rotation is 27.32 days.

7. Compare the tide-raising potentials of the Sun and Moon on the Earth. Assuming that the Earth is a homogeneous fluid (and neglecting its rotation), find approximate figures for the Earth when the three bodies are in a straight line and when the angle between the lines joining the Earth to the Sun and Moon is 90°.

8. Prove that the potential of a plane annulus bounded by concentric circles at a point on its axis is

$$2\pi G\rho(l' - l),$$

where ρ is the mass per unit area and l, l' are the distances of the point from the inner and outer edges.

A planet is at the center of a uniform plane annulus of mass M and inner and outer radii a and b, large compared with the planet's radius. Show that to a first approximation the effect of the ring on the figure of equilibrium of the planet is equivalent to that of a rotational velocity ω, where

$$\omega^2 = \frac{GM}{ab(a + b)}.$$

9. A homogeneous gravitating solid is in the form of a prolate spheroid of small ellipticity ϵ, where $\epsilon = (a - c)/a$ and a and c are the semiaxes of a meridian section. The spheroid is rotating about its axis with angular velocity ω. Prove that the direction of a plumb line at any point on the spheroid will pass through the center, provided

$$\omega^2 = \frac{6\epsilon g}{5a},$$

where g is the approximately constant value of gravity at the surface.

10. Two masses M are placed at distances c on opposite sides of the center of a gravitating sphere of liquid of radius a and total mass M'. Show that, neglecting powers of a/c above the third, the liquid is deformed into a prolate spheroid, the ratio of the minor axis to the major being

$$1 - \frac{15}{2} \cdot \frac{M}{M'} \left(\frac{a}{c}\right)^3.$$

If two more particles of the same mass M are placed at distances c from the center on an axis at right angles to the line joining the former pair, show that the surface becomes an oblate spheroid, the ratio of the axes being the same as in the previous case.

11. A planet consists of a point mass and an atmosphere of negligible mass. Investigate the degree of *small* distortions due to rotation and to tidal forces.

   Assuming that Jupiter is such a planet, compare the figures for the distortion and rotation with those of problem 2. What conclusions can be drawn?

Chapter 6 ** THE TWO-BODY PROBLEM

6.1 The Motion of the Center of Mass

The case of a central orbit described under an attraction μ/r^2 has already been considered. In this chapter we shall investigate the motion of two bodies that are subject only to their mutual attraction. It is assumed that the bodies are spherically symmetrical and that Newton's law holds; then the bodies can be considered to be point masses. The methods used will be general, but most of the applications and much of the language will apply specifically to a planet traveling around the Sun.

Let the bodies have masses m_1 and m_2, and position vectors $\mathbf{r}_1$ and $\mathbf{r}_2$ at some instant. Also let

$$\mathbf{r} = \mathbf{r}_1 - \mathbf{r}_2.$$

Instead of the Newtonian gravitational constant G, we shall substitute k^2, for reasons which will become apparent soon. Then the equations of motion are

$$m_1\ddot{\mathbf{r}}_1 = -k^2 m_1 m_2 \frac{\mathbf{r}_1 - \mathbf{r}_2}{r^3} \tag{6.1.1}$$

and

$$m_2\ddot{\mathbf{r}}_2 = -k^2 m_1 m_2 \frac{\mathbf{r}_2 - \mathbf{r}_1}{r^3}. \tag{6.1.2}$$

These are equivalent to six second-order differential equations, requiring twelve arbitrary constants for their complete solution. Adding (6.1.1) and (6.1.2), we get

$$m_1\ddot{\mathbf{r}}_1 + m_2\ddot{\mathbf{r}}_2 = 0$$

which can be integrated at once to give

$$m_1\mathbf{r}_1 + m_2\mathbf{r}_2 = \mathbf{a}t + \mathbf{b}, \tag{6.1.3}$$

where $\mathbf{a}$ and $\mathbf{b}$ are constant vectors, supplying six constants of integration and leaving six more to be found. Let

$$m_1 + m_2 = M$$

and

$$M\bar{\mathbf{r}} = m_1\mathbf{r}_1 + m_2\mathbf{r}_2,$$

so that $\bar{\mathbf{r}}$ is the center of mass of the two bodies. Then (6.1.3) shows that the center of mass moves in a straight line with constant speed.

In considering planetary motion, we are concerned with the orbit of one body about another without regard to their motion through space, so (6.1.3) does not provide any useful information. (It should be noted that the constants **a** and **b** can be changed at will by changing the inertial system of reference.) But the interpretation is important. One application is to the theory of double stars. Suppose that the observed paths of the components of a visual binary on the celestial sphere are the full lines in Figure 6.1. The center of mass must divide corresponding positions in a constant ratio, and since it moves in a straight line with constant speed, its path can be drawn and the ratio of the masses can be determined. In some cases only one star is observed, moving in a twisted path, and the existence of a companion body is inferred from this. The companion of Sirius was first discovered in this way by Bessel, and in a few recent cases bodies of planetary dimensions have been suspected as invisible companions to optically single stars, through similar reasoning.

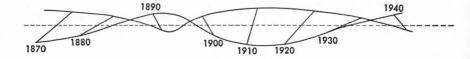

Figure 6.1 The orbits of Sirius A and B.

Problems

1. Find approximately the distance of the center of mass of the Sun and Jupiter from the center of the Sun, and the speed of the Sun's center in its orbit about this center of mass. (Ignore the effects of the other planets.)
2. Answer problem 1, substituting the Earth and the Moon for the Sun and Jupiter.
3. Two unequal bodies describe circular orbits around each other while their center of mass moves through space with speed v, with respect to some fixed reference system. Sketch the orbits in space with values of v giving paths with and without loops, and mark in relative positions at particular times. Find the relation between the orbit and v such that the space orbit has cusps.

6.2 The Relative Motion

Take a new origin at the center of mass so that

$$m_1\mathbf{r}_1 + m_2\mathbf{r}_2 = 0.$$

(6.1.1) can be written:

$$\ddot{\mathbf{r}}_1 = -k^2 \frac{m_2\mathbf{r}_1 - m_2\mathbf{r}_2}{r^3}$$

$$= -k^2 \frac{m_2\mathbf{r}_1 + m_1\mathbf{r}_1}{r^3}$$

$$= -k^2 M \frac{\mathbf{r}_1}{r^3}. \tag{6.2.1}$$

Similarly, (6.1.2) can be written:

$$\ddot{\mathbf{r}}_2 = -k^2 M \frac{\mathbf{r}_2}{r^3}. \tag{6.2.2}$$

Subtract (6.2.2) from (6.2.1), and put $k^2 M = \mu$. Then

$$\ddot{\mathbf{r}} = -\mu \frac{\mathbf{r}}{r^3}. \tag{6.2.3}$$

This is equivalent to three second-order differential equations requiring six constants of integration for their complete solution: finding and interpreting these constants constitutes the kernel of the two-body problem.

$\mathbf{r} \times$ (6.2.3) gives

$$\mathbf{r} \times \ddot{\mathbf{r}} = 0,$$

or, integrating,

$$\mathbf{r} \times \dot{\mathbf{r}} = \mathbf{h}, \tag{6.2.4}$$

where $\mathbf{h}$ is a constant vector supplying three constants of integration. (6.2.4) shows that the angular momentum of the system is constant, and that the motion takes place in the plane

$$\mathbf{r} \cdot \mathbf{h} = 0.$$

Now take $\mathbf{h} \times$ (6.2.3), using (6.2.4) on the right-hand side. We obtain

$$\mathbf{h} \times \ddot{\mathbf{r}} = -\frac{\mu}{r^3} \mathbf{h} \times \mathbf{r}$$

$$= -\frac{\mu}{r^3} (\mathbf{r} \times \dot{\mathbf{r}}) \times \mathbf{r}$$

$$= -\frac{\mu}{r^3} \{r^2\dot{\mathbf{r}} - (\mathbf{r} \cdot \dot{\mathbf{r}})\mathbf{r}\}$$

$$= -\frac{\mu}{r^3} \{r^2\dot{\mathbf{r}} - (r\dot{r})\mathbf{r}\}$$

$$= -\mu \left\{\frac{\dot{\mathbf{r}}}{r} - \frac{\mathbf{r}\dot{r}}{r^2}\right\}$$

$$= -\mu \frac{d}{dt} \left(\frac{\mathbf{r}}{r}\right)$$

$$= -\mu \frac{d\hat{\mathbf{r}}}{dt}.$$

(This step is due to Hamilton.) Integrating, we obtain

$$\mathbf{h} \times \dot{\mathbf{r}} = -\mu\hat{\mathbf{r}} - \mathbf{P}. \tag{6.2.5}$$

$\mathbf{P}$ is a constant vector and seems at first sight to supply the remaining three constants of integration. But its components are not independent, for $\mathbf{h} \cdot$ (6.2.5) gives

$$\mathbf{P}\cdot\mathbf{h} = 0, \tag{6.2.6}$$

since $\hat{\mathbf{r}}\cdot\mathbf{h} = 0$. So $\mathbf{P}$ supplies only two arbitrary constants, leaving one more to be found.

Taking $\mathbf{r}\cdot$(6.2.5) we obtain

$$\mathbf{r}\cdot(\mathbf{h} \times \dot{\mathbf{r}}) = -\mu r - \mathbf{P}\cdot\mathbf{r}$$

or

$$-\mathbf{h}\cdot(\mathbf{r} \times \dot{\mathbf{r}}) = -\mu r - \mathbf{P}\cdot\mathbf{r}$$

or

$$h^2 = \mu r + \mathbf{P}\cdot\mathbf{r}$$

or

$$\frac{h^2/\mu}{r} = 1 + \frac{\mathbf{P}}{\mu}\cdot\hat{\mathbf{r}}. \tag{6.2.7}$$

Let $\hat{\mathbf{r}}$ make an angle v with $\mathbf{P}$; then (6.2.7) is equivalent to

$$\frac{h^2/\mu}{r} = 1 + \frac{P}{\mu}\cos v. \tag{6.2.8}$$

This is the standard equation of a conic with the origin at one focus and with

$$\frac{P}{\mu} = e \tag{6.2.9}$$

and

$$\frac{h^2}{\mu} = p = a(1 - e^2) \text{ for an ellipse}$$

or

$$= a(e^2 - 1) \text{ for a hyperbola.} \tag{6.2.10}$$

For a hyperbola the condition that r is nonnegative shows that v varies between $\pm \cos^{-1}(-1/e)$, so that only one branch can be described, the relevant branch being concave toward the origin. $\mathbf{P}$ is a vector along the major axis of the orbit pointing toward the position of closest approach between the two bodies; in the case of a planet going around the Sun, it points toward perihelion. The angle v is known as the *true anomaly*; it is measured in the direction in which the orbit is described, starting from perihelion. The symbol "v" almost always replaces the conventional "θ" of polar coordinates in this context.

In some problems in astronomy it is necessary to consider motion under a repulsive force varying with the inverse square of the distance. For example the particles in a comet's tail suffer this repulsion from the Sun, owing to radiation pressure, which easily outweighs the gravitational attraction of the Sun. In this case the formal theory is the same, but the sign of k^2, or μ, is changed, and the equation of the orbit is

$$\frac{p}{r} = -1 + e \cos v.$$

Since r is positive, e is greater than one, and the orbit is a branch of a hyperbola. Also, v varies between $\pm \cos^{-1}(1/e)$, so that the branch described is convex toward the focus occupied by the Sun.

Problems

1. Using great care, derive equations of motion for the two bodies, A and B, in the following forms: A with respect to B as origin, B with respect to A, and each with respect to their center of mass.

   Prove that the resulting orbits are all conics with the same eccentricity but different major axes, and find the relations between the major axes. Compare the angular momenta of A about B, B about A, and each with respect to their center of mass.

2. A star A is initially at rest with respect to an inertial system of reference. Another star B is projected from infinity with a velocity that would carry it a distance c from A if there were no mutual attraction. Investigate the motion of the center of mass in the subsequent motion. If the relative orbit has eccentricity e, find the angle through which B is deflected, having passed A and receded to infinity, and the velocity which A has then acquired.

6.3   The Orbit in Time

The final constant of integration is found by integrating the equation that expresses the constancy of the modulus of the angular momentum. This can be written:

$$r^2 \frac{dv}{dt} = h = \sqrt{p\mu}. \tag{6.3.1}$$

The equation of the orbit can be written:

$$r = \frac{p}{1 + e \cos v} \tag{6.3.2}$$

so that, eliminating r, we get

$$\frac{dv}{(1 + e \cos v)^2} = \sqrt{\frac{\mu}{p^3}}\, dt. \tag{6.3.3}$$

This can be integrated for all e without much trouble, but except for $e = 0$ or 1, an extra substitution is needed to put the result in a useful form.

$e = 0$ gives a circular orbit described with constant speed. There is no difficulty in the formal theory here, and results can always be found by putting $e = 0$ in the corresponding formulas for elliptic motion, so that a separate discussion is not necessary.

For the parabolic orbit, $e = 1$. If q is the perihelion distance for an elliptic orbit, $q = a(1 - e)$ and $p = q(1 + e)$. Hence, for the parabolic orbit, $p = 2q$ and the equation can be written:

$$r = q \sec^2 \frac{v}{2}. \qquad (6.3.4)$$

Since the results will be applied to the motion of comets, M can be taken as the mass of the Sun, which will be considered as unit mass. Then we can put $\mu = k^2$. (6.3.3) can now be written as

$$\sec^4 \frac{v}{2} \, dv = \frac{k\sqrt{2}}{q^{3/2}} \, dt.$$

Writing the left-hand side as

$$\sec^2 \frac{v}{2} \left(1 + \tan^2 \frac{v}{2}\right)$$

we find that the equation can be integrated at once to give

$$\frac{1}{3} \tan^3 \frac{v}{2} + \tan \frac{v}{2} = \frac{k}{\sqrt{2q^3}} (t - T). \qquad (6.3.5)$$

T is the final constant of integration, giving the time when $v = 0$ or when the comet passes through perihelion.

Consider the solution of (6.3.5) for v when t is given. Let

$$F(v) \equiv \frac{1}{3} \tan^3 \frac{v}{2} + \tan \frac{v}{2} - \frac{k}{\sqrt{2q^3}} (t - T).$$

Then varying only v,

$$\frac{dF}{dv} \equiv \frac{1}{2} \sec^4 \frac{v}{2}$$

which is positive for all v. (6.3.5), being a cubic equation for $\tan(v/2)$, must have at least one root; since $F(v)$ is monotonic, increasing with v, there is *only* one root for any given value of t. In practice (6.3.5) is solved for v by the use of tables.

Now consider the elliptic orbit. Squaring equation (6.2.4) we get

$$h^2 = \dot{r}^2 r^2 - (\mathbf{r} \cdot \dot{\mathbf{r}})^2$$
$$= \dot{r}^2 r^2 - (r\dot{r})^2. \qquad (6.3.6)$$

Substituting for h and $\dot{r}^2$ (from the energy integral) for the elliptic orbit, we find

$$\mu\left(\frac{2}{r} - \frac{1}{a}\right) r^2 - r^2\dot{r}^2 = \mu a(1 - e^2). \tag{6.3.7}$$

Define E by

$$r = a(1 - e \cos E). \tag{6.3.8}$$

E is called the *eccentric anomaly*. As v varies from 0 to 360°, E also varies from 0 to 360°. Differentiating (6.3.8) we get

$$\dot{r} = ae \sin E\, \dot{E}.$$

Substituting into (6.3.7) and rearranging, we obtain, eventually,

$$\frac{a^3}{\mu}\, \dot{E}^2(1 - e \cos E)^2 = 1.$$

Now the orbit is described so that dE/dt is positive, so that

$$dt = \sqrt{\frac{a^3}{\mu}}\, (1 - e \cos E)dE. \tag{6.3.9}$$

Integrating over a complete orbit, we get for the period

$$P = 2\pi \sqrt{\frac{a^3}{\mu}}, \tag{6.3.10}$$

the result obtained in Chapter Four. The *mean notion*, n, is given by

$$n = \frac{2\pi}{P}$$

$$= \sqrt{\frac{\mu}{a^3}}. \tag{6.3.11}$$

n is measured in *radians per unit time*. If P is expressed in mean solar days, n is called the *mean daily motion*. (6.3.9) can now be written:

$$n\, dt = dE(1 - e \cos E)$$

which can be integrated immediately to give

$$n(t - T) = E - e \sin E. \tag{6.3.12}$$

T, the time of perihelion passage, is the final constant of integration for the elliptic orbit. (6.3.12) is *Kepler's equation*; it is often written in the form:

$$M = E - e \sin E,$$

where M is the *mean anomaly*, defined by

$$M = n(t - T).$$

A similar equation can be found for hyperbolic motion. In this case we make the substitutions

$$r = a(e \cosh F - 1) \qquad (6.3.13)$$

and

$$\nu = \sqrt{\frac{\mu}{a^3}} \qquad (6.3.14)$$

and we find

$$\nu(t - T) = e \sinh F - F. \qquad (6.3.15)$$

There is a simple but important derivation of Kepler's equation which explains the geometrical significance of E. The ellipse can be derived from the orthogonal projection of a circle called the *eccentric circle*. In the notation of Figure 6.2, the ellipse can be regarded as the locus of points P such that PD/QD

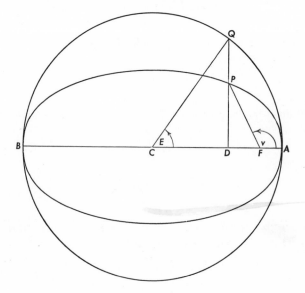

Figure 6.2

is constant, the value of the constant being the ratio of the minor to major axes of the ellipse. Here Q is any point on the eccentric circle, and QD is perpendicular to the diameter ACB, which is also the major axis of the ellipse, center C.

Let F be the relevant focus; then $FP = r$ and $\angle AFP = v$. Let $\angle QCA = E$;

then

$$r^2 = PD^2 + DF^2$$

$$= \left(\frac{b}{a}QD\right)^2 + (CF - CD)^2$$

$$= \left(\frac{b}{a}a\sin E\right)^2 + (ae - a\cos E)^2$$

$$= a^2(1 - e^2)\sin^2 E + a^2(e - \cos E)^2 \quad [\text{since } b^2 = a^2(1 - e^2)]$$

$$= a^2(1 - e\cos E)^2,$$

showing that E is defined as before.

The coordinates of P with respect to axes along the major and minor axes of the ellipse (the origin being at the center of the ellipse) are

$$\left. \begin{array}{l} x = a\cos E, \\ y = b\sin E = a\sqrt{1 - e^2}\sin E. \end{array} \right] \tag{6.3.16}$$

As the elliptic orbit is described by P, we have, by the law of areas,

$$\frac{M}{2\pi} = \frac{\text{area of sector } AFP}{\text{area of ellipse}}$$

$$= \frac{\text{area of sector } AFQ}{\text{area of circle}}.$$

Areas $AFQ = ACQ - FCQ$

$$= \tfrac{1}{2}a^2 E - \tfrac{1}{2}ae(a\sin E),$$

so we have

$$\frac{M}{2\pi} = \frac{a^2(E - e\sin E)}{2\pi a^2}$$

or

$$M = E - e\sin E.$$

A method for the solution of Kepler's equation will be described later. The equation of the elliptic orbit can be written:

$$r = \frac{a(1 - e^2)}{1 + e\cos v}.$$

Hence

$$1 - e\cos E = \frac{1 - e^2}{1 + e\cos v}$$

so

$$\cos v = \frac{\cos E - e}{1 - e\cos E}, \tag{6.3.17}$$

and

$$\sin v = \frac{\sqrt{1 - e^2}\sin E}{1 - e\cos E}. \tag{6.3.18}$$

Now

$$\tan^2 \frac{v}{2} = \frac{1 - \cos v}{1 + \cos v}$$

$$= \frac{(1 + e)(1 - \cos E)}{(1 - e)(1 + \cos E)}$$

$$= \frac{1 + e}{1 - e} \tan^2 \frac{E}{2}.$$

So

$$\tan \frac{v}{2} = \sqrt{\frac{1 + e}{1 - e}} \tan \frac{E}{2}. \qquad (6.3.19)$$

To illustrate the interpretation of the three anomalies, consider the Moon's libration in longitude. The period of rotation of the Moon on its axis is the same as the period of its revolution around the Earth (one *sidereal month*). If the Moon revolved around the Earth in a circular orbit, then one half of its surface would be constantly pointing toward the Earth, and we would see no part of the other half. Now the Moon moves in an elliptic orbit with the Earth, E, as a focus. Let the Moon have center O, and let P be that point on the surface of the Moon such that O, P, and E are collinear at perigee. At any time OP will make an angle with the major axis of the ellipse that is equal to the mean anomaly M of the Moon in its orbit, while the angle between OE and the major axis is the true anomaly v. Assuming for the moment that the axis of rotation of the Moon is perpendicular to the plane of the orbit, an observer on the Earth will see P as being displaced from the center of the Moon's disk by a longitude $(M - v)$, or he will see this extra longitude at the Moon's limb compared with what he observed at perigee. This is known as the *libration in longitude* of the Moon. To investigate its fullest extent, we find the maximum value of $(M - v)$; this occurs when

$$\frac{d(M - v)}{dt} = 0,$$

or

$$\frac{dv}{dt} = n.$$

From the angular momentum equation, the value of r at this point is found from

$$r^2 = \frac{h}{n},$$

and, substituting for h and n, we find

$$r = a(1 - e^2)^{1/4}.$$

The appropriate value of v can then be found from the equation of the orbit.

To find M, it is necessary first to find E, from (6.3.8), say, and then to solve Kepler's equation for M.

(For the Moon, three other types of libration must be considered. The axis of rotation is not perpendicular to the plane of its orbit, so an observer in the northern hemisphere of the Earth will sometimes see "over" the Moon's north pole, and sometimes "under" its south pole; this is *libration in latitude*. While looking at the Moon, an observer will be moving in space owing to the Earth's rotation; this will cause him to see a slightly different "half" at different times; this is *diurnal libration*. Also, because of its nonspherical shape, the Moon oscillates slightly; this effect, which is very small, leads to *physical libration*. The other three types of libration are classed as *optical librations*.)

Problems

1. A planet travels round the Sun in an elliptic orbit and rotates on an axis perpendicular to the plane of its orbit with a period equal to the period of the orbit. Find the maximum libration in longitude and where in the orbit this is achieved. Prove that if e^2 is neglected in the final answer, the maximum libration expressed in radians is $2e$, and that the time interval between perihelion and the following position of maximum libration is

$$\frac{1}{4} - \frac{5e}{8\pi}$$

   times the period.

2. Mercury rotates on its axis so that, on the average, it points the same face toward the Sun. Find the maximum libration in longitude and when and where in the orbit this is achieved. Hence find the proportion of the surface that never receives direct light from the Sun.

3. If ψ is the angle between the direction of a planet's motion and the direction perpendicular to the radius vector, prove that

$$\tan \psi = \frac{e \sin E}{\sqrt{1 - e^2}}.$$

4. A planet travels around the Sun in an ellipse of eccentricity e. Find the proportion of the time spent near the Sun between the ends of the minor axis to the total period.

5. Find the time during which a parabolic comet is inside the ends of the latus rectum of its path, in terms of q, its perihelion distance. If $q = 6 \times 10^7$ miles, show that the time is about 114 days.

6. The perihelion distance of a parabolic comet, measured in astronomical units, is q (less than one). Assuming that the Earth's orbit is circular and that the comet moves in the ecliptic, show that if t (measured in sidereal years) is the interval during which the comet is within the Earth's orbit,

then

$$t = \frac{1}{3\pi}(1 + 2q)\sqrt{2 - 2q}.$$

7. A planet describing a circular orbit receives a small impulse in the direction of its motion. At any future time it is at P, whereas if it had not received the impulse, it would have been at P'. Show that although the path of P is never far from the original circle, the length of PP' is not small. Discuss the case where the small impulse is radial.

8. Prove that

$$\sin\frac{1}{2}(v - E) = \sqrt{\frac{r}{p}}\sin\frac{1}{2}\phi\sin v,$$

$$\sin\frac{1}{2}(v + E) = \sqrt{\frac{r}{p}}\cos\frac{1}{2}\phi\sin v,$$

where $e = \sin\phi$. How would these formulas be useful in finding E when v and r are given and e is small?

9. Find the average value of r in an elliptic orbit, taking the true anomaly as the independent variable. (You can avoid the integration of

$$\int\frac{dv}{1 + e\cos v}$$

by changing the variable to E.)

10. Find the average values of the following quantities in an elliptic orbit, taking the time as the independent variable: (a) r; (b) dr/dt; (c) $1/r$; (d) dv/dt; (e) the potential energy; (f) the kinetic energy; (g) E. For the last, consider only half the orbit from perihelion to aphelion.

11. Derive the following average values for the elliptic orbit, taking the time as the independent variable:

(a) $\overline{\left(\frac{a}{r}\right)^3} = (1 - e^2)^{-3/2};$ (b) $\overline{\left(\frac{a}{r}\right)^4\cos v} = e(1 - e^2)^{-5/2};$

(c) $\overline{\left(\frac{a}{r}\right)^4} = \left(1 + \frac{1}{2}e^2\right)(1 - e^2)^{-5/2};$ (d) $\overline{\left(\frac{a}{r}\right)^5} = \left(1 + \frac{3}{2}e^2\right)(1 - e^2)^{-7/2};$

(e) $\overline{\left(\frac{a}{r}\right)^5\cos 2v} = \frac{3}{4}e^2(1 - e^2)^{-7/2}.$

12. Prove that the amount of heat received from the Sun by the planets, per unit area, in unit time, is on the average proportional to the reciprocals of the products of the major and minor axes of the orbits.

13. Find formulas for v in terms of F for the hyperbolic orbit. Find, for the hyperbolic orbit, those mean values mentioned above which are finite.

14. An ICBM is fired at an elevation of 45° with initial speed 5 km/sec from
     a point on a flat Earth (constant g). Find the range and the time of flight.
     Now, taking into account the shape of the Earth and its rotation, let
     the ICBM be launched with the same elevation and speed, due east from
     latitude 45°. Find the range and time of flight.
     What effect would air resistance have on your results?
     (Use the energy and angular momentum to find a and e for the orbit.)

15. A rocket is launched from latitude 45°N over the north pole. If it strikes
     the point of launching twelve sidereal hours later, find the initial con-
     ditions of launching.

6.4 Some Properties of the Motion

Taking $\mathbf{h} \times$ (6.2.5) we obtain

$$h^2\dot{\mathbf{r}} = \mu\mathbf{h} \times \hat{\mathbf{r}} + \mathbf{h} \times \mathbf{P}. \tag{6.4.1}$$

(6.4.1) shows that the velocity at any point is the sum of two vectors of constant
modulus. One, of length μ/h, is perpendicular to $\hat{\mathbf{r}}$, and the other, of length
$e(\mu/h)$, is perpendicular to the major axis of the orbit. It follows that the
hodograph of the motion is a circle of radius μ/h, with center a distance $e(\mu/h)$
from the origin. The hodograph for elliptic motion is sketched in Figure 6.3a,
with the corresponding position in the orbit shown in Figure 6.3b.

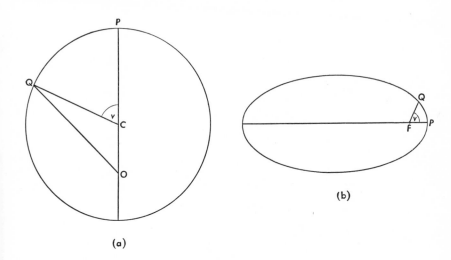

(a)

(b)

Figure 6.3

If Q is any point on the circle, **OQ** represents the velocity in the orbit at one
extremity of the focal chord that is at right angles to **CQ**. **OP** gives the velocity
at perihelion.

Figures 6.4 and 6.5 are the hodographs of parabolic and hyperbolic motion. For the hyperbolic case, let OA and OB be tangents to the circle. Then the angles COA and COB are each equal to $\sin^{-1}(1/e)$ and the angles PCA and PCB are each equal to $\cos^{-1}(-1/e)$; so only points on the arc APB are permissible. OA and OB are parallel to the asymptotes. The remaining arc would correspond to points on the branch of the hyperbola that is convex toward the center of force; it gives the hodograph for motion under an inverse square law of repulsion.

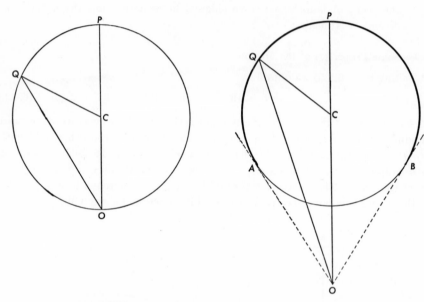

Figure 6.4   **Figure 6.5**

From Chapter 4 the energy integral is

$$V^2 = 2\frac{\mu}{r} + 2C,$$

where $C = -(\mu/2a)$, 0, $+(\mu/2a)$ for elliptic, parabolic, or hyperbolic orbits, respectively. The speed in a circular orbit of radius r is given by

$$V_c^2 = \frac{\mu}{r},$$

and in a parabolic orbit by

$$V_p^2 = 2\frac{\mu}{r}.$$

Suppose m_1 to be projected from a point distant r from m_2 with speed V relative to m_2. There are three possibilities:

$$V^2 <, \quad =, \quad \text{or} \; > 2\frac{\mu}{r},$$

giving elliptic, parabolic, or hyperbolic orbits. The parabolic speed is the velocity of escape. It should be remembered that the major axis, and therefore the period of the resulting orbit, depends only on r and V and not on the direction of projection. Also, a particle with speed V_p will be moving in a parabolic orbit regardless of the direction of its motion. When m_1 is distant r_1 from m_2, the relative speed will be given by

$$V_1^2 = V^2 + 2\mu\left(\frac{1}{r_1} - \frac{1}{r}\right).$$

Consider (6.3.10). Rearranging it, we find

$$\frac{P^2}{a^3}(m_1 + m_2) = \frac{4\pi^2}{k^2}. \tag{6.4.2}$$

This is the amended form of Kepler's third law. For any planet in the solar system $(m_1 + m_2)$ is very nearly equal to the mass of the Sun, so that P^2/a^3 is effectively constant. The right-hand side of (6.4.2) is a constant, the value of which depends on the units chosen. Provided consistent units are used, the quantity on the left-hand side will be the same for any pair of bodies.

The law provides a useful method for finding the masses of celestial bodies. For instance, if P and a are known for a double star, then the sum of the masses of the components can be found. In some cases this can be combined with the observations described in Section 6.1, giving the ratio of the masses, and then the individual masses can be found. Alternatively, if the sum of the masses is assumed (twice the mass of the Sun is a good value) and the orbit of one star about the other can be observed, then a can be calculated in terms of some definite unit of length. But the angle that a subtends at the distance of the Sun from the double star is observed; hence the distance of the system can be calculated: this is known as the *dynamical parallax*.

Suppose a planet of mass m_p has a satellite whose mass is very small compared with m_p and which has an orbit about the planet with semimajor axis a_1 and period P_1. If the corresponding values for the orbit of the planet around the Sun are a_2 and P_2, and the mass of the Sun, M, is much greater than m_p, then we can apply (6.4.2) to the satellite going around the planet and then to the planet going around the Sun, when we find:

$$\frac{P_1^2}{a_1^3}m_p = \frac{P_2^2}{a_2^3}M. \tag{6.4.3}$$

So, the mass of the planet can be measured in units of the mass of the Sun. If P is measured in sidereal years, a in astronomical units, and masses in terms of the Sun's mass, then each side of (6.4.3) must be equal to one.

Problems

1. Given that the eccentricity of the Earth's orbit is 0.01673 and the astronomical unit is 1.495×10^8 km, find the perihelion and aphelion distances

and the length of the semiminor axis of the orbit. Find also the speeds of the Earth at perihelion, aphelion, the ends of the minor axis, and the ends of the latus rectum.

2. Assuming that the Earth's orbit is circular and that meteors approach the Sun in elliptic and parabolic orbits, between what limits of relative speed will they hit the Earth's atmosphere, if the Earth's attraction is neglected? What effects on these limits will result if the eccentricity of the Earth's orbit is taken into account?

3. Two planets of equal mass moving in opposite directions collide and coalesce at a distance d from the Sun. At the time of their collision one planet is at perihelion and the other at aphelion, and both orbits have the same eccentricity e. Find the major axis of the orbit of the joint mass.

4. A comet moving in a parabolic orbit with perihelion distance q collides, when distant r from the Sun, and combines with a body of equal mass that is at rest before the collision. Find the major axis and eccentricity of the orbit of the combined mass.

5. At a certain point in an elliptic orbit under the force μ/r^2 the value of μ is changed by a small amount. If the eccentricities of the former and new orbits are the same, show that the point is at an extremity of the minor axis.

6. The Newtonian gravitation constant G is found from terrestrial experiments to be 6.670×10^{-8} cgs units. Using data for the Earth's orbit, find the mass of the Sun.

   If $g = 981$ cgs units, and the radius of the Earth is 6380 km, find the mass of the Earth.

7. Assuming that the Moon's orbit about the Earth is circular, with radius 60 times the radius of the Earth and with period 27d 8h, show that this information together with values for g and the Earth's radius given above furnishes one check for Newton's law of gravitation.

8. Prove that the greatest value of dr/dt in an elliptic orbit occurs at the ends of the latus rectum, and find this value for a planet whose orbit has semimajor axis a and eccentricity e. What is the value for the Earth's orbit?

9. An artificial satellite is launched vertically upward with initial speed u. When the vertical speed becomes zero, the satellite is given a transverse speed v. Find the resulting orbit in terms of u and v.

10. If an artificial satellite starts off in an elliptic orbit such that atmospheric drag occurs only at perigee, describe qualitatively how the orbit will change, showing that it will eventually become circular: what is the radius of the circle?

    Once the orbit has become circular, suppose that during one revolution it loses a small amount of energy, owing to atmospheric friction, but that the orbit remains circular, but with different radius. How will the energy lost be distributed between the kinetic and potential energies of the satellite?

11. When a periodic comet is at its greatest distance from the Sun, its speed receives a small increment δv. Show that the comet's least distance from the Sun will be increased by the quantity

$$4\delta v \sqrt{\frac{a^3}{\mu}} \sqrt{\frac{1-e}{1+e}}.$$

12. A particle is to be projected with given speed from a given point under a central Newtonian force, so that the line of apsides shall make a given angle θ with the initial radius vector. Show that there are two directions of projection making angles with this radius vector, whose sum is

$$\left(\theta + \frac{\pi}{2}\right) \quad \text{or} \quad \left(\theta + 3\frac{\pi}{2}\right).$$

13. If POP' is a focal chord of an elliptic path described around the Sun, show that the time from P to P' through perihelion is equal to the time of falling toward the Sun from a distance $2a$ to a distance $a(1 + \cos \alpha)$, where $\alpha = 2\pi - (E - E')$ and E and E' are the eccentric anomalies at P and P'.

14. Two stars of masses m_1 and m_2 move under their mutual gravitation. Prove that, if when m_1 is at rest, the velocity of m_2 is at right angles to the line joining the two masses and equal to

$$\sqrt{\frac{G(m_1 + m_2)}{d}}$$

where d is the distance of the two bodies, then the path of m_1 in space is a succession of cycloids, the body coming to rest at a cusp at equal intervals of time.

15. If particles are projected from a given point in the solar system with a given speed but in different directions, find the loci of the following points in their orbits: (a) the other focus; (b) perihelion; (c) aphelion; (d) the center of the ellipse; (e) the ends of the minor axis. (It is assumed that the speed of projection is less than the velocity of escape from the solar system.)

16. If the particles are now projected from a given point in the same direction but with different speeds, find the loci of the same points considered in problem 15.

17. Show that in elliptic motion under Newton's law, the projections on the external bisector of two radii, of the velocities corresponding to these radii, are equal. Show also that the sum of the projections on the inner

bisector is equal to the projection of a line constant in magnitude and direction.

18. Show that if a particle describes an ellipse under a force to a focus, the speed at the mean distance from the center of force is a mean proportional between the speeds at the ends of any diameter.

19. The components, of masses m_1 and m_2, forming a double star, describe elliptic orbits around each other in period P, their greatest and least distances apart being D_1 and D_2. Prove that the rotational momentum of the orbital motion of the system is

$$\frac{\pi}{P} \cdot \frac{m_1 m_2}{m_1 + m_2} \sqrt{D_1 D_2} \, (D_1 + D_2).$$

20. Two stars of masses M and m are initially at a great distance apart. M is at rest and m has a velocity V in a direction that passes M at a perpendicular distance σ. Prove that after the encounter, when m has again receded to a great distance, M will have acquired the velocity

$$2VGm\{G^2(M + m)^2 + \sigma^2 V^4\}^{-1/2},$$

and find its direction.

21. Two stars of masses M and m are at a great distance apart and move toward one another with relative velocity V, σ being the perpendicular distance between the directions of their velocities, which are parallel. Show that the least distance between them during the subsequent motion is given by

$$\frac{1}{d} = \frac{G(M + m)}{\sigma^2 V^2} \left\{ 1 + \left[1 + \frac{\sigma^2 V^4}{G^2(M + m)^2} \right]^{1/2} \right\}.$$

22. For the two stars of problem 21, let ϕ be the angle through which the relative velocity is turned by the complete encounter; prove that

$$\tan \frac{1}{2} \phi = \frac{G(M + m)}{\sigma V^2}.$$

Show further that if the two stars have equal masses and one is initially at rest, the final velocities are

$$V \cos \tfrac{1}{2}\phi \quad \text{and} \quad V \sin \tfrac{1}{2}\phi.$$

23. A comet of negligible mass is traveling initially in a parabolic orbit around the Sun. The orbit is disturbed by a close approach to Jupiter. Assume that during this approach, Jupiter is moving in a straight line and that the comet is subject only to Jupiter's gravitational attraction; also assume that the comet approaches Jupiter in either of the two directions tangential to Jupiter's orbital motion around the Sun. Investigate

the conditions under which the velocity of the comet *with respect to the Sun* will be increased or decreased by the encounter.

24.   A foreign body of negligible mass, traveling at velocity V relative to the Sun's motion, penetrates into the solar system and approaches to a distance D from the Sun before receding again. Prove that when it has left the system, its direction of relative motion is deflected through an angle ψ given by

$$\operatorname{cosec} \frac{\psi}{2} = 1 + \frac{DV^2}{D_0 V_0^2},$$

where V_0 is the orbital velocity of a planet revolving in a circular orbit at distance D_0. Calculate the deflection roughly when V is 28 km/sec, and D is 0.7 of an astronomical unit, the distance of Venus from the Sun.

25.   A particle is projected from a great distance from a star of mass M and radius r_0 with velocity V, such that, neglecting the attraction of the star, it would approach the star at a minimum distance σ. Write down the equations of energy and angular momentum, and find σ such that the particle will just graze the star.

A star of radius r_0 moves through a cloud of particles, of density ρ_0 particles per unit volume, with velocity V relative to the cloud. Assuming that the particles have no relative velocities (or that the cloud has zero temperature), particles within a tunnel of radius σ will be accreted by the star. Show that the rate of accretion is

$$A = \pi r_0^2 \rho_0 \left(V + \frac{2MG}{r_0 V} \right).$$

By considering probable figures for the Sun, show that the first term in the parentheses can usually be neglected. (This is Eddington's formula for accretion.)

26.   In another theory of accretion (due to Lyttelton) it is assumed that all particles collide on an axis through the center of the star, parallel to its direction of motion, and that the collisions are nonelastic, completely annulling the components of velocity perpendicular to this axis, but leaving the components along the axis unchanged.

Show that the component of velocity along this axis is V, and find the condition for a particle, after its collision, to fall into the star. Hence show that all particles within a tunnel of radius

$$\sigma = \frac{2MG}{V^2}$$

will be swept up, so that the rate of accretion is

$$A = \frac{4\pi M^2 G^2 \rho_0}{V^3}.$$

27. Find the mass of Jupiter compared with that of the Sun from the following data:

Period of Ganymede (a satellite) = 7.155 days,
Mean distance of Ganymede from Jupiter = 0.007156 astronomical units.

28. The sidereal period of Jupiter is 11.86 years; find the value of a. A body of negligible mass moves around the Sun with the same value of a; what is its period? If this body originally drifted away from Jupiter, how long would it be before it approached Jupiter again? (Assume both orbits are circular, and neglect the attraction of Jupiter.)

29. Procyon is a visual binary with period 40.33 years. The orbit of Procyon B about Procyon A has a value of a which subtends 4″.26 on the celestial sphere, while that of A about the center of mass of the system has $a = 1″.02$. Find the ratio of their masses.

If, at the distance of the system, the radius of the Earth's orbit around the Sun subtends an angle 0″.289, find the distance of the system, the separate masses of the components (compared with the mass of the Sun), and the physical dimensions of the orbit.

6.5 The Choice of Units

The values of the various constants used depend on the choice of units. If these are chosen as the astronomical unit (with a modification given below), the mass of the Sun, and the mean solar day, then the resulting value of k is the *Gaussian gravitational constant*. When it was first calculated the following data were used:

1 sidereal year = 365.256 3835 mean solar days;
The combined mass of the Earth and Moon,

$$m_{e+m} = \frac{1}{354\ 710} \text{ solar masses.}$$

Then

$$k = \frac{2\pi}{P\sqrt{1 + m_{e+m}}}$$

$$= 0.017\ 202\ 098\ 95.$$

These data have been revised, and the first figure is known to be steadily changing. The best figures available at the present time give

1 sidereal year = $365.256\ 365\ 56 - 0.000\ 000\ 11T$,

where T is measured in centuries from 1900, and

$$m_{e+m} = \frac{1}{328\ 466} \text{ solar masses.}$$

The value of k, as first defined, will be sensitive to revisions of the data and to long-term changes. It would be extremely inconvenient to alter its value; so, with the revised data, the unit of length is adjusted so that k retains its original value. At present the semimajor axis of the Earth's orbit is not 1 but 1.000 000 230 astronomical units.

The same situation arises when motion around the Earth is considered. Taking the units of length, mass, and time to be the Earth's equatorial radius, the mass of the Earth, and the minute, a value for k is furnished by suitable satellite or lunar observations. Having decided on a value for k, in this case

$$k_e = 0.074\ 365\ 74,$$

this is kept constant, and the unit of length is altered. The student will find a fuller discussion in Ref. 22, Chapter Five.

In some work it is convenient to choose the unit of time so that $k = 1$. Or we might choose k so that the unit of time would be the sidereal year. In all cases it is hardly necessary to stress that consistent units should be used throughout any calculation.

The student must beware of using G in his calculations. For instance, for motion around the Sun, we might take $G = 6.670 \times 10^{-8}$ and $M_{\text{Sun}} = 2.00 \times 10^{33}$ c.g.s. units, but these values are so poorly determined that the calculation would be of little use.

Problems

1. Find k when the units of length, mass, and time are as follows: (a) The astronomical unit, the mass of the Sun, the sidereal year. (b) The mean distance of the Moon from the Earth, the mass of the Earth, the sidereal month.
   If in each case the unit of time is altered so that $k = 1$, find that new unit of time.

2. The components of position and velocity of a comet are (8.134, -10.385, 1.746) in units of 10^7 km, and (18.43, 15.97, -4.62) km/sec. Express these in terms of astronomical units and mean solar days. Also express them in such units that make $k = 1$ when the units of length and mass are the astronomical unit and the mass of the Sun.

3. Find the maximum value of dr/dt in the Earth's orbit around the Sun in kilometers per second and astronomical units per mean solar day.

4. Show that for a parabolic comet

$$V = \frac{26.175}{\sqrt{r_{\text{AU}}}}\ \text{mps}$$

and find the corresponding result in kilometers per second and astronomical units per mean solar day.

5. A parabolic comet moving in the ecliptic has $q = 0.287\ 45$ AU. Calculate how long (in mean solar days) it lies in its orbit within that of (a) the Earth, (b) Mars, (c) Jupiter, and (d) Pluto, assuming that all these planets move in the ecliptic in circular orbits of radius a.

6. For the comet of problem 5, find the speed at perihelion, and the number of days after perihelion passage when its speed is 90, 80, and 50 per cent of this value. Also find the time when its speed is 30 km/sec. Calculate the true anomalies for these positions.

7. Find the orbital speed of Mercury at perihelion, aphelion, the ends of the minor axis, and the ends of the latus rectum. Give your answers in astronomical units per day.

8. The mean daily motions of the minor planets Ceres and Medusa are, respectively, $711''.2424$ and $1105''.8897$. Find their mean distances from the Sun in astronomical units.

9. Find the period and orbital speed of a satellite that just grazes the Earth's equator. Find the mean distance and orbital speed for a satellite with period 24 sidereal hours. If the unit of length is the Earth's equatorial radius, the unit of mass is the mass of the Earth, and the unit of time is chosen to make $k = 1$, find the unit of time and express the above results in these units.

10. In order to find k, it is necessary to know the mass of the Earth + Moon. To find this, we proceed as follows: Let a_1 be the semimajor axis of the Moon's orbit about the Earth, and P_1 its sidereal period. Show that

$$\frac{a_1^3}{P_1^2} = \frac{k^2 m}{4\pi^2},$$

where m is the mass of the Earth + Moon. Expressing a_1 in astronomical units and P_1 in sidereal years, show that

$$\frac{1}{m} + 1 = \frac{P_1^2}{a_1^3},$$

and that since m is in units of the solar mass, we can neglect the number 1 on the left. Hence show that

$$\frac{1}{m} = \left(\frac{\sin \pi_m}{\sin \pi_s}\right)^3 P_1^2,$$

Where π_m and π_s are the parallaxes of the Moon and Sun (i.e., the angles subtended by the Earth's equatorial radius at the mean distances of these objects). The principal error in this method comes from the smallness of π_s.

11. Using the result above and taking $1/m = 329\ 390$ (Newcomb's value) and

$\pi_s = 8''.79$ as initial values, show that the variation in $1/m$ caused by varying π_s is given by

$$\delta\left(\frac{1}{m}\right) = -112\,440\delta\pi_s,$$

where $\delta\pi_s$ is measured in seconds of arc. Thus show that evaluating $1/m$ is equivalent to measuring the solar parallax, or conversely, that the measurement of the solar parallax yields a value for $1/m$.

12. Using Gauss's value of $1/m$, show that

$$\delta k = [6.73480 - 20]\delta\left(\frac{1}{m}\right)$$

(where the square brackets mean that the number enclosed is the logarithm of the number required), and thus obtain

$$\delta k = -0.000\,000\,0172\delta\pi_s$$

as an approximate expression for changing k if it were not agreed to keep this quantity constant.

13. Consider the question of finding the value to ascribe to a for the Earth, as a result of better values of m and P than those used by Gauss, while retaining his value of k. Let m_1 and P_1 be new values for the mass and period in question, and show that

$$a = \left(\frac{1 + m_1}{1 + m}\right)^{1/3}\left(\frac{P_1}{P}\right)^{2/3},$$

and thus to terms of the first order

$$a = 1 + \frac{1}{3}\left(m_1 - m + 2\frac{P_1 - P}{P}\right).$$

Take Newcomb's values

$$\frac{1}{m_1} = 329\,390, \quad P_1 = 365.256\,360\,42$$

and show that they give $a = 1.000\,000\,030$.

6.6 Lambert's Theorem

Let E_1 and E_2 be the eccentric anomalies of two points P_1 and P_2 in an elliptic orbit such that E_2 is greater than E_1. Let

$$2G = E_2 + E_1$$

and

$$2g = E_2 - E_1 > 0.$$

Then
$$r_1 = a(1 - e \cos E_1) \quad \text{and} \quad r_2 = a(1 - e \cos E_2),$$
and
$$r_1 + r_2 = a[2 - e(\cos E_1 + \cos E_2)]$$
$$= 2a(1 - e \cos G \cos g).$$

Let the chord P_1P_2 have length c; then, using (6.3.16), we have
$$c^2 = a^2(\cos E_2 - \cos E_1)^2 + a^2(1 - e^2)(\sin E_2 - \sin E_1)^2$$
$$= 4a^2 \sin^2 G \sin^2 g + 4a^2(1 - e^2)\cos^2 G \sin^2 g.$$

Let
$$e \cos G = \cos j;$$
then
$$c^2 = 4a^2 \sin^2 g(1 - \cos^2 j),$$
or
$$c = 2a \sin g \sin j.$$
Also
$$r_1 + r_2 = 2a(1 - \cos g \cos j). \tag{6.6.1}$$

Now let
$$\epsilon = j + g$$
and
$$\delta = j - g.$$
Then
$$r_1 + r_2 + c = 2a[1 - \cos(g + j)] = 4a \sin^2 \tfrac{1}{2}\epsilon \tag{6.6.2}$$
and
$$r_1 + r_2 - c = 2a[1 - \cos(g - j)] = 4a \sin^2 \tfrac{1}{2}\delta. \tag{6.6.3}$$

If t is the time taken in the orbit between the two positions,
$$nt = E_2 - E_1 - e(\sin E_2 - \sin E_1)$$
$$= (\epsilon - \delta) - (\sin \epsilon - \sin \delta). \tag{6.6.4}$$

ϵ and δ are given by (6.6.2) and (6.6.3) in terms of $(r_1 + r_2)$, c, and a. These equations constitute Lambert's theorem for elliptic motion. The solutions for ϵ and δ are not unique, but for a small arc it is sufficient to take ϵ and δ as the smallest positive values satisfying the equations (6.6.2) and (6.6.3). A full geometrical discussion is given in Plummer's *Dynamical Astronomy*, p. 51 (Ref. 22).

An important limiting case of Lambert's theorem may be found for parabolic motion, when a tends to infinity. When a is large, ϵ and δ are small, so that, approximately,
$$a\epsilon^2 = r_1 + r_2 + c, \tag{6.6.5}$$
and
$$a\delta^2 = r_1 + r_2 - c. \tag{6.6.6}$$

Replacing n by $\sqrt{\mu/a^3}$, we get

$$\sqrt{\mu}\,t = \tfrac{1}{6}a^{3/2}(\epsilon^3 - \delta^3)$$
$$= \tfrac{1}{6}(r_1 + r_2 + c)^{3/2} \pm \tfrac{1}{6}(r_1 + r_2 - c)^{3/2}.$$

This is to be applied to the motion of comets, so that it can be written

$$6kt = (r_1 + r_2 + c)^{3/2} \pm (r_1 + r_2 - c)^{3/2}. \qquad (6.6.7)$$

This is *Euler's theorem.*

As regards the ambiguity of sign, for small arcs we must clearly use the minus sign. When the difference between the true anomalies is 180°, the second term is zero, and for larger differences we must use the plus sign. So, we have the result that the plus or minus sign is used depending on whether the arc contains or does not contain the focus.

Problems

1. Examine the limiting case of Lambert's theorem when the minor axis of the ellipse vanishes, so that the orbit is rectilinear.
2. Establish Euler's theorem directly from the formulas for parabolic motion.
3. Find equations analogous to those constituting Lambert's theorem for hyperbolic orbits.
4. Find equations analogous to those constituting Lambert's theorem for motion under an inverse square law of repulsion.

6.7   The Ratio of the Sector to the Triangle

An important quantity in the determination of orbits is the ratio, denoted by y, of the sector (i.e., the area swept out by the radius vector) to the triangle. Consider the case of elliptic motion. Since $n = h/ab$, twice the area of the sector is, by (6.6.4),

$$ht = ab[\epsilon - \delta - (\sin \epsilon - \sin \delta)].$$

If (x_1, y_1) and (x_2, y_2) are the coordinates of the extremities of the arc, P_1 and P_2, twice the area of the triangle is

$$2\Delta = (x_1 y_2 - x_2 y_1)$$
$$= ab[\sin E_2(\cos E_1 - e) - \sin E_1(\cos E_2 - e)]$$
$$= ab\left[\sin(E_2 - E_1) - 2e \cos \frac{E_2 + E_1}{2} \sin \frac{E_2 - E_1}{2}\right]$$
$$= ab[\sin 2g - 2 \cos j \sin g]$$
$$= ab[\sin(\epsilon - \delta) - (\sin \epsilon - \sin \delta)].$$

Hence

$$y = \frac{ht}{2\Delta}$$

$$= \frac{\epsilon - \delta - (\sin \epsilon - \sin \delta)}{\sin(\epsilon - \delta) - (\sin \epsilon - \sin \delta)}. \tag{6.7.1}$$

(6.7.1) contains a implicitly, and this quantity is to be eliminated.

Let

$$v_2 - v_1 = 2f,$$

where v_1 and v_2 are the true anomalies corresponding to P_1 and P_2. Then

$$c^2 = r_1^2 + r_2^2 - 2r_1 r_2 \cos 2f.$$

Now from (6.6.2) and (6.6.3),

$$
\begin{aligned}
4a^2[1 - \cos(j + g)][1 - \cos(j - g)] &= (r_1 + r_2 + c)(r_1 + r_2 - c) \\
&= (r_1 + r_2)^2 - r_1^2 - r_2^2 + 2r_1 r_2 \cos 2f \\
&= 4r_1 r_2 \cos^2 f.
\end{aligned}
$$

After some manipulation the left-hand side can be shown to be equal to

$$4a^2(\cos g - \cos j)^2,$$

so we have

$$2a(\cos g - \cos j) = 2\cos f \sqrt{r_1 r_2}. \tag{6.7.2}$$

Multiplying through by $\cos g$ and using (6.6.1), we find

$$r_1 + r_2 - 2\cos f \cos g \sqrt{r_1 r_2} = 2a \sin^2 g. \tag{6.7.3}$$

From (6.7.1),

$$y = \frac{nt}{\sin 2g - 2\sin g \cos j}$$

$$= \frac{ant}{2\sin g \cos f \sqrt{r_1 r_2}}. \tag{6.7.4}$$

Square (6.7.4), eliminate n^2 using $n^2 a^3 = \mu$, and then substitute for a from (6.7.2); we get

$$y^2(r_1 + r_2 - 2\cos f \cos g \sqrt{r_1 r_2}) = \frac{2\mu t^2}{4\cos^2 f \, r_1 r_2}. \tag{6.7.5}$$

Also from (6.7.1),

$$y - 1 = \frac{\epsilon - \delta - \sin(\epsilon - \delta)}{\sin(\epsilon - \delta) - (\sin \epsilon - \sin \delta)}$$

$$= \frac{2g - \sin 2g}{2\sin g(\cos g - \cos j)}$$

$$= \frac{a(2g - \sin 2g)}{2\sin g \cos f \sqrt{r_1 r_2}}. \tag{6.7.6}$$

Eliminating a between (6.7.4) and (6.7.6), we find

$$y^2(y-1) = \frac{\mu t^2}{(2 \cos f \sqrt{r_1 r_2})^3} \frac{2g - \sin 2g}{\sin^3 g}. \tag{6.7.7}$$

In the notation of Gauss write

$$1 + 2l = \frac{r_1 + r_2}{2 \cos f \sqrt{r_1 r_2}}$$

and

$$m^2 = \frac{\mu t^2}{(2 \cos f \sqrt{r_1 r_2})^3}.$$

Then (6.7.5) and (6.7.7) become

$$y^2 = \frac{m^2}{l + \sin^2 g/2} \tag{6.7.8}$$

and

$$y^3 - y^2 = m^2 \frac{2g - \sin 2g}{\sin^3 g}. \tag{6.7.9}$$

The appropriate value of y is found by solving this pair of equations for y and g by some method of approximation.

The corresponding ratio for parabolic motion can be derived by letting a become large, so that ϵ and δ become small. From (6.7.1),

$$y = \frac{\epsilon^3 - \delta^3}{-(\epsilon - \delta)^3 + \epsilon^3 - \delta^3}$$

$$= \frac{\epsilon^2 + \delta^2 + \epsilon\delta}{3\epsilon\delta}.$$

Let

$$c = (r_1 + r_2)\sin \gamma,$$

where $0 < \gamma < 90°$. Equations (6.6.5) and (6.6.6) give

$$a^2 \epsilon^2 \delta^2 = (r_1 + r_2)^2 - c^2$$
$$= (r_1 + r_2)^2 \cos^2 \gamma.$$

Also

$$a(\epsilon^2 + \delta^2) = 2(r_1 + r_2),$$

so

$$y = \frac{2(r_1 + r_2) + (r_1 + r_2)\cos \gamma}{3(r_1 + r_2)\cos \gamma}$$

$$= \tfrac{1}{3}(1 + 2 \sec \gamma). \tag{6.7.10}$$

Problems

1. Find analogous equations for the hyperbolic orbit.
2. Find analogous equations for motion under the inverse square law of repulsion.

6.8 Further Relations Between Position and Time

In this section we shall consider some relations between positions in an orbit and the time intervals separating them, assuming that these times are small (actually kt must be small).

Take a unit of time such that $k = 1$; in effect we let $t' = kt$, and then drop the prime. The equation of motion is

$$\mathbf{r}'' = -\frac{\mathbf{r}}{r^3},$$

where $\mathbf{r}'$ refers to the first derivative of $\mathbf{r}$ with respect to our new t, $\mathbf{r}''$ to the second derivative, and so on.

Let $\mathbf{r}_0$ be the position at time $t = 0$, and let the subscript $_0$ refer to values for this position. If $\mathbf{r}$ is the position at time t, then we can express $\mathbf{r}$ in a Taylor series as

$$\mathbf{r} = \mathbf{r}_0 + t\mathbf{r}_0' + \tfrac{1}{2}t^2\mathbf{r}_0'' + \tfrac{1}{6}t^3\mathbf{r}_0''' + \cdots \tag{6.8.1}$$

Define the three quantities σ, τ, and ω by

$$\frac{\mathbf{r}_0 \cdot \mathbf{r}_0}{r_0^5} = \frac{1}{r_0^3} = \sigma, \tag{6.8.2}$$

$$\frac{\mathbf{r}_0 \cdot \mathbf{r}_0'}{r_0^2} = \frac{r_0'}{r_0} = \tau, \tag{6.8.3}$$

and

$$\frac{\mathbf{r}_0' \cdot \mathbf{r}_0'}{r_0^2} = \omega. \tag{6.8.4}$$

Differentiating these and using the equation of motion to eliminate $\mathbf{r}_0''$, we have

$$\left.\begin{aligned} \sigma' &= -3\sigma\tau, \\ \tau' &= \omega - \sigma - 2\tau^2, \\ \omega' &= -2\tau(\sigma + \omega). \end{aligned}\right\} \tag{6.8.5}$$

and

Then

$$\tfrac{1}{2}\mathbf{r}_0'' = -\tfrac{1}{2}\sigma\mathbf{r}_0,$$

$$\tfrac{1}{6}\mathbf{r}_0''' = \tfrac{1}{2}\sigma\tau\mathbf{r}_0 - \tfrac{1}{6}\sigma\mathbf{r}_0',$$

$$\tfrac{1}{24}\mathbf{r}_0'''' = \tfrac{1}{24}\sigma(3\omega - 2\sigma - 15\tau^2)\mathbf{r}_0 + \tfrac{1}{4}\sigma\tau\mathbf{r}_0',$$

and so on. Substituting these expressions into (6.8.1) we find

$$\mathbf{r} = f\mathbf{r}_0 + g\mathbf{r}_0', \tag{6.8.6}$$

where

$$f = 1 - \tfrac{1}{2}\sigma t^2 + \tfrac{1}{2}\sigma\tau t^3 + \cdots \tag{6.8.7}$$

and

$$g = t - \tfrac{1}{6}\sigma t^3 + \cdots \tag{6.8.8}$$

Calculation of terms around t^6, although not formally difficult, becomes tedious and impracticable. These series converge rapidly for moderate t. They are known as the "f and g series".

An important relation concerning three positions and the time intervals between them was first given by Gibbs. Assume that

$$\mathbf{r} = \mathbf{a} + \mathbf{b}t + \mathbf{c}t^2 + \mathbf{d}t^3 + \mathbf{e}t^4 + \cdots$$

Let positions $\mathbf{r}_1$, $\mathbf{r}_2$, and $\mathbf{r}_3$ correspond to times t_1, 0, and t_3, respectively. If terms in t^5 are small enough to be neglected, we have

$$\mathbf{r}_1 = \mathbf{a} + \mathbf{b}t_1 + \mathbf{c}t_1^2 + \mathbf{d}t_1^3 + \mathbf{e}t_1^4,$$

$$\mathbf{r}_2 = \mathbf{a},$$

$$\mathbf{r}_3 = \mathbf{a} + \mathbf{b}t_3 + \mathbf{c}t_3^2 + \mathbf{d}t_3^3 + \mathbf{e}t_3^4.$$

Differentiating the series twice and applying the law of gravitation, we have, in general,

$$-\frac{\mathbf{r}}{r^3} = \mathbf{r}'' = 2\mathbf{c} + 6\mathbf{d}t + 12\mathbf{e}t^2,$$

so that for the three positions,

$$-\frac{\mathbf{r}_1}{r_1^3} = 2\mathbf{c} + 6\mathbf{d}t_1 + 12\mathbf{e}t_1^2,$$

$$-\frac{\mathbf{r}_2}{r_1^3} = 2\mathbf{c},$$

$$-\frac{\mathbf{r}_3}{r_3^3} = 2\mathbf{c} + 6\mathbf{d}t_3 + 12\mathbf{e}t_3^2.$$

So, we have six vector equations, from which the five vectors $\mathbf{a} \cdots \mathbf{e}$ can be eliminated. The algebra, which is straightforward, will not be included here; the result is

$$t_3\left[1 + \frac{1}{12r_1^3}(t_1^2 - t_1t_3 - t_3^2)\right]\mathbf{r}_1 - (t_3 - t_1)\left[1 - \frac{1}{12r_2^3}(t_1^2 - 3t_1t_3 + t_3^2)\right]\mathbf{r}_2$$

$$-t_1\left[1 - \frac{1}{12r_3^3}(t_1^2 + t_1t_3 - t_3^2)\right]\mathbf{r}_3 = 0. \quad (6.8.9)$$

The series for $\mathbf{r}$ was truncated at the term in t^4 because we had just enough information to eliminate the five vector coefficients. If we had more information, we could include further terms and find more accurate expressions.

The student should note carefully the difference between these two approaches. The f and g series are used to predict position for *any* time (within reasonable limits) when position and velocity are given at some epoch; the coefficients in the series are worked out explicitly. But in the Gibbsian approach several positions are used to eliminate as many as possible of the coefficients. An example of the application of this approach is described in Section 7.3. As another illustration consider the following problem: We are given values $\mathbf{r}_1$, $\mathbf{r}_2$, and $\mathbf{r}_3$, as before, and we want to find $\mathbf{r}_2'$. Now $\mathbf{r}_2' = \mathbf{b}$; and this and the preceding six equations can be solved for $\mathbf{r}_2'$ in terms of the data, where now we are able to include another term in the series—$\mathbf{f}t^5$. The final answer will therefore be accurate to the order of t^5.

Problems

1. Evaluate the f and g series up to terms in t^5.

2. Find the value of $f'g - fg'$.

3. Modify the f and g series to give $\mathbf{r}'$ (instead of $\mathbf{r}$).

4. Using the principle of the f and g series, find similar series to calculate r and r' (scalars) for any time when r_0 and r_0' are given. (Use the relation $r'' - h^2/r^3 = -1/r^2$.)

5. Given $\mathbf{r}_1$ and $\mathbf{r}_2$ at times t_1 and t_2 use the Gibbsian approach to find an expression for $\mathbf{r}_2'$.

6. Given $\mathbf{r}_0$ and $\mathbf{r}_0'$, use the Gibbsian approach to find an expression for $\mathbf{r}$ at any time. Compare your result with that found using the f and g series.

6.9 The Solution of Kepler's Equation

Very many methods exist for the solution of Kepler's equation. Here we shall be content to describe only one. This is much in favor among some computers, but other methods are used, depending on the individual and the machine available (see problem 4 in this section).

An important fact to remember when solving Kepler's equation is that in its derivation, all the angles occurred as natural numbers, which means that they are measured in radians. If E and M are expressed in degrees, as is usually the case, then the *scale* of E and M must be changed from radians to degrees in Kepler's equation, *and the same must be done for* e. To express e in degrees, we have

$$e_{\text{degrees}} = \frac{360}{2\pi}\, e_{\text{radians}}.$$

Then Kepler's equation can be written

$$M° = E° - e° \sin E.$$

If E and e are known, there is, of course, no difficulty in writing down M. But if M and e are known (and this is the usual order of events), there is no direct way of writing down the solution for E, and some method of successive approximations must be used. First it is necessary to prove that the equation always has one and only one solution.

Consider
$$F(E) \equiv E - e \sin E - M.$$

Suppose that $n\pi < M < (n + 1)\pi$, where n is an integer. Then
$$F(n\pi) = n\pi - M < 0,$$
and
$$F[(n + 1)\pi] = (n + 1)\pi - M > 0.$$

So, there is at least one root in the range $n\pi < E < (n + 1)\pi$. Now
$$\frac{dF(E)}{dE} \equiv 1 - e \cos E$$

which is positive for all E. So $F(E)$ is monatonic, increasing with E, and there is only one root.

The first step in the solution of Kepler's equation is to find a rough solution. If solutions are required for a run of dates (as, for example, in the preparation of an ephemeris), a rough solution can be found by extrapolation, once solutions for the first few dates are known. Alternatively, it can be found fairly quickly by trial and error, using a slide rule. There are many graphical methods, one of the simplest of which is to plot the two curves
$$y = \sin E$$
and
$$y = \frac{1}{e}(E - M)$$

in the same figure, and use the value of E for which they intersect. There are also tables that can be used.

Once the rough solution, E_0, say, has been found, a better one can easily be obtained. Let
$$M_0 = E_0 - e \sin E_0$$
and
$$\Delta M_0 = M - M_0.$$

Also let
$$E = E_0 + \Delta E_0,$$

where E is the correct solution; we want, therefore, to determine ΔE_0. M and E satisfy
$$M = E - e \sin E$$
so
$$M_0 + \Delta M_0 = E_0 + \Delta E_0 - e \sin(E_0 + \Delta E_0).$$

ΔE_0 is small, so we have, approximately,
$$\Delta M_0 = \Delta E_0 - e \Delta E_0 \cos E_0,$$
so that
$$\Delta E_0 = \frac{\Delta M_0}{1 - e \cos E_0}. \tag{6.9.1}$$

The value of e used in (6.9.1) is expressed in *radians*.

Once ΔE_0 is found, we have a better value of E, E_1, say. The corresponding value M_1 is then found. If, to the order of accuracy required, $M = M_1$, then E_1 is the final answer; if not, then another differential correction, ΔE_1, must be found. This process is rapidly convergent, even when the initial solution is not very accurate. Any computation of E must always end up with a check; i.e., the corresponding value of M must be found.

As an illustration of this method, the value of E will be found when $e = 0.2$ and $M = 45°$. Five figure tables with degrees and decimals have been used; if these are not available, then the change to degrees and minutes should be included at each stage. The modifications when using logarithm tables follow fairly obviously.

$M = 45°$
$e = 0.2$ radian
$e = 11.459$ degrees
$E_0 = 53°$ (using slide rule)
$\sin E_0 = 0.79864$
$\cos E_0 = 0.60182$
$e° \sin E_0 = 9°.1517$
$e \cos E_0 = 0.12036$ (Here e is in radians. See note below.)
$M_0 = 43°.8483$
$\Delta M_0 = 1°.1517$
$1 - e \cos E_0 = 0.87964$
$\Delta E_0 = 1°.3093$
$E_1 = 54°.3093$
$\sin E_1 = 0.81218$
$\cos E_1 = 0.58341$
$e° \sin E_1 = 9°.3069$
$e \cos E_1 = 0.1167$

(Note: With the improving solution, this quantity need not be calculated so accurately.)

$M_1 = 45°.00241$
$\Delta M_1 = -0°.00241$
$1 - e \cos E_1 = 0.8833$
$\Delta E_1 = -0°.0027$
$E_2 = 54°.3066$
$\sin E_2 = 0.81216$
$e° \sin E_2 = 9°.3066$
$M_2 = 45°.0000.$

So, E_2 is correct to four decimal places.

It is wise in this type of calculation to include every stage of the work so that it is easier to check. It is axiomatic that every stage should be checked.

The initial value used could have been improved with a slide rule, but a crude value was deliberately chosen to show the rapidity of the convergence of the approximations. In general, a slide rule is not accurate enough for this work, but it can be used with advantage in the calculation of some differential corrections, such as ΔE_1, since only a few figures are involved.

Problems

1. The appropriate elements for a comet are

$$e = 0.528\ 4019$$
$$a = 3.408\ 4162$$
$$T = 1957 \text{ November } 24.7969.$$

Calculate n. Find M, and then solve Kepler's equation for the dates Jan. 2, Feb. 1, March 3, April 2, May 2, June 1, July 1, July 31, August 30, and Sept. 29, all of 1957.

Find r and v for each date. Sketch the ellipse and mark in the positions at each date, checking, with a geometrical construction, that the values of v are correct (with respect to those of E).

(Use as many significant figures as tables allow; do not use a slide rule. Set out the work in rows and columns on a large sheet of paper. At this stage the student might read Sections 10.1 and 10.6.)

2. If $e = \sin \phi$, prove that

$$\tan \tfrac{1}{2} v = \tan(45° + \tfrac{1}{2}\phi) \tan \tfrac{1}{2}E.$$

3. Show that when powers of e above the second are neglected, the value of E satisfying Kepler's equation is given by

$$\tan E = \sec \phi \tan 2\chi,$$

where

$$\tan \chi = \tan(45° + \tfrac{1}{2}\phi)\tan \tfrac{1}{2}M,$$

and

$$\tan E = \frac{\sin M}{\cos M - e}.$$

4. Discuss the question of solving Kepler's equation by successive substitutions

$$E_{i+1} = M + e° \sin E_i, \quad E_1 = M,$$

if a calculating machine is available and one has a table of natural sines with respect to degrees and decimals of a degree.

5. The longitude of perihelion of the Earth's orbit (measured from the vernal equinox) is $101° \, 45' \, 13''.6$. Find the lengths of the seasons between the equinoxes and solstices.

6.10 Some Expansions in Elliptic Motion

Although the formulas for elliptic motion make it possible to calculate the position of a planet in its orbit at any time, it would be useful to have this position given directly by one formula. Unfortunately Kepler's equation provides a stumbling block to this, but if it can be solved as a series, then we can find series expansions for r and v, in particular, in terms of M and e. The development of these series for their useful application (particularly to perturbation theory) demands the use of Bessel functions, and is considered outside the scope of this text. The student should consult the texts by Smart or Plummer (Refs. 22, 23) for full accounts. Here we shall be content to find the first few terms in three expansions.

Consider Kepler's equation

$$M = E - e \sin E.$$

If $e = 0$, then $E = M$, and if e is very small, M will be a reasonable first approximation to E. If we write Kepler's equation in the form

$$E = M + e \sin E,$$

then, given some value E_i which is approximate, a better one is

$$E_{i+1} = M + e \sin E_i.$$

So, starting off with $E_1 = M$, we have

$$E_2 = M + e \sin M,$$

and

$$
\begin{aligned}
E_3 &= M + e \sin(M + e \sin M) \\
&= M + e[\sin M \cos(e \sin M) + \cos M \sin(e \sin M)].
\end{aligned}
$$

E_3 is only an approximate value, correct to the order e^2; so,

$$E_3 = M + e \sin M + e^2 \sin M \cos M.$$

If e^3 is negligible, this solution will be good enough; if not, we can find the term in e^3 by writing down E_4 and neglecting e^4. We find

$$E_4 = M + e \sin M + \tfrac{1}{2}e^2 \sin 2M + \tfrac{1}{8}e^3(3 \sin 3M - \sin M). \qquad (6.10.1)$$

This process can be continued indefinitely, although the later terms obviously become unwieldy.

The following method for finding r in terms of e and M is due to MacMillan, as given by Moulton (Ref. 17). From Kepler's equation

$$e \frac{\partial E}{\partial e} = \frac{e \sin E}{1 - e \cos E},$$

and

$$dM = (1 - e \cos E)dE,$$

so that

$$e \frac{\partial E}{\partial e} dM = e \sin E \, dE.$$

This can be integrated to give

$$e \int_0^M \frac{\partial E}{\partial e} dM = -e \cos E + \text{constant.}$$

Substituting the series for E in terms of e and M, we find

$$-e \cos E = \text{constant} + e \int_0^M (\sin M + e \sin 2M + \cdots) dM$$

or, since $r/a = 1 - e \cos E$,

$$\frac{r}{a} = 1 + c - e \cos M - \frac{1}{2} e^2 \cos 2M + \cdots$$

where c is a constant still to be found. Assuming that the series is uniformly convergent (which is the case for moderate e), we can integrate both sides of the equation with respect to M between the limits $M = 0$ to $M = 2\pi$, integrating the series term by term. Hence

$$\int_0^{2\pi} \frac{r}{a} dM = 2\pi(1 + c) - e \int_0^{2\pi} \cos M \, dM - \cdots$$

The trigonometric terms all vanish when integrated between these limits. To evaluate the left-hand side, we note that r/a and dM can easily be put in terms of E and dE, and we find

$$2\pi(1 + \tfrac{1}{2}e^2) = 2\pi(1 + c),$$

so that $c = \tfrac{1}{2}e^2$. Then

$$\frac{r}{a} = 1 - e \cos M - \frac{1}{2} e^2(\cos 2M - 1) - \frac{1}{8} e^3(3 \cos 3M - 3 \cos M) - \cdots$$

$$(6.10.2)$$

To find the series for v, differentiate equation (6.3.17), and eliminate $\sin v$, using (6.3.18); then

$$dv = \frac{\sqrt{1 - e^2}}{(1 - e \cos E)^2} dM,$$

and by Kepler's equation this reduces to

$$dv = \sqrt{1 - e^2} \left(\frac{dE}{dM}\right)^2 dM.$$

The procedure is to use the series for E in terms of M to find dE/dM, square it, multiply it into $\sqrt{1 - e^2}$ as a power series in e, and then integrate. The final result is

$$v = M + 2e \sin M + \tfrac{5}{4}e^2 \sin 2M + \tfrac{1}{12}e^3(13 \sin 3M - 3 \sin M) + \cdots$$

$$(6.10.3)$$

It is obvious that in this case we have no trouble over the constant of integration. This expansion [or, more specifically, the expansion of $(v - M)$] is called the *equation of the center.*

The student will find additional expansions in Appendix D.

Problems

1. Prove that if fourth and higher powers of e are neglected, then

$$E = M + \frac{e \sin M}{1 - e \cos M} - \frac{1}{2}\left(\frac{e \sin M}{1 - e \cos M}\right)^3$$

   is a solution of Kepler's equation.

2. Prove that the equation of the center, $(v - M)$, is given in terms of the true anomaly v by the expression

$$\sum_{p=1}^{\infty} (-1)^{p-1} \frac{2\lambda^p\{(p + 1) - (p - 1)\lambda^2\}}{p(1 + \lambda^2)} \sin pv,$$

   where $\lambda = \dfrac{e}{1 + \sqrt{1 - e^2}},$

   e being the eccentricity of the orbit. Show that the maximum value of the equation of the center occurs approximately when

$$v = \frac{\pi}{2} + \sin^{-1}\left(\frac{3e}{4}\right),$$

   e being small.

3. Show that if the eccentricity e is small and e^3 is neglected,

$$r = a(1 - e \cos nt + e^2 \sin^2 nt)$$

   and

$$\omega = n(1 + \tfrac{1}{2}e^2 \cos 2nt),$$

   where r is the radius vector, t the time measured from the nearer apsis, $2\pi/n$ the period, a the semimajor axis, and ω the angular velocity about the empty focus.

   Hence prove that the Moon always very nearly turns the same face to that focus of its orbit in which the Earth is not situated.

4. If the origin is at the center of force and the x-axis points toward

perihelion, show that the coordinates in an elliptic orbit are (x,y), where

$$\frac{x}{a} = \cos M + \frac{1}{2} e(\cos 2M - 3) + \frac{1}{8} e^2(3 \cos 3M - 3 \cos M) + \cdots$$

and

$$\frac{y}{a} = \sin M + \frac{1}{2} e \sin 2M + \frac{1}{24} e^2(9 \sin 3M - 15 \sin M) + \cdots$$

5.   Derive two extra terms for each of the three series developed in this section.

6.11   The Orbit in Space

The six constants of integration found in Sections 6.2 and 6.3 complete the formal solution to the problem, but they are not in a form that is immediately useful to the astronomer. Any set of six independent constants will suffice, but those usually used will now be described: they are known as the *elements of the orbit*.

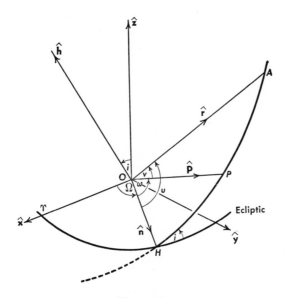

Figure 6.6

In Figure 6.6 the Sun is at O, Ox points toward the vernal equinox and Oz toward the north pole of the ecliptic. Let the plane of the orbit cut the celestial sphere in the great circle HPA, where H is the point where the body in its orbit rises north of the ecliptic, called the *ascending node*. The point at which the body crosses the ecliptic, moving south, is the *descending node*. The angle xOH is the *longitude of the ascending node*; it is written Ω. This angle is measured eastward around the ecliptic. The angle between the plane of the orbit and the ecliptic (or the angle between $\hat{\mathbf{h}}$ and $\hat{\mathbf{z}}$) is called *the inclination*; it is written i. i always lies between 0 and 180°. For $0 \leqslant i < 90°$ the orbit is *direct*; for $90° < i < 180°$ the orbit is *retrograde*. If **OP** is the direction of perihelion, the angle HOP is called the *argument of perihelion*; it is written ω. The angle $\tilde{\omega}$, defined by

$$\tilde{\omega} = \Omega + \omega$$

is the *longitude of perihelion*; it is measured first in the ecliptic to the ascending node, and then in the plane of the orbit to the direction of perihelion. The remaining three elements of the elliptic orbit are a, e, and T. For a parabolic orbit only five elements are needed; q, the perihelion distance, replaces a and e.

$\tilde{\omega}$ is an element that can be used instead of ω. There are other alternatives to the elements defined above. For instance it may be convenient to replace T by

$$\chi = -nT.$$

The *true longitude* of a planet is the angle measured from the vernal equinox, first along the ecliptic to the ascending node, and then in the direction of the orbit to the planet. Denoting this by L, we have

$$L = \tilde{\omega} + v = \Omega + \omega + v = \Omega + u,$$

where u is the angle HOA, A being the position of the planet on the celestial sphere; u is called *the argument of the latitude* of the planet. The *mean longitude l* of the planet is defined by

$$l = \tilde{\omega} + n(t - T) = \tilde{\omega} + M.$$

When $t = 0$ we have an *epoch* (which can, of course, be any convenient date); the value of l when $t = 0$ is

$$\epsilon = \tilde{\omega} - nT = \tilde{\omega} + \chi,$$

which is *the mean longitude at the epoch*.

The angles Ω and i depend on the direction of **h**. Let $\hat{\mathbf{h}}$ have components $(\hat{h}_x, \hat{h}_y, \hat{h}_z)$. Then

$$\hat{h}_z = \hat{\mathbf{h}} \cdot \hat{\mathbf{z}} = \cos i.$$

Let the unit vector along OH be $\hat{\mathbf{n}}$; this has components $(\cos\Omega, \sin\Omega, 0)$. But $\hat{\mathbf{z}} \times \hat{\mathbf{h}} = \hat{\mathbf{n}} \sin i$, so

$$(-\hat{h}_y, \hat{h}_x, 0) = \sin i(\cos\Omega, \sin\Omega, 0),$$

and

$$\left.\begin{aligned}
\hat{h}_x &= \sin \Omega \sin i, \\
-\hat{h}_y &= \cos \Omega \sin i, \\
\hat{h}_z &= \cos i.
\end{aligned}\right] \tag{6.11.1}$$

The angle ω can be found formally from the unit vector **P**.

Problem

Elements for comet Kopff (see Section 6.9, problem 1) are

ω	169°8833	e	0.528 4019
Ω	110°1459	a	3.408 4162
i	1°6074	T	1957 November 24.7969.

Find χ and $\tilde{\omega}$; also find ϵ for the epoch 1957 January 0.5.

Sketch the orbit as accurately as possible as it would be observed from the north pole of the ecliptic, distinguishing the parts that are above or below the ecliptic. Mark the positions occupied by the comet and the Earth on the dates considered in Section 6.9, problem 1, and measure the distances between them. Describe how the comet will appear to move among the stars, as observed from the Earth.

6.12 The Determination of the Elements from r and r′

An important process in the determination of orbits is the computation of the elements when the position and velocity at some time are known. In fact the components of **r** and **r′** at some instant comprise an alternative form of the six constants of integration. In the work that follows, it will be assumed that the body has negligible mass and that the unit of time is chosen to make $k = 1$; the units of length and mass are the astronomical unit and the mass of the Sun.

The angular momentum

$$\mathbf{h} = \mathbf{r} \times \mathbf{r'} \tag{6.12.1}$$

can be found at once (but care must be taken with the signs), and hence h and $\hat{\mathbf{h}}$. The components of $\hat{\mathbf{h}}$ immediately give Ω and i, by equations (6.11.1), assuming that the data are given with respect to the axes considered in Section 6.11.

r and $\mathbf{r'}^2$ can be calculated without difficulty, so that a can be found from

$$\mathbf{r'}^2 = \frac{2}{r} - \frac{1}{a}, \tag{6.12.2}$$

assuming the orbit to be an ellipse. If it is not, a in (6.12.2) will be negative. Once a is known, P and n can be found.

Next r' is found from

$$r' = \frac{\mathbf{r} \cdot \mathbf{r'}}{r}. \tag{6.12.3}$$

From the equation of the orbit,

$$e \cos v = \frac{h^2}{r} - 1. \tag{6.12.4}$$

Differentiating this with respect to the time, and using the angular momentum equation to eliminate dv/dt, we find

$$e \sin v = hr'. \tag{6.12.5}$$

Equations (6.12.4) and (6.12.5) determine e and v. h can be found from the components of $\mathbf{h}$, or, better, from

$$h^2 = r^2 V^2 - r^2 r'^2.$$

Now

$$r \cos u = \mathbf{r} \cdot \hat{\mathbf{n}}$$

$$= x \cos \Omega + y \sin \Omega. \qquad (6.12.6)$$

Also

$$\hat{\mathbf{n}} \times \hat{\mathbf{r}} = \hat{\mathbf{h}} \sin u,$$

of which the x-component gives [using (6.11.1)]

$$\frac{z}{r} \sin \Omega = \sin \Omega \sin i \sin u$$

so that

$$\sin u = \frac{z}{r} \operatorname{cosec} i. \qquad (6.12.7)$$

Equations (6.12.6) and (6.12.7) uniquely determine u, after which ω can be found from

$$\omega = u - v, \qquad (6.12.8)$$

where an extra 360° may have to be added to make ω lie between 0 and 360°.

Finally E is found from (6.3.19), and T can then be found from Kepler's equation.

This order of computation is not unique, and other selections of formulas for the elliptic orbit can be used. The compilation of alternative methods is left to the student, but an important alternative will be described at the end of Section 6.14.

Problems

1. Consider the elements of comet Kopff. Choose any date, and compute $\mathbf{r}$ and $\mathbf{r}'$. Using these values, recompute the elements.
2. If

$$\mathbf{r} = (+2.795\ 526,\ +1.399\ 919,\ +0.846\ 807)$$

and

$$\mathbf{r}' = (-0.230\ 40,\ +0.483\ 17,\ -0.102\ 25),$$

on November 26.7480, 1910 (the coordinates being based on the ecliptic), derive the elements

ω	267° 16′ 36″.6		a	3.120 500
Ω	260 40 11 .8		e	0.048 8747
i	18 29 41 .8		χ	139° 17′ 19″.3.

3. If
$$\mathbf{r} = (+2.246\ 6000,\ -0.647\ 4707,\ -0.245\ 1240)$$
and
$$\mathbf{r'} = (+0.249\ 757,\ +0.658\ 181,\ +0.084\ 632)$$

on September 2.9067, 1935 (the coordinates being based on the celestial equator), derive the elements

ω	152°3358	a	2.873 4707
Ω	165.8334	e	0.193 9539
i	15.1752	T	June 13.53.

6.13 The Determination of the Elements from r_1 and r_2

In the method of orbit determination due to Gauss, the elements are found from two values of position and the corresponding times. A similar situation arises in astrodynamics, when the times and positions of launching and impact are known and the necessary orbit must be found. To do this, it is usual to use the theory of Section 6.7. l and m are found from the data and then equations (6.7.8) and (6.7.9) are solved for y by some method of approximation.

Now y is the ratio of the sector to the triangle. The area of the triangle is known (i.e., $\frac{1}{2}r_1r_2 \sin 2f$), so that the area of the sector can be found. Then, since the time from $\mathbf{r}_1$ to $\mathbf{r}_2$ is known, the areal velocity and then h can be found. From h, p is found, and the two geometrical equations

$$\frac{p}{r_1} = 1 + e \cos v_1 \quad \text{and} \quad \frac{p}{r_2} = 1 + e \cos v_2$$

can be solved for e and the v's. Then a is found from

$$p = a(1 - e^2).$$

u, ω, E, and T are found as in Section 6.12. Ω and i can be found from the direction of $\mathbf{r}_1 \times \mathbf{r}_2$, since this vector is parallel to $\mathbf{h}$.

The solution for y might be accomplished in the following way: A trial value y_1 leads, from (6.7.8), to a value g_1 for g. If this is now substituted into (6.7.9), the equation can be solved for y, leading to a value y_2 which is unlikely to be equal to y_1. However, if y_2 is used as a trial value, the process can be repeated until eventually the two values of y agree.

An alternative approach, which avoids the use of y altogether, was recently developed by Herrick and Liu. This starts with a trial value of p; from this value it is possible to predict the interval between the positions $\mathbf{r}_1$ and $\mathbf{r}_2$. This will not be the same as the actual interval, so another value of p is tried. Let the actual interval be T. If values p_1 and p_2 lead to computed intervals T_1 and T_2, let

$$mT_1 + nT_2 = T, \quad m + n = 1;$$

then $mp_1 + np_2$ will be a better value of p; and so on. To see how a value of p leads to the time interval, we note that e, v_1, v_2, and a can be found as before. Then E_1 and E_2, and hence M_1 and M_2, can be found, and since n is known from a, the value of the time interval follows at once.

In some cases only an approximate solution is needed. Assume

$$\mathbf{r} = \mathbf{a} + \mathbf{b}t + \mathbf{c}t^2 + \mathbf{d}t^3 + \mathbf{e}t^4 + \cdots$$

so that, by the law of gravitation,

$$-\frac{\mathbf{r}}{r^3} = 2\mathbf{c} + 6\mathbf{d}t + 12\mathbf{e}t^2 + \cdots$$

as in Section 6.8. If $t = 0$ corresponds to $\mathbf{r}_1$, then

$$\mathbf{r}_1 = \mathbf{a},$$

$$\mathbf{r}_2 = \mathbf{a} + \mathbf{b}t + \mathbf{c}t^2 + \mathbf{d}t^3 + \cdots$$

$$-\frac{\mathbf{r}_1}{r_1^3} = 2\mathbf{c},$$

$$-\frac{\mathbf{r}_2}{r_2^3} = 2\mathbf{c} + 6\mathbf{d}t + \cdots$$

We also have

$$\mathbf{r}_1' = \mathbf{b}.$$

From these five equations it is possible to eliminate the constant coefficients up to $\mathbf{d}$; then we have an expression which gives $\mathbf{r}_1'$ in terms of $\mathbf{r}_1$, $\mathbf{r}_2$, and t, which is accurate to the order t^3. The solution for the elements follows from $\mathbf{r}_1$ and $\mathbf{r}_1'$.

Problems

1. Calculate $\mathbf{r}$ for two dates (not too far apart) in the orbit of comet Kopff. Recompute the elements from these.
2. Find the expression for $\mathbf{r}_1'$ in terms of $\mathbf{r}_1$, $\mathbf{r}_2$, and t.
3. Using the result of problem 2, compute approximate elements from the values of $\mathbf{r}$ of problem 1.

6.14   The Geocentric Coordinates

For observational purposes, equatorial coordinates are used, so that the cartesian coordinates of a planet must be found with respect to equatorial axes, the particular equator involved being defined for some definite epoch. With origin at the Sun, let OX point toward the vernal equinox and OZ toward the north celestial pole. Also let OP point toward perihelion and OQ toward the point in the orbit for which the true anomaly is $90°$. The coordinates of the planet with respect to the axes OP and OQ are

$$(r \cos v, r \sin v)$$

or

$$[a(\cos E - e), b \sin E].$$

Let $\hat{\mathbf{P}}$ and $\hat{\mathbf{Q}}$ be the unit vectors along OP and OQ, and let them have components (P_x, P_y, P_z) and (Q_x, Q_y, Q_z) with respect to the equatorial axes. Then the coordinates of a planet with respect to these axes are

$$\left. \begin{array}{l} x = aP_x(\cos E - e) + bQ_x \sin E, \\ y = aP_y(\cos E - e) + bQ_y \sin E, \\ z = aP_z(\cos E - e) + bQ_z \sin E. \end{array} \right] \tag{6.14.1}$$

The components of $\hat{\mathbf{P}}$ and $\hat{\mathbf{Q}}$ are most easily derived by the methods of Appendix B. As an alternative method we will find them first with respect to the ecliptic system of axes used in Section 6.11. Let these components be (l_1, m_1, n_1) and (l_2, m_2, n_2); then by the formulas of spherical trigonometry, we have, from the triangles PxH, PyH, and PzH,

$$\left. \begin{array}{l} l_1 = \cos \Omega \cos \omega - \sin \Omega \sin \omega \cos i, \\ m_1 = \sin \Omega \cos \omega + \cos \Omega \sin \omega \cos i, \\ n_1 = \sin \omega \sin i. \end{array} \right] \tag{6.14.2}$$

Similarly,

$$\left. \begin{array}{l} l_2 = -\cos \Omega \sin \omega - \sin \Omega \cos \omega \cos i, \\ m_2 = -\sin \Omega \sin \omega + \cos \Omega \cos \omega \cos i, \\ n_2 = \cos \omega \sin i. \end{array} \right] \tag{6.14.3}$$

To get to equatorial axes, the ecliptic axes must be rotated about OX through an angle ϵ, so that, finally, we have

$$\left. \begin{array}{ll} P_x = l_1, & Q_x = l_2, \\ P_y = m_1 \cos \epsilon - n_1 \sin \epsilon, & Q_y = m_2 \cos \epsilon - n_2 \sin \epsilon, \\ P_z = m_1 \sin \epsilon + n_1 \cos \epsilon, & Q_z = m_2 \sin \epsilon + n_2 \cos \epsilon. \end{array} \right] \tag{6.14.4}$$

When computing these, it is wise to apply the checks

$$\hat{\mathbf{P}}^2 = P_x^2 + P_y^2 + P_z^2 = 1,$$
$$\hat{\mathbf{Q}}^2 = Q_x^2 + Q_y^2 + Q_z^2 = 1,$$
$$\hat{\mathbf{P}} \cdot \hat{\mathbf{Q}} = P_x Q_x + P_y Q_y + P_z Q_z = 0.$$

The student should remember that $\hat{\mathbf{P}}$ and $\hat{\mathbf{Q}}$ are vectors; their components need not be given by the above formulas, but can be referred to any convenient set of axes. For instance in considering the orbit of a satellite around the Earth it is convenient to refer the elements not to the ecliptic but to the celestial equator. In this case ϵ would not appear in the expressions for the components. Equations (6.14.1) give the heliocentric equatorial coordinates of the planet.

To find the geocentric equatorial coordinates, the origin must be moved to the center of the Earth. If, after this has been done, the Sun is at

$$\mathbf{R} = (X, Y, Z),$$

then the planet is at

$$\boldsymbol{\rho} = (\xi, \eta, \zeta)$$

where

$$\boldsymbol{\rho} = \mathbf{r} + \mathbf{R}. \tag{6.14.5}$$

The components of $\mathbf{r}$ are found from (6.14.1). The components of $\mathbf{R}$ are tabulated in almanacs.

Finally the right ascension and declination of the planet are found from

$$\boldsymbol{\rho} = \rho(\cos \alpha \cos \delta, \sin \alpha \cos \delta, \sin \delta),$$
$$= (\xi, \eta, \zeta),$$

so that

$$\tan \alpha = \frac{\eta}{\xi} \quad \text{and} \quad \tan \delta = \frac{\zeta}{\sqrt{\xi^2 + \eta^2}}. \tag{6.14.6}$$

If we are given $\mathbf{r}$ and $\mathbf{r}'$ for some epoch and we want to construct an ephemeris from these data, it is not necessary to find the elements and then use these to calculate the components of $\hat{\mathbf{P}}$ and $\hat{\mathbf{Q}}$. Differentiating

$$\mathbf{r} = a\,\hat{\mathbf{P}}(\cos E - e) + b\,\hat{\mathbf{Q}} \sin E$$

we find

$$\mathbf{r}' = \frac{1}{r\sqrt{a}}\,(b\,\hat{\mathbf{Q}} \cos E - a\,\hat{\mathbf{P}} \sin E).$$

We also have

$$e \cos E = rV^2 - 1,$$
$$\sqrt{a}\, e \sin E = \mathbf{r} \cdot \mathbf{r}',$$

and

$$\frac{1}{a} = \frac{2}{r} - V^2.$$

Hence a, e, and E are known, and the first two equations can be solved for the components of $\hat{\mathbf{P}}$ and $\hat{\mathbf{Q}}$. We notice that $a\hat{\mathbf{P}}$, $b\hat{\mathbf{Q}}$, and T comprise an alternative set of elements.

Problems

1. Find the equatorial components of $\hat{\mathbf{R}}$ such that $\hat{\mathbf{P}} \times \hat{\mathbf{Q}} = \hat{\mathbf{R}}$.

2. Consider comet Kopff once more. Find the components of $\hat{\mathbf{P}}$ and $\hat{\mathbf{Q}}$, and check them. Find the coordinates (x, y, z) for each date previously considered, and with the tabulated values of (X, Y, Z) given below, find the geocentric distances ρ, which should check with those measured previously. Finally check the equatorial coordinates in the following ephemeris.

1957	h m	° ′	X	Y	Z
Jan. 2	12 24.6	+ 3 57	+0.191 704	−0.884 824	−0.383 719
Feb. 1	12 36.5	4 18	656 535	674 219	292 386
March 3	12 29.8	6 50	943 229	−0.280 262	−0.121 540
April 2	12 06.0	10 25	978 259	+0.188 965	+0.081 948
May 2	11 44.7	12 08	758 125	609 435	264 291
June 1	11 45.3	10 38	+0.344 645	875 057	379 482
July 1	12 08.9	6 35	−0.155 319	921 843	399 772
July 31	12 50.4	+ 0 46	616 735	739 679	320 774
Aug. 30	13 46.1	− 6 08	924 083	+0.373 080	+0.161 794
Sept. 29	14 55.3	−13 16	−0.997 062	−0.087 699	−0.038 029

6.15   The Effects of Planetary Aberration and Parallax

Let us suppose that the computed right ascension and declination have been corrected for the effects of precession and annual and diurnal aberration. Neglecting refraction effects in the Earth's atmosphere, there will still be two factors leading to a difference between the observed and computed values. Since light moves with a finite speed, the position observed corresponds to some time before the instant of observation. This effect is called *planetary aberration* (it should not be confused with other types of aberration). If t is the time of observation, the observed position will correspond to a time

$$t - \frac{\rho}{c}$$

where c is the speed of light.

Also, the published values of (X, Y, Z) are with respect to the center of the Earth. The fact that the observer is elsewhere will mean that the position of the planet on the celestial sphere will be changed by an amount which, among other things, will depend on the value of ρ. Finding the change amounts to *correcting for parallax*. The formulas involved are quoted below; proofs may be found in standard works on spherical astronomy.

Let a be the radius of the Earth to the point of observation, measured in terms of the equatorial radius.

Let ϕ be the geocentric latitude of the place of observation.

Let ρ be the geocentric distance, measured in astronomical units.

Let α and δ be the observed, or topocentric coordinates.

Let $\Delta\alpha^s$ and $\Delta\delta''$ be the corrections to be added to obtain the geocentric coordinates.

Let θ be the local sidereal time of observation.

Then

$$\left.\begin{aligned}
\rho\,\Delta\alpha &= \tfrac{1}{15}a \times 8.80 \times \cos\phi \sec\delta \sin(\theta - \alpha), \\
\rho\,\Delta\delta &= a \times 8.80 \times \sin\phi \operatorname{cosec} G \sin(G - \delta),
\end{aligned}\right\} \qquad (6.15.1)$$

where

$$\tan G = \tan\phi \sec(\theta - \alpha), \quad G < 180°.$$

Chapter 7 ** THE DETERMINATION OF ORBITS

7.1 Introduction

In Chapter Six we have seen how, once the elements of an orbit are known, the geocentric position on the celestial sphere can be calculated for any time. In this chapter we shall be concerned with the reverse situation, that of finding the elements of an orbit from observations. For convenience we shall refer to the observed body as a comet, but it could equally well be a minor planet or an interplanetary rocket; with slight modifications to the methods used, it could be an artificial satellite. The roughest glance at the process of ephemeris computation described in Section 6.14 will show that the work cannot practically be reversed, so that some new technique must be found. In fact no direct way is known for finding the elements of an orbit from observations, and it is necessary to proceed by approximations.

An observer on another star would recognize the bodies in the solar system as moving in elliptic orbits about the Sun; but observations from the Earth are affected by the motion of the Earth. The observed geocentric path will obviously not be an ellipse, and Figure 7.1, showing part of the path of comet Arend-Roland (1956 h), demonstrates how complicated the observed path can become. The position of the Earth in the solar system at any time is, of course, accurately known. If we could observe the distance of the comet, then there would be no difficulty in calculating its position in the solar system; unfortunately only its direction can be observed, and the calculation of its distance is one of the processes of orbit determination. In astrodynamics more and different information may be available from observations. The processes of orbit determination can be modified (and simplified) to take advantage of this extra information.

For interest we shall describe in principle the method used by Kepler to find the distance, and thence the orbit, of Mars. The sidereal period of Mars was accurately known, and Figure 7.2 shows the situation for two observations separated by one sidereal period, so that Mars has returned to the same position

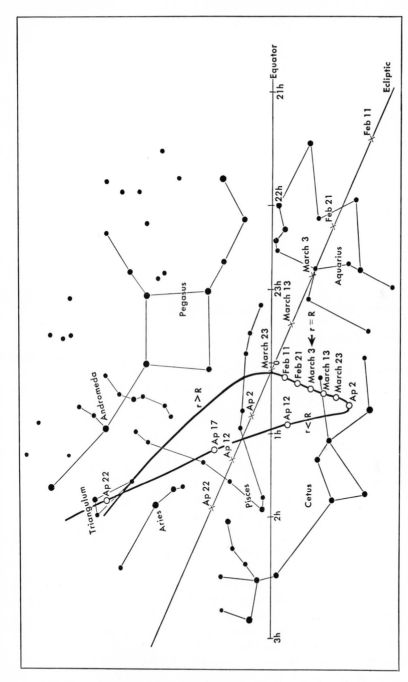

Figure 7.1. The chart is a central projection, so that all great circles are straight lines.

in the solar system. Since the sidereal period is 1.88 years, the Earth will have revolved through approximately 677°, so that the angle E_1SE_2 is known, as is the distance E_1E_2 (but only in terms of the astronomical unit). Observations furnish the angles E_1E_2M and E_2E_1M, so that the triangle E_1E_2M can be solved to find the lengths of the sides, and ultimately the distance MS.

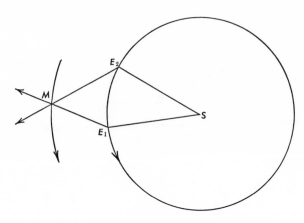

Figure 7.2

The price of the simplicity of Kepler's method is that observations are needed over many revolutions, and this is a luxury that we cannot afford. The history of the discovery of Ceres will illustrate this. Ceres, the first of the minor planets to be discovered, was found by Piazzi in 1801, but only a few observations were possible before it approached conjunction and became too close to the Sun to be observed. Ceres is a faint object, and it was obviously

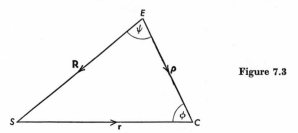

Figure 7.3

important to predict when and where it could be observed again; this prediction could not be based on the leisurely study of several revolutions but had to depend on a small arc of one revolution. In this case the occasion was doubly historic because Gauss evolved a new method for orbit determination; the principles of this will be described later.

A single observation yields two angles and the time. Since six unknowns must be found before the orbit is determined, a minimum of three observations is necessary. An accurate orbit, the *definitive orbit*, is found from many more observations, but since three are enough, we shall be concerned here with the problem of determining the orbit from these.

It is instructive at this stage to consider the observed path geometrically. Throughout this chapter we shall use the notation of Figure 7.3, where S, E, and C apply to the Sun, the Earth, and the comet, respectively. The observed quantity is the unit vector $\hat{\boldsymbol{\rho}}$, and it traces out a curve on the celestial sphere (which we assume to have unit radius). Then

$$\frac{d\hat{\boldsymbol{\rho}}}{ds} = \hat{\boldsymbol{\rho}}' = \hat{\mathbf{t}},$$

where s is distance measured along the curve and $\hat{\mathbf{t}}$ is the unit vector tangent to the curve at $\hat{\boldsymbol{\rho}}$. (The prime will denote differentiation with respect to s in this section only.) Let

$$\hat{\mathbf{n}} = \hat{\boldsymbol{\rho}} \times \hat{\mathbf{t}}.$$

Since $\hat{\mathbf{t}}'$ is perpendicular to $\hat{\mathbf{t}}$, it can be resolved along $\hat{\boldsymbol{\rho}}$ and $\hat{\mathbf{n}}$, so that

$$\hat{\mathbf{t}}' = \lambda\hat{\boldsymbol{\rho}} + \kappa\hat{\mathbf{n}},$$

where, by differentiating $\hat{\boldsymbol{\rho}}\cdot\hat{\mathbf{t}} = 0$, we see that $\lambda = -1$. The component of $\hat{\mathbf{t}}'$ at right angles to the line of sight is $\kappa\hat{\mathbf{n}}$, and Figure 7.4 shows the situation where κ is positive; in this case the curve is concave toward the direction $\hat{\mathbf{n}}$.

Figure 7.4

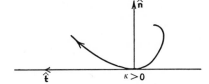

When κ is negative, the curve is convex toward $\hat{\mathbf{n}}$. Now

$$\mathbf{r} + \mathbf{R} = \boldsymbol{\rho} = \rho\hat{\boldsymbol{\rho}},$$

so

$$\dot{\mathbf{r}} + \dot{\mathbf{R}} = \dot{\rho}\hat{\boldsymbol{\rho}} + \rho\dot{\hat{\boldsymbol{\rho}}}$$

$$= \dot{\rho}\hat{\boldsymbol{\rho}} + \rho\frac{ds}{dt}\hat{\mathbf{t}}, \quad (dt \text{ refers to the time})$$

and

$$\ddot{\mathbf{r}} + \ddot{\mathbf{R}} = \ddot{\rho}\hat{\boldsymbol{\rho}} + 2\dot{\rho}\frac{ds}{dt}\hat{\mathbf{t}} + \rho\frac{d^2s}{dt^2}\hat{\mathbf{t}} + \rho\left(\frac{ds}{dt}\right)^2(-\hat{\boldsymbol{\rho}} + \kappa\hat{\mathbf{n}}).$$

Multiply by $\cdot\hat{\mathbf{n}}$; then

$$(\ddot{\mathbf{r}} + \ddot{\mathbf{R}})\cdot\hat{\mathbf{n}} = \rho\left(\frac{ds}{dt}\right)^2\kappa. \tag{7.1.1}$$

Now both the Earth and the comet move subject to the gravitational attraction of the Sun, and the mass of each can be neglected compared with the mass of the Sun. Hence

$$\ddot{\mathbf{r}} = -\mu\frac{\mathbf{r}}{r^3} \quad \text{and} \quad \ddot{\mathbf{R}} = -\mu\frac{\mathbf{R}}{R^3},$$

and so

$$\ddot{\mathbf{r}} + \ddot{\mathbf{R}} = -\mu \left(\frac{\mathbf{r}}{r^3} + \frac{\mathbf{R}}{R^3} \right)$$
$$= -\mu \left(\frac{\boldsymbol{\rho} - \mathbf{R}}{r^3} + \frac{\mathbf{R}}{R^3} \right).$$

Multiply by $\cdot \hat{\mathbf{n}}$; then from (7.1.1) we find

$$\mu \left(\frac{1}{r^3} - \frac{1}{R^3} \right) \mathbf{R} \cdot \hat{\mathbf{n}} = \rho \left(\frac{ds}{dt} \right)^2 \kappa. \qquad (7.1.2)$$

Now suppose κ is positive; then $(r - R)$ and $\mathbf{R} \cdot \hat{\mathbf{n}}$ have opposite signs. If $r > R$, then the direction of the Sun makes an angle of more than 90° with $\hat{\mathbf{n}}$, and the curve is convex toward the Sun. If $r < R$, then the curve is concave toward the Sun. These results are not altered if κ is negative. Hence we have Lambert's theorem that the apparent path is convex toward the Sun when $r > R$ and concave toward the Sun when $r < R$. This is illustrated in Figure 7.1.

From the triangle *SEC* we have

$$r^2 = \rho^2 + R^2 - 2R\rho \cos \psi,$$

and, formally, this and (7.1.2) can be solved for the two unknowns r and ρ. But if $\mathbf{R} \cdot \hat{\mathbf{n}} = 0$, a solution is impossible. This will happen if the orbit lies in the ecliptic (in this case three observations are inadequate, for they are not truly independent). It can also happen accidentally as the comet crosses the ecliptic. We shall also be in difficulties if $\mathbf{R} \cdot \hat{\mathbf{n}}$ is very small. There will also be trouble if κ is very small; in this case the three observations lie nearly on a great circle. In fact the prospect of a satisfactory solution depends primarily on the deviation of the observed arc from a great circle. (There is another cause of uncertainty; this is discussed in the following section.)

It must be emphasized that this chapter is not a practical manual for orbit determination. Rather it is intended that the student should become familiar with some of the theoretical background so that in practical work, and in any work that may involve orbit determination, he will know what is going on. For the practical computation of orbits, the student should consult *The Computation of Orbits* by P. Herget (Ref. 27), for which there is at present no substitute.* The author is indebted to this work for most of his knowledge of the subject and for much of the substance of this chapter.

7.2 Laplace's Method

The basic formulas for Laplace's method are

$$\mathbf{r} + \mathbf{R} = \rho \hat{\boldsymbol{\rho}}, \qquad (7.2.1)$$
$$\mathbf{r}' + \mathbf{R}' = \rho' \hat{\boldsymbol{\rho}} + \rho \hat{\boldsymbol{\rho}}', \qquad (7.2.2)$$
$$-\frac{\boldsymbol{\rho}}{r^3} + \left(\frac{1}{r^3} - \frac{1}{R^3} \right) \mathbf{R} = \rho'' \hat{\boldsymbol{\rho}} + 2\rho' \hat{\boldsymbol{\rho}}' + \rho \hat{\boldsymbol{\rho}}'', \qquad (7.2.3)$$

---

* At the time of composition, *The Determination of Orbits* by A. D. Dubyago had not been published. This book is also highly recommended.

and

$$r^2 = \rho^2 + R^2 - 2R\rho \cos \psi. \tag{7.2.4}$$

Here we have chosen the unit of time to make $k = 1$, and the unit of mass to be the mass of the Sun. If the modified time is referred to as τ, measured from some epoch t_0, then

$$\tau = k(t - t_0).$$

A prime will denote differentiation with respect to τ.

The observations furnish three values of $\hat{\rho}$ for three values of τ. The four formulas given above represent exactly the geometrical and gravitational aspects of the motion. The initial approximation in Laplace's method involves finding values for $\hat{\rho}'$ and $\hat{\rho}''$ at some instant. Let this instant be t_0; then for small τ, $\hat{\rho}$ can be expanded by a Taylor series as

$$\hat{\rho} = (\hat{\rho})_{\tau=0} + \tau(\hat{\rho}')_0 + \tfrac{1}{2}\tau^2(\hat{\rho}'')_0 + \cdots \tag{7.2.5}$$

If this series is truncated after the third term, then three observations are sufficient to determine $(\hat{\rho}')_0$ and $(\hat{\rho}'')_0$. These values are not exact, so that the observed positions (and therefore the geometry of the problem) will not be represented accurately. It is possible to choose t_0 so that the errors are minimized (see problems 10 and 11 at the end of this chapter), but it is usual to take it to be the time of the second observation. If more than three observations are available, we can, of course, find better values for $(\hat{\rho}')_0$ and $(\hat{\rho}'')_0$.

Let us assume that $\hat{\rho}'$ and $\hat{\rho}''$ have been found. Taking $(\hat{\rho} \times \hat{\rho}') \cdot (7.2.3)$, we find

$$\left(\frac{1}{r^3} - \frac{1}{R^3}\right)[\hat{\rho},\hat{\rho}',\mathbf{R}] = \rho[\hat{\rho},\hat{\rho}',\hat{\rho}''], \tag{7.2.6}$$

an equation which is similar to (7.1.2). Also from $(\hat{\rho} \times \hat{\rho}'') \cdot (7.2.3)$, we find

$$\left(\frac{1}{r^3} - \frac{1}{R^3}\right)[\hat{\rho},\hat{\rho}'',\mathbf{R}] = -2\rho'[\hat{\rho},\hat{\rho}',\hat{\rho}'']. \tag{7.2.7}$$

Assuming that (7.2.4) and (7.2.6) can be solved for r and ρ, (7.2.7) can then be solved for ρ'. Then from (7.2.1) and (7.2.2), $\mathbf{r}$ and $\mathbf{r}'$ can be found, and the elements of the orbit can be calculated from these.

If these elements are then used to predict the positions at the first and third times of observation (assuming that $\tau = 0$ corresponds to the second observation), the answers will not agree with the original observations. This is because we truncated the series (7.2.5). Some method must be found to improve the orbit, but before discussing this, we shall consider in more detail the solution of (7.2.4) and (7.2.6) from a theoretical angle; their practical solution is described in problem 4 at the end of this chapter.

By eliminating r, we can obtain an algebraic equation of the eighth degree in ρ, but rather than attempting to solve this, it is easier to make the following substitutions. From the triangle SEC we have (see Figure 7.3)

$$\frac{R}{\sin \phi} = \frac{r}{\sin \psi} = \frac{\rho}{\sin(\phi + \psi)}. \tag{7.2.8}$$

Write (7.2.6) in the form

$$\rho = A \left(\frac{1}{R^3} - \frac{1}{r^3} \right); \tag{7.2.9}$$

then, using (7.2.8), we find

$$R \sin \psi \cos \phi + \left(R \cos \psi - \frac{A}{R^3} \right) \sin \phi = - \frac{A}{R^3} \frac{\sin^4 \phi}{\sin^3 \psi}.$$

In order to simplify this, let

$$\left. \begin{aligned}
N \sin m &= R \sin \psi, \\[2mm]
N \cos m &= R \cos \psi - \frac{A}{R^3}, \\[2mm]
M &= - \frac{N R^3}{A} \sin^3 \psi,
\end{aligned} \right] \tag{7.2.10}$$

where the sign of N is chosen to make M positive.

Substituting into (7.2.9) and simplifying, we find, eventually,

$$\sin^4 \phi = M \sin(\phi + m). \tag{7.2.11}$$

The quantities M and m are known; assuming that a unique solution exists, (7.2.11) can be solved by successive approximations. (See problem 3 at the end of this chapter.)

It can easily be verified that the position of the observer satisfies the equations, so that $\phi = \pi - \psi$ is a solution which must be rejected. Also, from the geometry of the triangle SEC,

$$\phi < \pi - \psi.$$

The solutions of (7.2.11) are the intersections of the curves

$$y_1 = \sin^4 \phi$$

and

$$y_2 = M \sin(\phi + m).$$

Figure 7.5 shows these curves for m negative and M somewhat less than one. In this case there are three solutions, and in general we shall have either one or three real solutions for ϕ lying between 0 and π. But if there is only one solution, it must be $\phi = \pi - \psi$; then no solution is left for the comet, and the problem has no meaning.

Consider the case when A is positive. Then $r > R$, and since $\sin \psi$ is not negative, N must be negative; then m lies in the third or fourth quadrant.

Figure 7.5 shows m in the fourth quadrant; as m decreases, the curve y_2 slides to the right and there will be a critical value of m, after which there is only one real solution (see problem 5). Since we require three roots, m certainly cannot lie in the third quadrant. Similarly, if A is negative, it can be shown that m must certainly lie in the first quadrant.

Let the three roots be ϕ_1, ϕ_2, and ϕ_3, where $\phi_1 \leqslant \phi_2 \leqslant \phi_3$. If $\phi_1 = \pi - \psi$, the problem has no solution. If $\phi_2 = \pi - \psi$, there is a unique solution, ϕ_1; this can be found without difficulty by solving (7.2.11). If $\phi_3 = \pi - \psi$, there are two possible solutions, ϕ_1 and ϕ_2. It might be possible to judge between these, since one might require a solution for r which would be unreasonably large, but it may be necessary to use a fourth observation. In the latter case (7.2.11) might be formed for two choices of three dates from the four, having a common central date; the solution common to both would be used. (Or see problem 12 at the end of this chapter.)

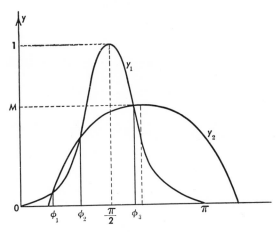

Figure 7.5

To find the condition for a unique solution, consider

$$F(\phi) \equiv \sin^4 \phi - M \sin(\phi + m),$$

so that

$$\frac{\partial F}{\partial \phi} \equiv 4 \sin^3 \phi \cos \phi - M \cos(\phi + m).$$

Suppose A to be positive. If there are three solutions, we see from Figure 7.5 that

$$\frac{\partial F(\phi_2)}{\partial \phi} > 0.$$

The derivatives at the other two roots are negative, so that for a unique solution it is necessary and sufficient that

$$\phi_2 = \pi - \psi$$

and

$$-4 \sin^3 \psi \cos \psi + M \cos(\psi - m) > 0.$$

Using (7.2.10), this becomes

$$\frac{4MA \cos \psi}{NR^3} + \frac{M}{N} \left\{ \cos \psi \left(R \cos \psi - \frac{A}{R^3} \right) + R \sin^2 \psi \right\} > 0$$

or

$$\frac{MR}{N} \left(1 + \frac{3A \cos \psi}{R^4} \right) > 0.$$

Then, since N is negative, we have

$$1 + \frac{3A \cos \psi}{R^4} < 0. \tag{7.2.12}$$

It can easily be shown that the same condition holds if A is negative.

Consider the limiting case when

$$1 + \frac{3A \cos \psi}{R^4} = 0.$$

Eliminating $\cos \psi$ by means of (7.2.4), and using (7.2.9), we find

$$\rho^2 = r^2 + \frac{2}{3} \frac{R^5}{r^3} - \frac{5}{3} R^2. \tag{7.2.13}$$

This is the equation of a surface of revolution about the line SE. A section through SE is shown in Figure 7.6. The sign of the left-hand side of (7.2.12)

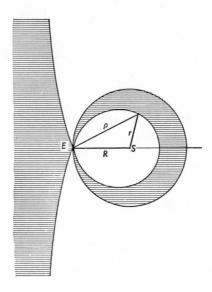

Figure 7.6

changes on crossing the surface, and it can be verified that the inequality is satisfied in the shaded areas of the figure.

We shall now consider the problem of improving the approximate orbit. Now that we have approximate values for ρ, we can adjust for parallax and for planetary aberration. But the adjustments will not affect the discrepancies between the computed and observed positions for the first and third times of observation, and the removal of these is the main problem. The method given below is due to Leuschner.

To find the predicted right ascension and declination for the two times of observation, we use the series

$$\mathbf{r} = f\mathbf{r}_0 + g\mathbf{r}_0'$$

(see Section 6.8) to find the values of $\mathbf{r}$. ($\mathbf{r}_0$ and $\mathbf{r}_0'$ apply to the second observation and are known.) Then we use the formulas (6.14.6) to find α and δ. Let the subscripts 1 and 3 apply to the first and third times of observation, and let $\Delta\alpha_1$ and $\Delta\delta_1$, etc., be the discrepancies between the observed and calculated values in the sense that they are corrections to be added to the calculated values. We than have four residuals, $\Delta\alpha_1$, $\Delta\delta_1$, $\Delta\alpha_3$, and $\Delta\delta_3$.

The errors in $\mathbf{r}$ stem from an incorrect value of ρ, while those in $\mathbf{r}'$ are due to a variety of causes; hence we want to find corrections $\Delta\rho$ and $\Delta\mathbf{r}'$ (four in all) in terms of the four residuals. $\mathbf{R}$ is, of course, not affected; so, from (7.2.1) we have, in general,

$$\Delta\mathbf{r} = \Delta\boldsymbol{\rho} = \Delta\rho\hat{\boldsymbol{\rho}} + \rho\,\Delta\hat{\boldsymbol{\rho}}. \tag{7.2.14}$$

Multiply by $\cdot\hat{\boldsymbol{\rho}}$; then

$$\Delta\rho = \hat{\boldsymbol{\rho}}\cdot\Delta\mathbf{r}$$

so

$$\rho\,\Delta\hat{\boldsymbol{\rho}} = \Delta\mathbf{r} - \hat{\boldsymbol{\rho}}(\hat{\boldsymbol{\rho}}\cdot\Delta\mathbf{r}). \tag{7.2.15}$$

$\Delta\mathbf{r}$ here is the correction to be applied to $\mathbf{r}$. If we assume that all corrections are of the first order of small quantities, and we neglect their squares and products, we find, from the equation of motion for the comet,

$$\mathbf{r}'' + \Delta\mathbf{r}'' = -\frac{\mathbf{r}}{r^3} - \frac{\Delta\mathbf{r}}{r^3} + 3r\frac{\Delta r}{r^4},$$

so that

$$\Delta\mathbf{r}'' = -\frac{\Delta\mathbf{r}}{r^3} + 3r\frac{\Delta r}{r^4}.$$

But from (7.2.4),

$$r\,\Delta r = (\rho - R\cos\psi)\,\Delta\rho.$$

Now let $\Delta\mathbf{r}''$ be evaluated at the time of the second observation, when $\Delta\hat{\boldsymbol{\rho}} = 0$; so $\Delta\mathbf{r} = \hat{\boldsymbol{\rho}}\,\Delta\rho$. Then

$$\Delta\mathbf{r}'' = \left\{-\frac{\hat{\boldsymbol{\rho}}}{r^3} + \frac{3\mathbf{r}}{r^5}(\rho - R\cos\psi)\right\}\Delta\rho$$

$$= \mathbf{H}\,\Delta\rho, \text{ say.} \tag{7.2.16}$$

Now

$$\Delta \mathbf{r}_1 = \Delta \mathbf{r} + \Delta \mathbf{r}' \tau_1 + \tfrac{1}{2} \Delta \mathbf{r}'' \tau_1^2 + \cdots \tag{7.2.17}$$

and, ignoring terms of the order τ_1^3, we have

$$\Delta \mathbf{r}_1 = (\hat{\boldsymbol{\rho}} + \tfrac{1}{2} \mathbf{H} \tau_1^2) \, \Delta \rho + \tau_1 \, \Delta \mathbf{r}'. \tag{7.2.18}$$

Substituting into (7.2.15), we have the three equations that are components of

$$\rho_1 \, \Delta \hat{\boldsymbol{\rho}}_1 = \Delta \mathbf{r}_1 - \hat{\boldsymbol{\rho}}_1 (\hat{\boldsymbol{\rho}}_1 \cdot \Delta \mathbf{r}_1) \tag{7.2.19}$$

for the first time of observation, and another three for the third. The residuals $\Delta \hat{\boldsymbol{\rho}}_1$ and $\Delta \hat{\boldsymbol{\rho}}_3$ are known (if we let $\hat{\boldsymbol{\rho}} = (\lambda, \mu, \nu)$, they are $\Delta \lambda_1, \Delta \mu_1, \Delta \nu_1$, etc.), and it appears for a moment that we have six equations for the four unknowns $\Delta \rho$ and $\Delta \mathbf{r}'$. But the six equations are not independent, and it is better to work with the residuals $\Delta \alpha$ and $\Delta \delta$, where we have

$$\left.\begin{array}{ll} \cos^2 \delta_1 \, \Delta \alpha_1 = \lambda_1 \, \Delta \mu_1 - \mu_1 \, \Delta \lambda_1, \\ \cos \delta_1 \, \Delta \delta_1 \; = \Delta \nu_1, \\ \cos^2 \delta_3 \, \Delta \alpha_3 = \lambda_3 \, \Delta \mu_3 - \mu_3 \, \Delta \lambda_3, \\ \cos \delta_3 \, \Delta \delta_3 \; = \Delta \nu_3. \end{array}\right\} \tag{7.2.20}$$

Substituting from (7.2.19) for the components $\Delta \lambda_1, \Delta \mu_1, \Delta \nu_1$, and doing the same for the third observation, we have four linear simultaneous equations for the unknowns $\Delta \rho$ and $\Delta \mathbf{r}'$, and these can be solved by determinants in the usual way.

If these residuals are applied as corrections to the original values of $\mathbf{r}$ and $\mathbf{r}'$, a better orbit will have been found, but it may still not be successful in predicting the observations for the first and third dates; however, the residuals should be less than they were in the first place. The entire process can now be repeated, and this is continued until the residuals become negligible. It should be noted that once the equations (7.2.20) have been set up, the coefficients of $\Delta \rho$ and $\Delta \mathbf{r}'$ will not vary through the successive approximations, so that later approximations can be accomplished relatively easily.

If extra observations are available, more residuals can be found; we are then able to set up more equations than there are unknowns, and these can be solved by the method of least squares. The resulting corrections to the orbit arise from more than three observations and are therefore more dependable than those found above. Observations over a longer arc can be used if, instead of the truncated series (7.2.17), the f and g series are used, so that

$$\Delta \mathbf{r} = \mathbf{r}_0 \Delta f + \mathbf{r}_0' \Delta g + f \Delta \mathbf{r}_0 + g \Delta \mathbf{r}_0'.$$

The resulting equations are more complicated than those described above; they are given by Herget (Ref. 27).

(We have now entered the realm of *orbit correction*, a subject outside the scope of this text. Various techniques are used; the main ones are described by Herget (Ref. 27). The student should also consult Ref. 22, Section 6.6, Ref. 26, and Sections *G* and *H* of *Notes of the Summer Institute in Dynamical Astronomy at Yale University* (Ref. 29). If *any* quantity can be predicted, and then checked by observation, the resulting residual can be used to improve the orbit. Also, apart from finding corrections to the six elements of the orbit (whether they be $\mathbf{r}_0$, $\mathbf{r}_0'$, or the conventional elements, or any other set of six suitable quantities) any other quantities can be corrected. For instance we might decide to correct the Earth's orbit, on which the tabulated values of $\mathbf{R}$ are based; or we might improve the value of some physical constant. The general principle behind these corrections is that they are so small that their squares and products can be neglected. Then if *m* residuals, $\Delta O_1, \Delta O_2, \cdots, \Delta O_m$, can be observed, and *n* quantities, $A_1, A_2, \cdots, A_n$, are to be corrected,

$$[\Delta O_1 \cdots \Delta O_m] = [\Delta A_1 \cdots \Delta A_n] \begin{bmatrix} a_{11} & \cdots & & & & & & a_{1m} \\ \cdot & & & & & & & \cdot \\ \cdot & & & & & & & \cdot \\ \cdot & & & & & & & \cdot \\ \cdot & & & & & & & \cdot \\ \cdot & & & & & & & \cdot \\ \cdot & & & & & & & \cdot \\ \cdot & & & & & & & \cdot \\ a_{n1} & \cdots & & & & & & a_{nm} \end{bmatrix}$$

where $a_{ij} = \partial O_j/\partial A_i$ and is evaluated using the uncorrected quantities.)

A further modification to Laplace's method is described in Section 7.4.

7.3 Gauss' Method

In Laplace's method the Taylor series for $\hat{\boldsymbol{\rho}}$ was truncated to allow rough values of $\hat{\boldsymbol{\rho}}'$ and $\hat{\boldsymbol{\rho}}''$ to be found; as a result the observations were not accurately represented, but the law of gravitation was introduced rigorously. In Gauss' method the series to be truncated are the *f* and *g* series of Section 6.8; thus the approximation is introduced into the dynamics of the problem: the geometry remains rigorous.

Since the motion takes place in a plane, we can write

$$\mathbf{r}_2 = c_1 \mathbf{r}_1 + c_3 \mathbf{r}_3. \tag{7.3.1}$$

Then

$$\mathbf{r}_2 \times \mathbf{r}_3 = c_1 \mathbf{r}_1 \times \mathbf{r}_3$$

and

$$c_1 = \frac{[r_2, r_3]}{[r_1, r_3]}, \tag{7.3.2}$$

where $[r_i, r_j]$ is the area of the triangle with sides $\mathbf{r}_i$ and $\mathbf{r}_j$. Similarly

$$c_3 = \frac{[r_1, r_2]}{[r_1, r_3]}. \tag{7.3.3}$$

If the c's are known, (7.3.1) represents three equations for the $\mathbf{r}$'s. These are not linearly independent, but if the relation

$$\mathbf{r} = \boldsymbol{\rho} - \mathbf{R}$$

is used, we have

$$c_1\boldsymbol{\rho}_1 - \boldsymbol{\rho}_2 + c_3\boldsymbol{\rho}_3 = c_1\mathbf{R}_1 - \mathbf{R}_2 + c_3\mathbf{R}_3, \tag{7.3.4}$$

and this represents three linearly independent equations for the $\boldsymbol{\rho}$'s. The problem, then, is to find the c's. (If the values of $\mathbf{R}$ used in forming (7.3.4) are position vectors of the Sun with respect to *the observer*, rather than the center of the Earth, then no correction need be made later for parallax.)

Let $T_1 = k(t_3 - t_2)$, $T_2 = k(t_3 - t_1)$ and $T_3 = k(t_2 - t_1)$. Then $T_3 = -\tau_1$, $T_1 = \tau_3$ and $T_2 = \tau_3 - \tau_1$; all the T's are positive. We have

$$\mathbf{r}_1 = f_1\mathbf{r}_2 + g_1\mathbf{r}_2', \quad \text{and} \quad \mathbf{r}_3 = f_3\mathbf{r}_2 + g_3\mathbf{r}_2',$$

where, approximately,

$$f_1 = 1 - \tfrac{1}{2}\sigma T_3^2, \quad g_1 = -T_3(1 - \tfrac{1}{6}\sigma T_3^2),$$

$$f_3 = 1 - \tfrac{1}{2}\sigma T_1^2, \quad g_3 = T_1(1 - \tfrac{1}{6}\sigma T_1^2),$$

and $\sigma = 1/r_2^3$. (To carry the series further would involve r_2', and this would introduce too many unknowns at present.) Now

$$[r_2, r_3] : [r_1, r_2] : [r_1, r_3] = g_3 : -g_1 : (f_1 g_3 - f_3 g_1).$$

Substituting the c's and expanding in powers of T, we find

$$\left. \begin{array}{l} c_1 = \dfrac{T_1}{T_2}\left\{1 + \dfrac{1}{6}\sigma(T_2^2 - T_1^2)\right\}, \\[2mm] c_3 = \dfrac{T_3}{T_2}\left\{1 + \dfrac{1}{6}\sigma(T_2^2 - T_3^2)\right\}. \end{array} \right] \tag{7.3.6}$$

A better way to find the c's is to use the formula (6.8.9) of Gibbs. Multiplying by $\mathbf{r}_3 \times$ and $\mathbf{r}_1 \times$ results in values for c_1 and c_3, respectively; the final results are

$$c_1 : c_3 : 1 = T_1\left(1 + \dfrac{B_1}{r_1^3}\right) : T_3\left(1 + \dfrac{B_3}{r_3^3}\right) : T_2\left(1 - \dfrac{B_2}{r_2^3}\right),$$

where

$$\left. \begin{array}{l} B_1 = \tfrac{1}{12}\{T_1T_3 + T_2(T_3 - T_1)\}, \\[1mm] B_2 = \tfrac{1}{12}\{T_1T_3 + T_2^2\}, \\[1mm] B_3 = \tfrac{1}{12}\{T_1T_3 - T_2(T_3 - T_1)\}. \end{array} \right] \tag{7.3.7}$$

If we multiply (7.3.4) scalarly by $(\hat{\boldsymbol{\rho}}_1 \times \hat{\boldsymbol{\rho}}_3)$, and substitute for the c's from (7.3.6) or (7.3.7) (in which r_1 and r_3 in the denominators are put equal to r_2), we obtain an equation of the form

$$\rho_2 = A + \frac{B}{r_2^3}. \tag{7.3.8}$$

This can be combined with the cosine formula (7.2.4) to give r_2 and ρ_2 as in Laplace's method.

Once ρ_2 has been found, (7.3.4) gives ρ_1 and ρ_3, and from these $\mathbf{r}_1$, $\mathbf{r}_2$, and $\mathbf{r}_3$ can be found. The elements of the orbit can now be found from $\mathbf{r}_1$ and $\mathbf{r}_3$, or we can find $\mathbf{r}_2'$ by a Gibbsian procedure and use $\mathbf{r}_2$ and $\mathbf{r}_2'$, proceeding according to Laplace's method. However, any orbit computed from the three values of $\mathbf{r}$ will be approximate and must be improved. One approach is to calculate the ratios

$$y_1 = \frac{(r_2, r_3)}{[r_2, r_3]}, \quad y_2 = \frac{(r_1, r_3)}{[r_1, r_3]}, \quad y_3 = \frac{(r_1, r_2)}{[r_1, r_2]},$$

where (r_i, r_j) is the area of the sector.
Now

$$c_1 = \frac{[r_2, r_3]}{[r_1, r_3]} = \frac{(r_2, r_3)}{(r_1, r_3)} \cdot \frac{[r_2, r_3]}{(r_2, r_3)} \cdot \frac{(r_1, r_3)}{[r_1, r_3]}$$

$$= \frac{T_1}{T_2} \frac{y_2}{y_1}. \tag{7.3.9}$$

Similarly,

$$c_3 = \frac{T_3}{T_2} \frac{y_2}{y_3}. \tag{7.3.10}$$

The solution can be revised with these improved c's, and this process can be continued until two successive approximations give the same result. After this the elements are computed.

Alternatively, Gibbs' formulas can be used to obtain improved values for the c's. From the three values of r, a value of r_2' can be found, and this can be used in a more accurate version of (7.3.6) to get better values for the c's.

A more elementary method (but one that can lead to difficulties over the convergence of the iterations) is to use the approximate values of $\mathbf{r}_1$, $\mathbf{r}_2$, and $\mathbf{r}_3$ directly to calculate the c's from

$$c_1 = \frac{|\mathbf{r}_2 \times \mathbf{r}_3|}{|\mathbf{r}_1 \times \mathbf{r}_3|} \quad \text{and} \quad c_3 = \frac{|\mathbf{r}_1 \times \mathbf{r}_2|}{|\mathbf{r}_1 \times \mathbf{r}_3|}.$$

7.4   The Use of the Ratios of the Direction Cosines

Modifications of the methods of Laplace and Gauss, which make use of the ratios of the observed direction cosines, together with the practical formulas, are given by Herget (Ref. 27, pp. 42, 43, 60–62). The modification of Laplace's method is due to Stumpff. The accounts given here are based on those given by Herget.

Let

$$U = \frac{y + Y}{x + X} = \tan \alpha, \tag{7.4.1}$$

$$V = \frac{z + Z}{x + X} = \sec \alpha \tan \delta, \tag{7.4.2}$$

$$P = Y - UX, \tag{7.4.3}$$

and

$$Q = Z - VX. \tag{7.4.4}$$

U and V are observed; X, Y, and Z are found from tables. Solving (7.4.1) for y, we find

$$y = U(x + X) - Y = Ux - P. \tag{7.4.5}$$

Similarly,

$$z = Vx - Q. \tag{7.4.6}$$

Differentiating these two equations twice, we find

$$y' = U'x + Ux' - P',$$
$$y'' = U''x + 2U'x' + Ux'' - P'',$$
$$z' = V'x + Vx' - Q',$$
$$z'' = V''x + 2V'x' + Vx'' - Q''.$$

Now

$$\mathbf{r}'' = -\frac{\mathbf{r}}{r^3}.$$

Substituting the components of this into the equations for y'' and z'', we have

$$U''x + 2U'x' = P'' + \frac{P}{r^3}$$

and

$$V''x + 2V'x' = Q'' + \frac{Q}{r^3}.$$

Let

$$2D = U''V' - V''U'. \tag{7.4.7}$$

Then

$$2Dx = P''V' - Q''U' + \frac{PV' - QU'}{r^3} \tag{7.4.8}$$

and

$$4Dx' = Q''U'' - P''V'' + \frac{U''Q - V''P}{r^3}. \tag{7.4.9}$$

Also

$$r^2 = x^2 + y^2 + z^2$$
$$= (1 + U^2 + V^2)x^2 - 2(UP + VQ)x + (P^2 + Q^2). \tag{7.4.10}$$

Approximate values for U', U'', V', and V'' are found as in Laplace's method for the time of the second observation. Then (7.4.8) and (7.4.10) are solved by iteration to find r_2 and x_2. (For instance, an initial guess for r_2 gives x_2 from (7.4.8), and this value gives another value of r_2 when substituted into (7.4.10); this is then substituted into (7.4.8), and so on.) x_2' is next found from (7.4.9), and then y_2, z_2, y_2', and z_2' can be found. Now $\mathbf{r}_2$ and $\mathbf{r}_2'$ are known, and we proceed as before.

In using the ratios of the direction cosines, we reduce the determinants from the third order to the second. A drawback with ratios is that a denominator may be small; this is due essentially to the choice of reference system, and the trouble can be avoided by changing the reference system, or better, by modifying the ratios that are used. All necessary procedures are given by Herget.

These substitutions can be applied to the basic formulas of Gauss' method. From (7.3.1) we have

$$y_2 = c_1 y_1 + c_3 y_3$$
$$= c_1(U_1 x_1 - P_1) + c_3(U_3 x_3 - P_3),$$

and

$$z_2 = c_1(V_1 x_1 - Q_1) + c_3(V_3 x_3 - Q_3),$$

where, from the definitions,

$$y_2 = U_2 x_2 - P_2$$
$$= U_2(c_1 x_1 + c_3 x_3) - P_2,$$

and

$$z_2 = V_2(c_1 x_1 + c_3 x_3) - Q_2.$$

Eliminating y_2 and z_2, we find

$$c_1(U_1 - U_2)x_1 + c_3(U_3 - U_2)x_3 = c_1 P_1 - P_2 + c_3 P_3 = P$$

and

$$c_1(V_1 - V_2)x_1 + c_3(V_3 - V_2)x_3 = c_1 Q_1 - Q_2 + c_3 Q_3 = Q.$$

Now let

$$D = (U_1 - U_2)(V_3 - V_2) - (U_3 - U_2)(V_1 - V_2).$$

Then, solving for the x's, we find

$$\left. \begin{array}{l} c_1 D x_1 = P(V_3 - V_2) - Q(U_3 - U_2) \\[2mm] c_3 D x_3 = Q(U_1 - U_2) - P(V_1 - V_2). \end{array} \right] \qquad (7.4.11)$$

and

These equations can be solved by using approximate values for the c's, and the solutions used to find better values of the c's, and so on. This is the case in principle; important modifications are given by Herget.

7.5   Parabolic Orbits: Olbers' Method

Consider Euler's equation for parabolic motion, (6.6.7), in the form

$$(r_1 + r_3 + c)^{3/2} - (r_1 + r_3 - c)^{3/2} = 6k(t_3 - t_1) = 6T_2. \qquad (7.5.1)$$

c is the length of the chord $(r_3 - r_1)$. Divide through by $(r_1 + r_3)^{3/2}$ and put

$$\frac{2T_2}{(r_1 + r_2)^{3/2}} = \eta;$$

then

$$\left(1 + \frac{c}{r_1 + r_2}\right)^{3/2} - \left(1 - \frac{c}{r_1 + r_2}\right)^{3/2} = 3\eta.$$

This equation can be solved for $c/(r_1 + r_2)$ as a function of η, $f(\eta)$, say, and f can be tabulated; this has been done in several references (such as Ref. 27).

Now consider (7.3.4) in the form

$$c_1\boldsymbol{\rho}_1 - \boldsymbol{\rho}_2 + c_3\boldsymbol{\rho}_3 = c_1\mathbf{R}_1 - \mathbf{R}_2 + c_3\mathbf{R}_3 = \mathbf{V}. \qquad (7.5.2)$$

Let $\mathbf{U}$ be some vector coplanar with $\mathbf{V}$ and $\boldsymbol{\rho}_2$, which will be specified later. Multiply (7.5.2) scalarly by $(\hat{\boldsymbol{\rho}}_2 \times \mathbf{U})$; then only the terms in ρ_1 and ρ_3 remain, and we have

$$\left. \begin{aligned} \rho_3 &= -\frac{c_1}{c_3}\frac{[\hat{\boldsymbol{\rho}}_1,\hat{\boldsymbol{\rho}}_3,\mathbf{U}]}{[\hat{\boldsymbol{\rho}}_3,\hat{\boldsymbol{\rho}}_2,\mathbf{U}]}\rho_1 \\[4pt] &= M\rho_1, \text{ say.} \end{aligned} \right] \qquad (7.5.3)$$

Now

$$r_1^2 = (\mathbf{R}_1 - \boldsymbol{\rho}_1)^2 = a_1 + b_1\rho_1 + c_1\rho_1^2, \qquad (7.5.4)$$

and

$$\begin{aligned} r_3^2 = (\mathbf{R}_3 - \boldsymbol{\rho}_3)^2 &= (\mathbf{R}_3 - M\rho_1\hat{\boldsymbol{\rho}}_3)^2 \\ &= a_2 + b_2\rho_1 + c_2\rho_1^2. \end{aligned} \qquad (7.5.5)$$

Also

$$\begin{aligned} c^2 = (\mathbf{r}_3 - \mathbf{r}_1)^2 &= \{(M\hat{\boldsymbol{\rho}}_3 - \hat{\boldsymbol{\rho}}_1)\rho_1 - (\mathbf{R}_3 - \mathbf{R}_1)\}^2 \\ &= a_3 + b_3\rho_1 + c_3\rho_1^2. \end{aligned} \qquad (7.5.6)$$

Assuming that $\mathbf{U}$ is known, then M is known, and so are all the coefficients.

Suppose we take a trial value of ρ_1. We can calculate c from (7.5.6); but we can also find η and $f(\eta)$ and then find c from

$$c = (r_1 + r_3)f(\eta).$$

These two values are unlikely to agree; their difference will depend on the initial trial value of ρ_1, so we can call this difference $\Delta(\rho_1)$. By varying ρ_1, we can construct a table of $\Delta(\rho_1)$ as a function of ρ_1. It is unlikely that the function will vanish at a tabular point, but as long as the table includes positive and negative values, it will be possible by inverse interpolation to find the appropriate value of ρ_1 that makes $\Delta(\rho_1)$ zero. Once this ρ_1 has been found, ρ_3 and

r_1 and r_3 can be found as before, and thence the elements. q is found from the value of η, and v, the true anomaly, from

$$\tan^2 \frac{v}{2} = \frac{r - q}{q}.$$

The approximation in this method is introduced into the preliminary value of **U**. We have

$$\mathbf{R}_2 = C_1\mathbf{R}_1 + C_3\mathbf{R}_3,$$

where C_1 and C_3 are the triangle ratios for the motion of the Earth about the Sun. To a good approximation

$$\frac{C_1}{C_3} = \frac{T_1}{T_3}.$$

If the time intervals are short, then a first approximation to the ratios of the c's is also T_1/T_3; so, to this order we can write

$$c_1 = aC_1 \quad \text{and} \quad c_3 = aC_3$$

for some unspecified a. Now

$$\begin{aligned}
\mathbf{V} &= c_1\mathbf{R}_1 - \mathbf{R}_2 + c_3\mathbf{R}_3 \\
&= aC_1\mathbf{R}_1 - \mathbf{R}_2 + aC_3\mathbf{R}_3 \\
&= \mathbf{R}_2(a - 1).
\end{aligned}$$

Hence for our first approximation we can take

$$\mathbf{U} = \mathbf{R}_2 \quad \text{and} \quad \frac{c^2}{c_3} = \frac{T_1}{T_3}.$$

Once r_1 and r_3 are known, r_2 can be found from (7.3.4). When only a rough value of r_2 is known, better values can be found for the c's, and an improved value found. From the final value we can find the predicted right ascension and declination for the time of the second observation, and these are unlikely to agree with the observed values. To get rid of the discrepancies, it is possible to use the improved values of the c's to find **V**, and then to take $\mathbf{U} = \mathbf{V}$ and repeat the solution. Or the solution might be repeated with slightly different values of M, and the best result found by inverse interpolation.

Another method, due to Strömgren, the method of "false position", is described by Herget as follows:

"If **U** is held fixed, then M may be considered as a function of $\hat{\rho}_2$. Since $\hat{\rho}_2$(observed) produces a solution that yields the middle position at $\hat{\rho}_2$(computed), then if we use a fictitious

$$\hat{\rho}_2 = 2\hat{\rho}_2(\text{observed}) - \hat{\rho}_2(\text{computed})$$

in M, we may expect to get a solution that yields the middle position at $\hat{\rho}_2$(observed). Therefore M is recomputed exactly as before, except for the use of this fictitious $\hat{\rho}_2$ (i.e., the 'false position'), and the solution is repeated".

It may happen that the residuals will refuse to disappear; this will be due to the fact that the orbit is not parabolic. Three observations provide, in general, too many quantities for the five unknowns of a parabolic orbit, so that this type of orbit cannot necessarily be imposed. However, when a comet is discovered, it will probably be moving in a nearly parabolic orbit. Certainly a preliminary solution for a parabolic orbit may provide a useful ephemeris for searching for the object shortly after discovery, but it would be useless to attempt to apply a parabolic orbit to a newly found minor planet. It is interesting to note that when Uranus was discovered, it was at first assumed to be a comet and was not recognized as a planet until attempts to represent its orbit as a parabola had failed.

7.6 Circular Orbits

This section is included mainly for the sake of completeness. Since only four elements are needed to specify a circular orbit, two observations will be adequate. But a preliminary circular orbit found from only two observations is unlikely to be of any value unless the actual orbit has small eccentricity. This might be the case for a minor planet; it would not be so for a comet.

Let the times of observation be t_1 and t_2, and let

$$T = k(t_2 - t_1).$$

During the time from t_1 to t_2, the body will have revolved through an angle M about the Sun where

$$\frac{M}{2\pi} = \frac{T}{\text{period}}.$$

But the period is $2\pi a^{3/2}$; so

$$M = Ta^{-3/2}. \tag{7.6.1}$$

Now

$$r_1 = r_2 = a,$$

so

$$|\mathbf{r}_1 \times \mathbf{r}_2| = a^2 \sin M$$

$$= a^2(M - \tfrac{1}{6}M^3 + \cdots)$$

$$= \sqrt{a}\,T(1 - \frac{1}{6}\frac{T^2}{a^3} + \frac{1}{120}\frac{T^4}{a^6} - \cdots). \tag{7.6.2}$$

Also, since $r_1^2 = a^2 = r_2^2$,

$$\rho_1^2 - 2R_1\rho_1 \cos\psi_1 + R_1^2 = a^2 = \rho_2^2 - 2R_2\rho_2 \cos\psi_2 + R_2^2. \tag{7.6.3}$$

If a value of ρ_1 is assumed, then a, ρ_2, $\mathbf{r}_1$, and $\mathbf{r}_2$ can be found. From these each side of (7.6.2) can be calculated independently. These are unlikely to be the same, but if their difference is tabulated as a function of ρ_1, inverse interpolation can be used to find the value that makes this difference zero so that (7.6.2) is satisfied. This gives the solution.

Problems

1. Show how the value of cos ψ can be calculated directly from the observations and from appropriate tables.
2. Discuss the problem of orbit determination, using (7.2.6) instead of (7.1.2). Show the relationships between the determinants of (7.2.6) and quantities such as κ or $\mathbf{R} \cdot \hat{\mathbf{n}}$.
3. Consider the solution of (7.2.11). If an approximate value ϕ_0 is found, show that a correction $\Delta\phi_0$ can be calculated from

$$\Delta\phi_0 = -\frac{\sin^4 \phi_0 - M \sin(\phi_0 + m)}{4 \sin^3 \phi_0 \cos \phi_0 - M \cos(\phi_0 + m)}.$$

Discuss the case when the denominator is small.
4. Show that the equations (7.2.4) and (7.2.6) can be solved by substituting trial values of ρ into (7.2.4) to find r and then substituting this value of r into (7.2.6) to find ρ. Use this method to solve

$$r^2 = 0.9734 + 1.1493\rho + \rho^2,$$

$$\rho = 2.703 - \frac{2.596}{r^3}.$$

(The answer is $\rho = 2.631$.)
5. Show that the condition for (7.2.11) to have a double root is

$$4 \sin^3 \phi \cos \phi - M \cos(\phi + m) = 0.$$

Hence show that m should satisfy the inequality

$$9 - 16 \tan^2 m \geqslant 0,$$

for there to be a possible solution to the problem, and find the possible limits of m and the corresponding limits of ϕ. Finally show that the maximum value of M which can result in (7.2.11) having three real roots is approximately 1.431.
6. Prove the inequality (7.2.12) when A is negative.
7. Prove that the left-hand side of (7.2.12) changes sign on crossing a boundary in Figure 7.6, and that the solution for ρ is unique in the shaded region of the figure.
8. Find the octic equation for ρ_2 by eliminating r_2 between (7.2.4) and (7.2.6).
9. Consider the solution of (7.2.4) and (7.2.6) as follows: Take, for convenience, $R = 1$, and (7.2.6) in the form

$$l\rho = 1 - \frac{1}{r^3}.$$

Eliminate ρ, obtaining an octic in r, in which the coefficients of r^i for $i = 1$, 2, 4, 5, 7 are zero. Show that if the coefficient of r^8 is positive, then that of r^6 is negative and that of r^3 is positive. Hence, from the theory of equations, show that the octic has three positive, one negative, and four complex roots. Show that $r = 1$ is a real root, and that if the other two positive roots lie on either side of 1, then it is possible to distinguish between them in the solution. Show that the condition for this is that

$$l(l - 3 \cos \psi) < 0.$$

10. Suppose we have three observations of λ, λ_1, λ_2, and λ_3, and that values λ_0, λ_0' and λ_0'', for time t_0 are found by assuming

$$\lambda = \lambda_0 + \lambda_0' \tau_0 + \tfrac{1}{2} \lambda_0'' \tau_0^2.$$

Better values, $\lambda_0 + \Delta \lambda_0$, etc., would be found if we could assume

$$\lambda = \lambda_0 + \lambda_0' \tau_0 + \tfrac{1}{2} \lambda_0'' \tau_0^2 + \tfrac{1}{6} \lambda_0''' \tau_0^3 + \tfrac{1}{24} \lambda_0'''' \tau_0^4.$$

Find $\Delta \lambda_0$, $\Delta \lambda_0'$, and $\Delta \lambda_0''$ in terms of λ_0''' and λ_0'''', and discuss the errors involved in finding λ_0, λ_0', and λ_0'' from three observations (of which t_0 need not be a time of observation). Show that the error in λ_0'' is minimized if

$$\tau_1 + \tau_2 + \tau_3 = 0$$

and find the corresponding value of t_0.

11. Suppose we have four observations of λ from which we want to find values of λ_0, λ_0', and λ_0''. Show that the error in λ_0'' is minimized if

$$\sum_{i<j=1}^{4} \tau_i \tau_j = 0.$$

Show that this leads to a quadratic in t_0 with real roots.

12. Given four observations, show that ρ can be found in the following way: From (7.2.6) and (7.2.7) we can find an expression of the form $\rho' = B\rho$; B depends on the derivatives of the direction cosines up to the second. Now, by differentiating this, we find $\rho'' = (B' + B^2)\rho$; B' involves third derivatives, but these can be found from four observations. Now find another relation between ρ and ρ'' (using (7.2.3)) of the form $\rho'' = C + D\rho$. Hence solve for ρ by eliminating ρ''.

13. Find approximations for the first and second derivatives of the direction cosines for the time of the second observation for the following set of observations:

Date			
Nov. 7.8205	$+0.902\,897$	$+0.060\,606$	$+0.425\,562$
Nov. 26.7480	$+0.922\,476$	$+0.051\,857$	$+0.382\,554$
Dec. 18.6262	$+0.934\,768$	$+0.080\,227$	$+0.346\,080$.

(*Answer:* $\lambda' = +0.047\,391$ $\mu' = +0.020\,560$ $\nu' = -0.115\,775$
$\lambda'' = -0.078\,250$ $\mu'' = +0.291\,339$ $\nu'' = +0.100\,251$)

14. Using an almanac choose three positions from the ephemeris of a minor planet. From the elements, work out the values of ρ, $\mathbf{r}$, and $\mathbf{r}'$ for the second of these positions. Now apply Laplace's method, and see how accurately it predicts these values at the first approximation. Next use extra positions from the ephemeris to find improved values for $\hat{\rho}'$ and $\hat{\rho}''$, and repeat the comparison.

15. Using the same three positions as in problem 14, find $\mathbf{r}_1$, $\mathbf{r}_2$, and $\mathbf{r}_3$ from the elements, and also accurate values for the c's. Now find out how accurately the orbit is found by Gauss' method at the first approximation.

16. Establish the following values for the c's:

$$c_1 = \frac{T_1}{T_2}\left\{1 + \frac{1}{6}\sigma(T_2^2 - T_1^2) + \frac{1}{4}\sigma\tau T_3(T_2 T_3 - T_1^2) + \cdots\right\},$$

$$c_3 = \frac{T_3}{T_2}\left\{1 + \frac{1}{6}\sigma(T_2^2 - T_3^2) - \frac{1}{4}\sigma\tau T_1(T_2 T_1 - T_3^2) + \cdots\right\},$$

where

$$\sigma = \frac{1}{r_2^3} \quad \text{and} \quad \tau = \frac{r_2'}{r_2}.$$

17. Show that from Euler's equation for parabolic motion we have

$$\frac{c}{r_1 + r_3} = \eta\zeta$$

where

$$\zeta = 1 + \tfrac{1}{24}\eta^2 + \tfrac{5}{384}\eta^4 + 0(\eta^6).$$

18. List, in order of application, the equations to be used in computing the elements of a parabolic orbit from the values of $\mathbf{r}_1$ and $\mathbf{r}_3$.

19. If the apparent path of a body on the celestial sphere has a point of inflection, prove that the tangent at that point passes through the Sun.

20. If the apparent path of a body on the celestial sphere has a loop, prove that (to the degree of approximation attained by assuming that the ratio of the sectors is equal to the ratio of the triangles) the great circle joining any point of the loop to the corresponding position of the Sun passes through the double point. Hence deduce a theorem (due to Klinkerfues) that if any three points on a loop be joined to the corresponding positions of the Sun, the three great circles will meet in one point, which is also a point on the apparent orbit. Comment on the degree of approximation, with reference to Figure 7.1.

21. Discuss the adaptation of the methods of orbit determination described in this chapter to apply to satellite orbits round the Earth.

22. Discuss ways in which observations of radial velocity and perhaps range can be used in the determination of orbits.

23. Given r_1, r_2, and r_3, show that

$$r_2 = c_1r_1 + c_3r_3,$$

and that if this equation is multiplied by $\cdot\hat{P}$, then an equation relating p and e results. Using the relation $\hat{Q} = \hat{h} \times \hat{P}$, and expressing $\hat{h}$ in terms of r_1 and r_3, show how an equation for e can be found. Find an expression for $\hat{P}$, and show how the remaining elements can be found.

Chapter 8 ** THE THREE-BODY PROBLEM

8.1 The Restricted Three-Body Problem: Jacobi's Integral

The general problem of the motion of three bodies (assumed to be point masses), subject only to their mutual gravitational attractions has not been solved, although many particular solutions have been found. We shall start with a discussion of the "restricted three-body problem"; here two bodies of finite mass revolve around one another in circular orbits, and a third body of infinitesimal mass moves in their field: this situation is approximately realized in many instances in the solar system.

Figure 8.1

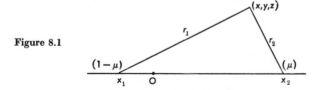

Let the origin be at the center of mass of the two finite masses and take axes rotating with the masses, such that they lie along the x-axis. Take the unit of mass to be the sum of their masses, and let the separate masses be μ and $(1 - \mu)$, where $\mu \leqslant \frac{1}{2}$. The axes will be rotating with constant angular velocity, ω, say, and the bodies will be fixed at $(x_2,0,0)$ and $(x_1,0,0)$, where x_1 is negative. (See Figure 8.1.) Let the unit of distance be $(-x_1 + x_2)$, and let the unit of time be such as to make $k = 1$. Then, in these units,

$$\omega = k \sqrt{\frac{(1 - \mu) + \mu}{(-x_1 + x_2)^3}}$$
$$= 1.$$

Let the infinitesimal mass be at (x,y,z) and let

$$(x - x_1)^2 + y^2 + z^2 = r_1^2$$

187

and

$$(x - x_2)^2 + y^2 + z^2 = r_2^2.$$

If v is the speed of the infinitesimal mass with respect to the moving axes,

$$v^2 = \dot{x}^2 + \dot{y}^2 + \dot{z}^2$$

and the modified energy integral (see (3.4.8)) is

$$v^2 = x^2 + y^2 + \frac{2(1 - \mu)}{r_1} + \frac{2\mu}{r_2} - C, \qquad (8.1.1)$$

where C is a constant. (8.1.1) is *Jacobi's integral*.

Five more integrals are needed to complete the solution (angular momentum obviously tells us nothing here), but these are not known. However, many properties of the motion can be found from a discussion of (8.1.1), and the following few sections will be devoted to this.

8.2   Tisserand's Criterion for the Identification of Comets

Let the infinitesimal mass have position vector $\mathbf{r}'$ with respect to nonrotating axes, with the same origin as before; then if $\hat{\mathbf{z}}$ is the axis of rotation,

$$\frac{d\mathbf{r}}{dt} = \frac{d\mathbf{r}'}{dt} - \hat{\mathbf{z}} \times \boldsymbol{\rho},$$

where $\boldsymbol{\rho}$ is the vector with components $(x',y',0)$ or $(x,y,0)$. Then

$$\begin{aligned}
\left(\frac{d\mathbf{r}}{dt}\right)^2 &= \left(\frac{d\mathbf{r}'}{dt}\right)^2 - 2\left(\frac{d\mathbf{r}'}{dt}\right)\cdot(\hat{\mathbf{z}} \times \boldsymbol{\rho}) + \rho^2 \\
&= \left(\frac{d\mathbf{r}'}{dt}\right)^2 - 2\hat{\mathbf{z}}\cdot\left(\boldsymbol{\rho} \times \frac{d\mathbf{r}'}{dt}\right) + \rho^2 \\
&= \left(\frac{d\mathbf{r}'}{dt}\right)^2 - 2\hat{\mathbf{z}}\cdot\left(\mathbf{r}' \times \frac{d\mathbf{r}'}{dt}\right) + x^2 + y^2.
\end{aligned}$$

Jacobi's integral becomes

$$\dot{\mathbf{r}}'^2 - 2\hat{\mathbf{z}}\cdot(\mathbf{r}' \times \dot{\mathbf{r}}') = \frac{2(1 - \mu)}{r_1} + \frac{2\mu}{r_2} - C. \qquad (8.2.1)$$

Now let the infinitesimal mass be a periodic comet, and $(1 - \mu)$ and μ the masses of the Sun and Jupiter, respectively, so that $\mu \sim 10^{-3}$. If we find the position and velocity of the comet at any time, from observations, we shall calculate elements from

$$\dot{\mathbf{r}}'^2 = \frac{2}{r} - \frac{1}{a}$$

and

$$\hat{\mathbf{z}}\cdot(\mathbf{r}' \times \dot{\mathbf{r}}') = \hat{\mathbf{z}}\cdot\mathbf{h} = \sqrt{a(1 - e^2)}\cos i.$$

Substituting these expressions into (8.2.1), we find

$$\frac{1}{a} + 2\sqrt{a(1-e^2)}\cos i = \frac{2}{r} - \frac{2(1-\mu)}{r_1} - \frac{2\mu}{r_2} + C.$$

Now r is nearly equal to r_1 so that, approximately,

$$\frac{1}{a} + 2\sqrt{a(1-e^2)}\cos i = 2\mu\left(\frac{1}{r_1} - \frac{1}{r_2}\right) + C. \tag{8.2.2}$$

Suppose the comet to be observed before and after a close approach to Jupiter; provided the comet is far from Jupiter when observed, r_1 and r_2 will be large and nearly equal, and we have approximately

$$\frac{1}{a} + 2\sqrt{a(1-e^2)}\cos i = C. \tag{8.2.3}$$

Now, because of perturbations by Jupiter, the elements of the comet will have changed, and it is possible that they will have changed so considerably that identification is difficult (i.e., we are not sure whether it is the old comet or a new one). But C is constant throughout, so if a_1, e_1, i_1 refer to the old orbit and a_2, e_2, i_2 to the new orbit, we must have approximately

$$\frac{1}{a_1} + 2\sqrt{a_1(1-e_1^2)}\cos i_1 = \frac{1}{a_2} + 2\sqrt{a_2(1-e_2^2)}\cos i_2.$$

This criterion is due to Tisserand.

8.3   The Surfaces of Zero Relative Velocity

If we put $v = 0$ in (8.1.1), we have the equation

$$x^2 + y^2 + \frac{2(1-\mu)}{r_1} + \frac{2\mu}{r_2} = C. \tag{8.3.1}$$

For some value of C this will be the locus of surfaces in space to be described shortly. If we consider (8.1.1) as a function of v^2, then we see that v^2 changes sign when a surface is crossed (as long as the crossing does not take place at a double point). Hence the motion can take place on one side of the surface but not on the other. This is similar to the theorem in the problem of two bodies, that the finite motion is restricted within a circle of radius $2a$ (also deduced from the energy integral).

The construction of the surfaces is described in some detail in Moulton (Ref. 18, pp. 281–290); we shall give only a rough description here. If C is large (it must, of course, be positive), we have the three alternatives:

$$x^2 + y^2 = C \quad \text{(nearly)}$$

or

$$r_1 \text{ is very small}$$

or

$$r_2 \text{ is very small.}$$

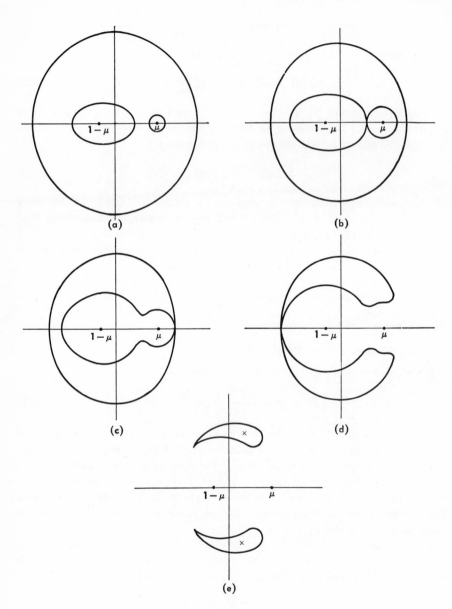

Figure 8.2

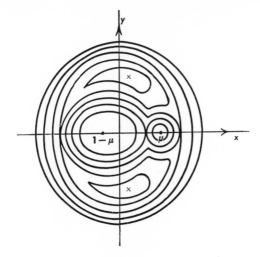

Figure 8.3

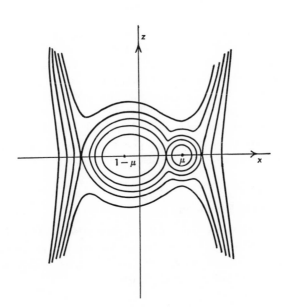

Figure 8.4

Hence we have, roughly, a cylinder with circular cross-section, parallel to the z-axis, and two small ovoids surrounding the finite masses. The larger ovoid is around the heavier mass, $1 - \mu$. For this value of C the motion of the infinitesimal body can take place outside the cylinder or inside one of the ovoids. The situation in the x-y plane is illustrated in Figure 8.2a.

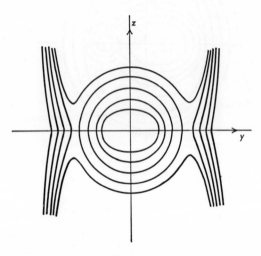

Figure 8.5

Now let C decrease. The "cylinder" shrinks (and acquires a "waist" in the x-y plane), and the ovoids expand until they coalesce; this will take place in the x-y plane at a point closer to μ than to $1 - \mu$. This is illustrated in Figure 8.2b.

As C decreases further, the wall of the cylinder meets the smaller and later the larger of the ovoids (see Figures 8.2c and 8.2d). Finally we are left with two tadpole-like shapes that eventually shrink to points (see Figure 8.2e). The parts of Figure 8.2 can be combined into one, and this is shown in Figure 8.3. Similar sections in the x-z and y-z planes are shown in Figures 8.4 and 8.5.

These limiting surfaces were first discussed by Hill in relation to the motion of the Moon.

8.4 The Positions of Equilibrium

All the double points involved in the surfaces discussed in Section 8.3 occur in the x-y plane. We might expect these to have some significance in the solution, and they are, in fact, positions of equilibrium, as we shall now show.

Let V be the "modified potential"; then

$$-V = \frac{1}{2}(x^2 + y^2) + \frac{1 - \mu}{r_1} + \frac{\mu}{r_2}. \tag{8.4.1}$$

The equation of motion is

$$\ddot{\mathbf{r}} + \hat{\mathbf{z}} \times \dot{\boldsymbol{\rho}} = -\nabla V. \tag{8.4.2}$$

Suppose the infinitesimal body to be initially at rest (with respect to the rotating axes); it will start to move off in the direction of $-\nabla V$.

The surfaces described in Section 8.3 are given by the function

$$F(x,y,z) \equiv V + \tfrac{1}{2}C = 0. \tag{8.4.3}$$

Now the normal at any point on a surface has direction cosines that are proportional to $\partial F/\partial x$, $\partial F/\partial y$, and $\partial F/\partial z$, so it is in the direction of $-\nabla V$. Therefore the infinitesimal body, initially at rest, will start to move off in the direction of the normal to the surface through the point which it occupies. But suppose this to be a double point; then there is not a unique normal. The body has no reason for moving off in one direction rather than another, and unless it receives a small nudge it will stay where it is. (This is similar to the situation of the student, who, having two lectures of equal importance at the same time, goes to neither.) The double points are therefore positions of equilibrium.

The double points occur at stationary values of F, the condition for this being

$$\frac{\partial F}{\partial x} = \frac{\partial F}{\partial y} = \frac{\partial F}{\partial z} = 0.$$

Now we have

$$\frac{\partial F}{\partial z} \equiv z \left(\frac{1 - \mu}{r_1^3} + \frac{\mu}{r_2^3} \right)$$

so that any double point occurs in the x-y plane, for which $z = 0$. Then we can put $z = 0$, and find the conditions for $\partial F/\partial x = 0$ and $\partial F/\partial y = 0$. They are

$$x - (1 - \mu)\frac{x - x_1}{r_1^3} - \mu \frac{x - x_2}{r_2^3} = 0 \tag{8.4.4}$$

and

$$y - (1 - \mu)\frac{y}{r_1^3} - \mu \frac{y}{r_2^3} = 0. \tag{8.4.5}$$

(8.4.5) is satisfied if $y = 0$, and in this case (8.4.4) becomes

$$x - (1 - \mu)\frac{x - x_1}{|x - x_1|^3} - \mu \frac{x - x_2}{|x - x_2|^3} = 0. \tag{8.4.6}$$

(Here $|a|$ indicates that the positive value of a is used.) The left-hand side of (8.4.6), considered as a function of x, has a graph of the form shown in Figure 8.6. The verification of this graph (after the fashion of that of Figure 5.6) is left as an exercise to the student. There are, then, three real roots, and this was to be expected from the three double points on the x-axis appearing in Figure 8.3.

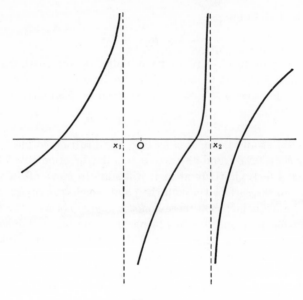

Figure 8.6

Now consider what happens when $y \neq 0$. (8.4.5) becomes

$$1 - \frac{1 - \mu}{r_1^3} - \frac{\mu}{r_2^3} = 0.$$

Multiply this by $(x - x_2)$ and $(x - x_1)$ and subtract the products separately from (8.4.4). We find

$$x_2 - (1 - \mu) \frac{x_2 - x_1}{r_1^3} = 0$$

and

$$x_1 - \mu \frac{x_1 - x_2}{r_1^3} = 0.$$

But $x_2 = 1 - \mu$ and $x_1 = -\mu$, since the origin is at the center of mass of the finite masses, so that these equations reduce to

$$r_1 = r_2 = 1.$$

These points of equilibrium form equilateral triangles in the x-y plane with the two finite masses.

8.5 The Stability of the Points of Equilibrium

In the preceding section we argued that the infinitesimal body would remain at a double point unless it received a slight nudge. If, for *any* such nudge, the motion that follows consists of small oscillations about the double point, the position of equilibrium is said to be *stable*; if, for *some* possible nudges, the body recedes indefinitely from the double point, the position is *unstable*. Therefore, to find out whether a position of equilibrium found above is stable, we must investigate the motion of the infinitesimal body if it is slightly displaced from that position. In practice (unless we assume the three bodies to be totally isolated) this will be constantly happening as a result of perturbations.

Let the position of equilibrium be at (x,y,z) and let the body be displaced to $(x + \xi, y + \eta, z + \zeta)$, where ξ, η, and ζ are small; we assume, until it may be proved to the contrary, that these quantities remain small. If we neglect their squares and products and remember that $\partial V/\partial x = 0$, etc., at (x,y,z), then the equations of motion are

$$\left. \begin{array}{l} \ddot{\xi} - 2\dot{\eta} = -\xi V_{xx} - \eta V_{xy} - \zeta V_{xz}, \\ \ddot{\eta} + 2\dot{\xi} = -\xi V_{yx} - \eta V_{yy} - \zeta V_{yz}, \\ \ddot{\zeta} \qquad = -\xi V_{zx} - \eta V_{zy} - \zeta V_{zz}, \end{array} \right\} \qquad (8.5.1)$$

where V_{yz} stands for $\partial^2 V/\partial y\,\partial z$, etc., and these quantities are evaluated at the point of equilibrium so that they have constant values.

Now

$$-V = \tfrac{1}{2}(x^2 + y^2) + (1 - \mu)\{(x - x_1)^2 + y^2 + z^2\}^{-1/2} + \mu\{(x - x_2)^2 + y^2 + z^2\}^{-1/2}.$$

Define α and β by

$$\alpha = \frac{1 - \mu}{r_1^3} + \frac{\mu}{r_2^3}$$

and

$$\beta = \frac{1 - \mu}{r_1^5} + \frac{\mu}{r_2^5};$$

then we find

$$V_{xx} = -1 + \alpha - 3(1 - \mu)\frac{(x - x_1)^2}{r_1^5} - 3\mu\frac{(x - x_2)^2}{r_2^5},$$

$$V_{yy} = -1 + \alpha - 3y^2\beta,$$

$$V_{zz} = \qquad + \alpha - 3z^2\beta,$$

$$V_{yz} = -3yz\beta, \quad V_{zx} = -3zx\beta, \quad V_{xy} = -3xy\beta.$$

For a straight-line solution for which $y = z = 0$ and $x = x_0$, say, we have

$$r_1^2 = (x_0 - x_1)^2 \quad \text{and} \quad r_2^2 = (x_0 - x_2)^2.$$

Also

$$V_{yz} = V_{zx} = V_{xy} = 0,$$

so the equations of motion following a small displacement are

$$\ddot{\xi} - 2\dot{\eta} = \xi(1 + 2\alpha),$$

$$\ddot{\eta} + 2\dot{\xi} = \eta(1 - \alpha),$$

$$\ddot{\zeta} \qquad = -\zeta\alpha.$$

Since α is positive, the oscillations in the z-direction are finite and small, and therefore stable, and we can concentrate on the first two equations.

We try a solution $\xi = Ke^{\lambda t}$, $\eta = Le^{\lambda t}$. If λ is purely imaginary, then the solution can be put entirely in the form of sines and cosines, and the motion, consisting of finite oscillations, will be stable. Otherwise the solution must involve hyperbolic functions; then ξ and η will increase without limit, and the motion is unstable. Substituting the trial solutions into the equations of motion, we have

$$K\lambda^2 - 2L\lambda = K(1 + 2\alpha)$$

and

$$L\lambda^2 + 2K\lambda = L(1 - \alpha).$$

Eliminating K and L, we find

$$\begin{vmatrix} \lambda^2 - (1 + 2\alpha) & -2\lambda \\ 2\lambda & \lambda^2 - (1 - \alpha) \end{vmatrix} = 0$$

or

$$\lambda^4 + \lambda^2(2 - \alpha) + (1 + 2\alpha)(1 - \alpha) = 0.$$

For stability λ must be purely imaginary so that there must be two real negative roots for λ^2; for this to be so, we must at least have

$$1 - \alpha > 0,$$

since the product of the roots must be positive, or

$$1 - \frac{1}{r_1^3} + \mu \left(\frac{1}{r_1^3} - \frac{1}{r_2^3} \right) > 0.$$

From Figure 8.6 we see that (8.4.6) has:

a positive root greater than x_2, when r_1 is greater than r_2;

a positive root between x_1 and x_2, when r_1 is greater than r_2;

a negative root less than x_1, when r_1 is less than r_2.

Now (8.4.6) can be written in the form

$$x_0(1 - \alpha) + (1 - \mu) \frac{x_1}{r_1^3} + \mu \frac{x_2}{r_2^3} = 0$$

or, since $x_1 = -\mu$ and $x_2 = 1 - \mu$,

$$x_0(1 - \alpha) - \mu(1 - \mu) \left\{ \frac{1}{r_1^3} - \frac{1}{r_2^3} \right\} = 0.$$

So

$$(1 - \alpha) = \frac{\mu(1 - \mu)}{x_0} \left\{ \frac{1}{r_1^3} - \frac{1}{r_2^3} \right\}.$$

It is clear from inspection that for each solution $(1 - \alpha)$ is negative. Therefore the straight-line solutions are unstable. Actually some displacements lead to finite oscillations (such as the oscillations in the z-direction), but for stability all possible displacements must lead to these. When testing for stability, it is not sufficient to try some special displacements.

If we assume that the orbit of the Earth around the Sun is circular, we can find the three straight-line positions of equilibrium, one of which is on the side of the Earth away from the Sun. It has been argued that meteoric material may be temporarily trapped in this position and that this explains a very faint glow seen in the night sky in a position exactly opposite the (invisible) Sun, called the *gegenschein*; the glow would be the reflection of sunlight from the trapped material. A meteoric particle trapped in this position might remain there for a short time if it were lucky in its perturbations, but it would eventually move away. The student may object to the statement made earlier that the particle would "recede indefinitely" from the position of equilibrium; the objection is valid, since in this example the displaced meteoric material will remain indefinitely within the solar system. But the phrase is intended to apply only to the perturbed equations (8.5.1), which are approximate, and not necessarily to motion farther afield.

Next consider the stability of the triangular solutions. We have $r_1 = r_2 = 1$, so that

$$x = \frac{1}{2}(1 - 2\mu), \quad y = \pm \frac{\sqrt{3}}{2}, \quad \text{and} \quad z = 0.$$

We can take the positive sign for y without loss of generality. The values of V_{ij} that are not zero are

$$V_{xx} = -\frac{3}{4},$$

$$V_{yy} = -\frac{9}{4},$$

$$V_{zz} = 1,$$

$$V_{xy} = -\frac{3\sqrt{3}}{4}(1 - 2\mu).$$

The equations of motion are

$$\ddot{\xi} - 2\dot{\eta} = \frac{3}{4}\xi + \frac{3\sqrt{3}}{4}(1 - 2\mu)\eta,$$

$$\ddot{\eta} + 2\dot{\xi} = \frac{9}{4}\eta + \frac{3\sqrt{3}}{4}(1 - 2\mu)\xi,$$

$$\ddot{\zeta} \qquad = -\zeta.$$

The oscillations in the z-direction are stable, the period being the same as that of the revolution of the finite bodies. To investigate the first two equations, we again try $\xi = Ke^{\lambda t}$, $\eta = Le^{\lambda t}$. Substituting, and eliminating K and L as before, we find

$$\lambda^4 + \lambda^2 + \frac{27}{4}\mu(1 - \mu) = 0.$$

Considered as a quadratic for λ^2, this equation must have real negative roots for stability. But the sum of the roots is negative and their product is positive; so, provided the roots are real, they must be negative. Hence, to find the condition for stability, it is sufficient to find the condition for real roots. This is

$$1 - 4\cdot\frac{27}{4}\mu(1 - \mu) > 0$$

or

$$1 - 27\mu(1 - \mu) > 0.$$

Putting the left-hand side equal to ϵ, and solving the resulting quadratic for μ, we find

$$\mu = \frac{1}{2} \pm \sqrt{\frac{23 + 4\epsilon}{108}}.$$

Since $\mu \leqslant \frac{1}{2}$, we take the lower sign. The condition for stability is $\epsilon > 0$, or

$$\mu < \frac{1}{2} - \sqrt{\frac{23}{108}} = 0.0385.$$

This condition is satisfied for Jupiter and the Sun, and in fact we do find some minor planets, called *the Trojans*, oscillating about the triangular positions. These oscillations are considerable, amounting to as much as 20° in longitude, so that the small oscillations considered above cannot be applied to the actual motion; they merely ensure stability.

8.6   The Lagrangian Solutions for the Motion of Three Finite Bodies

The equations of motion for three finite bodies are

$$\left.\begin{array}{l}
\ddot{\mathbf{r}}_1 = -m_2\dfrac{\mathbf{r}_1 - \mathbf{r}_2}{r_{12}^3} - m_3\dfrac{\mathbf{r}_1 - \mathbf{r}_3}{r_{13}^3}, \\[2ex]
\ddot{\mathbf{r}}_2 = -m_3\dfrac{\mathbf{r}_2 - \mathbf{r}_3}{r_{23}^3} - m_1\dfrac{\mathbf{r}_2 - \mathbf{r}_1}{r_{21}^3}, \\[2ex]
\ddot{\mathbf{r}}_3 = -m_1\dfrac{\mathbf{r}_3 - \mathbf{r}_1}{r_{31}^3} - m_2\dfrac{\mathbf{r}_3 - \mathbf{r}_2}{r_{32}^3}.
\end{array}\right\} \qquad (8.6.1)$$

Here $r_{ij} = |\mathbf{r}_j - \mathbf{r}_i|$; the unit of time is chosen to make $k = 1$.

If the equations are multiplied by m_1, m_2, and m_3, respectively, and added, the terms on the right-hand side vanish, and the equation can be integrated to yield the fact that the center of mass of the three bodies moves in a straight line with constant speed. We can, then, take the center of mass as a new origin, so that

$$m_1\mathbf{r}_1 + m_2\mathbf{r}_2 + m_3\mathbf{r}_3 = 0. \tag{8.6.2}$$

We shall look for solutions for which the geometrical form of the configuration remains the same. The scale can change and the figure can rotate, but that is all. We have already found two such solutions for the restricted three-body problem, where the scale remains constant. We shall start by seeing whether the equations (8.6.1) can be satisfied if the configuration is an equilateral triangle. In this case,

$$r_{23} = r_{31} = r_{12} = r,$$

where r need not be constant. On substitution, the first equation of (8.6.1) becomes

$$\ddot{\mathbf{r}}_1 = -\frac{1}{r^3}[m_2(\mathbf{r}_1 - \mathbf{r}_2) + m_3(\mathbf{r}_1 - \mathbf{r}_3)]. \tag{8.6.3}$$

From (8.6.2) we have

$$m_2(\mathbf{r}_1 - \mathbf{r}_2) + m_3(\mathbf{r}_1 - \mathbf{r}_3) = \mathbf{r}_1(m_1 + m_2 + m_3) \tag{8.6.4}$$

so that (8.6.3) becomes

$$\ddot{\mathbf{r}}_1 = -(m_1 + m_2 + m_3)\frac{\mathbf{r}_1}{r^3}. \tag{8.6.5}$$

Squaring (8.6.4), we find

$$\mathbf{r}_1^2(m_1 + m_2 + m_3)^2 = m_2^2 r_{12}^2 + 2m_2 m_3 r_{12} r_{13} \cos 60° + m_3^2 r_{13}^2$$
$$= r^2(m_2^2 + m_2 m_3 + m_3^2).$$

So (8.6.5) becomes

$$\ddot{\mathbf{r}}_1 = -M_1 \frac{\mathbf{r}_1}{r_1^3}, \tag{8.6.6}$$

where

$$M_1 = \frac{(m_2^2 + m_2 m_3 + m_3^2)^{3/2}}{(m_1 + m_2 + m_3)^2}.$$

Hence m_1 moves in a central orbit around the fixed center of mass as though a mass M_1 were located there; it will continue to do so as long as the configuration of the three bodies is maintained. Similar results follow for the other two bodies. Then, as long as the initial conditions are right, the equations of motion will ensure that the figure remains an equilateral triangle. Initially, we must obviously have the masses at the apices of an equilateral triangle, and the velocities must be such as to cause the figure to remain an equilateral triangle, independently of the accelerations caused by the gravitational forces. For this to be so, the initial velocities must be proportional to the distances r_i, and must make equal angles with the directions $\hat{\mathbf{r}}_i$.

We notice that in the case considered above, the resultant force $\mathbf{F}_i$ acting on m_i passes through the center of mass, and that if F_i is force per unit mass, then

$$F_1 : F_2 : F_3 = r_1 : r_2 : r_3. \qquad (8.6.7)$$

These two conditions, together with those ensuring that the initial conditions are right, are necessary and sufficient for the configuration of masses to remain in the same geometrical form, as we shall now show.

We start by showing that the first condition is necessary. The fact that the shape of the configuration is maintained means that the relative distances are given by

$$\frac{r_{23}}{\mathring{r}_{23}} = \frac{r_{31}}{\mathring{r}_{31}} = \frac{r_{12}}{\mathring{r}_{12}} = \lambda(t),$$

where the zero superscript indicates the value at t_0. (8.6.4) is true generally; squaring both sides we find

$$(m_1 + m_2 + m_3)^2 r_1^2 = m_2^2 r_{12}^2 + m_3^2 r_{13}^2 + 2 m_2 m_3 r_{12} r_{13} \cos \theta_{23}$$
$$= [\lambda(t)]^2 (m_2^2 \mathring{r}_{12}^2 + m_3^2 \mathring{r}_{13}^2 + 2 m_2 m_3 \mathring{r}_{12} \mathring{r}_{13} \cos \theta_{23}).$$

Here θ_{23} is the angle between $(\mathbf{r}_1 - \mathbf{r}_2)$ and $(\mathbf{r}_1 - \mathbf{r}_3)$; since this angle is constant we deduce

$$r_1 = \mathring{r}_1 \lambda(t),$$

and, generally,

$$r_i = \mathring{r}_i \lambda(t).$$

It follows that the shape of a triangle formed by the origin and any two masses is constant, and therefore that the angle subtended at the origin by the line joining any two masses is constant. Then if $\dot{\theta}_i$ is the angular velocity of m_i about the origin, we must have

$$\dot{\theta}_1 = \dot{\theta}_2 = \dot{\theta}_3 = \dot{\theta}(t).$$

But the total angular momentum of the system about the origin is constant and equal to

$$(m_1 \mathring{r}_1^2 + m_2 \mathring{r}_2^2 + m_3 \mathring{r}_3^2) \lambda^2 \dot{\theta}.$$

Hence the angular momentum of each individual mass about the origin is constant, so that the net force acting on that mass passes through the origin.

The equation of motion for m_i can be written

$$m_i F_i = m_i (\ddot{r}_i - r_i \dot{\theta}_i^2)$$
$$= r_i m_i \left(\frac{\ddot{\lambda}}{\lambda} - \dot{\theta}^2 \right).$$

Hence we have the condition (8.6.7), which must, therefore, be necessary.

To show that the conditions are sufficient, we simply follow up their consequences. We have $\mathbf{r}_1 \times \mathbf{F}_1 = 0$, or $\mathbf{r}_1 \times \ddot{\mathbf{r}}_1 = 0$. Applying this condition to the first equation of (8.6.1) we find

$$\mathbf{r}_1 \times \left\{ \frac{m_2\mathbf{r}_2}{r_{12}^3} + \frac{m_3\mathbf{r}_3}{r_{13}^3} \right\} = 0$$

or, using (8.6.2),

$$m_2\mathbf{r}_1 \times \mathbf{r}_2 \left\{ \frac{1}{r_{12}^3} - \frac{1}{r_{13}^3} \right\} = 0,$$

with similar results for the other masses. For these equations to be satisfied, we must either have

$$r_{23} = r_{31} = r_{12},$$

the case that we have already investigated, or

$$\mathbf{r}_2 \times \mathbf{r}_3 = \mathbf{r}_3 \times \mathbf{r}_1 = \mathbf{r}_1 \times \mathbf{r}_2 = 0,$$

so that the particles lie in a straight line; this satisfies our geometrical conditions. There are no other possibilities.

We might have suspected the possibility of straight-line solutions by analogy with the restricted three-body problem; now we have to justify them for the motion of three finite bodies and find the number of possible solutions. Let the line be the x-axis, and let it rotate with angular velocity $\dot{\theta}$. We have $x_i = \mathring{x}_i \lambda(t)$. The force acting on m_1 is

$$F_1 = -m_2 \frac{x_1 - x_2}{x_{12}^3} - m_3 \frac{x_1 - x_3}{x_{13}^3}$$

$$= -\frac{1}{\lambda^2} \left\{ m_2 \frac{\mathring{x}_1 - \mathring{x}_2}{\mathring{x}_{12}^3} - m_3 \frac{\mathring{x}_1 - \mathring{x}_3}{\mathring{x}_{13}^3} \right\}.$$

Now λ is proportional to the distance, so that m_1 is effectively acted upon by a force directed toward the center of mass and obeying the inverse square law; it will move in a conic orbit and so will the other two masses.

To show that this solution is possible, we must impose the condition

$$F_1 : F_2 : F_3 = x_1 : x_2 : x_3.$$

If this is true initially, it will always be true, so it is sufficient to prove that for the initial conditions,

$$Rx_1 = m_2 \frac{x_1 - x_2}{x_{12}^3} + m_3 \frac{x_1 - x_3}{x_{13}^3}, \tag{8.6.8}$$

$$Rx_2 = m_3 \frac{x_2 - x_3}{x_{23}^3} + m_1 \frac{x_2 - x_1}{x_{21}^3}, \tag{8.6.9}$$

$$Rx_3 = m_1 \frac{x_3 - x_1}{x_{31}^3} + m_2 \frac{x_3 - x_2}{x_{32}^3}. \tag{8.6.10}$$

Here R is a constant that depends on the initial conditions.

Let us prescribe a scale such that the initial distance $x_1 - x_2 = 1$. We need to show that the third body can be given some value of x such that the initial conditions are satisfied. Let

$$x_2 - x_3 = X.$$

We shall investigate whether there is an x_3 such that x_2 lies between x_1 and x_3; in this case X must be positive. Subtracting (8.6.9) from (8.6.8), and (8.6.10) from (8.6.9), we find

$$R = m_1 + m_2 - \frac{m_3}{X^2} + \frac{m_3}{(1 + X)^2},$$

and

$$RX = \frac{m_3}{X^2} - m_1 + \frac{m_1}{(1 + X)^2} + \frac{m_2}{X^2}.$$

$$(8.6.11)$$

If we eliminate R, remove fractions, and arrange in powers of X, we obtain the quintic

$$(m_1 + m_2)X^5 + (3m_1 + 2m_2)X^4 + (3m_1 + m_2)X^3$$
$$- (m_1 + 3m_3)X^2 - (2m_2 + 3m_3)X - (m_2 + m_3) = 0. \quad (8.6.12)$$

The coefficients of the powers of X change sign only once, so that by Descartes' rule of signs there is one positive root and one only. Hence there is one and only one position of m_3 such that $x_1 > x_2 > x_3$. If we want x_3 to lie between x_1 and x_2, equations (8.6.11) are slightly different, but we again finish with a quintic that has only one relevant root. The same applies if we want x_1 to lie between x_2 and x_3. Accordingly, there are three possible straight-line configurations and three only; these correspond to those found for the restricted three-body problem.

This completes the discussion of these solutions, called the *Lagrangian solutions*, to the three-body problem. The equilateral triangle solutions and the straight-line solutions are the only ones satisfying the geometrical conditions that there can only be rotation and change of scale. If there is no change of scale, the solutions are called *stationary*, and the positions of the bodies are called *libration points*. Thus the Trojan planets oscillate about libration points, and the gegenschein (if the suggested explanation is correct) is at a libration point, the other bodies being the Sun and Jupiter, and the Sun and the Earth, respectively.

Problems

1. Amend the criterion for the recognition of comets to apply to parabolic orbits. Show that the perturbations by Jupiter on a parabolic comet moving in the plane of Jupiter's orbit cannot result in the orbit's remaining parabolic, and find the relation between a and e of the resulting orbit. Consider some particular cases.

2. Show that if a parabolic comet is perturbed by Jupiter into another parabolic orbit, the relation between the old and new inclinations is given by

$$\cos i_1 = \sqrt{2} \cos i_2.$$

3. Prove analytically that the double point in the restricted three-body problem, which lies between the two finite masses, is closer to the lighter of the masses, and also that it is closer to μ than the double point lying on the far side.

4. Investigate the straight-line solution on the far side of the lighter mass when μ is small. Show that if $x = 1 - \mu + \rho$, then ρ can be expanded in a power series in $\mu^{1/3}$, in which the first three terms are

$$\rho = \left(\frac{\mu}{3}\right)^{1/3} + \frac{1}{3}\left(\frac{\mu}{3}\right)^{2/3} - \frac{1}{9}\left(\frac{\mu}{3}\right)^{3/3}.$$

5. Find series, corresponding to that in problem 4, for the other straight-line solutions.

6. Assuming that the suggestion made in the text about the gegenschein is correct, verify that the position of the libration point is not such that the meteors will lie in the Earth's shadow.

7. Consider motion in the x-y plane in the restricted three-body problem. Show that the equation of a limiting curve can be written

$$(1 - \mu)\left(r_1^2 + \frac{2}{r_1}\right) + \mu\left(r_2^2 + \frac{2}{r_2}\right) = C + \mu(1 - \mu),$$

and hence show that the minimum value of C is $3 - \mu(1 - \mu)$.

8. Show that, to the first order of small quantities, periodic orbits exist in the x-y plane about the straight-line points of libration in the restricted three-body problem. Also show that these are ellipses with major axes parallel to the y-axis, and are such that the eccentricity is independent of the initial displacement, but depends only on the distribution of the masses.

9. If $(1 - \mu)$ and μ are the Sun and the Earth, respectively, prove that the period of oscillation parallel to the z-axis for an infinitesimal body slightly displaced from the point of libration opposite the Sun is 183.304 mean solar days.

10. For the situation of problem 9, show that the period of small oscillations in the x-y plane is 177.0 days.

11. Prove that for small values of μ, the periods of oscillation both parallel to the z-axis and in the x-y plane are, in general, longest for the point opposite to μ with respect to $(1 - \mu)$ as origin; next longest for the point opposite to $(1 - \mu)$ with respect to μ as origin; and shortest for the point between $(1 - \mu)$ and μ.

12. Three bodies move in accordance with a Lagrangian solution. Prove that the orbit of any one about any other, taken as origin, is a conic.

    Suppose that the masses are equal and that they form an equilateral triangle at any time. Let P be the period in which they revolve around their center of mass and a be the semi-major axis of the orbit of any one body taken with respect to any other. Prove that the radius of the circle in which a particle would revolve around one of the bodies in the time P is $a \cdot 3^{-1/3}$.

13. Prove that the equilateral triangle circular solutions hold for the law of force μ/r^n. Investigate the general equilateral triangle solutions for this law, and also consider more complicated laws of central force.

14. Find the number of colinear solutions for the law of force μ/r^n.

15. Investigate the colinear solutions when the law of force is μ/r^3.

16. Prove that when the law of force varies inversely with the fifth power of the distance, one solution is that each of the bodies moves in a circle through their center of mass in such a way that the three bodies are always at the vertices of an equilateral triangle.

17. Prove that if the three bodies are placed at rest in any one of the configurations admitting circular solutions, they will fall to the center of mass in the same time in straight lines.

18. Find the distribution of mass among the three bodies for which the time of falling to their center of mass (see problem 17) will be (a) the least and (b) the greatest.

19. Solve completely the three-body problem when the law of force is proportional to the distance.

20. Investigate the possibility of a solution to the four-body problem when the masses are at the vertices of a regular tetrahedron.

21. Consider Jacobi's integral when applied approximately to the Sun, the Earth, and the (massless) Moon. Find the value of C, and investigate the size and shape of the Hill limiting surface for the motion of the Moon.

22. Consider small oscillations about the libration points for the Trojan planets. Show that of the two periods one is nearly the same as that of Jupiter, and the other is nearly 148 years. Considering the oscillation of longer period (usually known as *the libration*), show that the approximate ratio of the amplitudes along and perpendicular to the radius vector is $3\sqrt{\mu} : 1$, or $1 : 18.7$.

Chapter 9 ** THE n-BODY PROBLEM

9.1 The Center of Mass and the Invariable Plane

In this chapter we shall examine formally the equations of the n-body problem and their known solutions, and put them into a form that is readily useful in work on perturbations.

Let a system of n bodies consist of point masses m_i at $\mathbf{r}_i$, where $i = 1, 2, \cdots n$, and the $\mathbf{r}_i$ are expressed with respect to an inertial frame of reference. Let

$$r_{ij} = |\mathbf{r}_j - \mathbf{r}_i|, \quad (r_{ij} = r_{ji})$$

then the equation of motion of m_i is

$$m_i\ddot{\mathbf{r}}_i = -k^2 m_i \sum_{j=1}^{n} m_j \frac{\mathbf{r}_i - \mathbf{r}_j}{r_{ij}^3}. \tag{9.1.1}$$

Here the summation excludes $j = i$, and this case will automatically be excluded from future summations in this chapter where it would result in the vanishing of a denominator. For a complete solution of the n-body problem, $6n$ constants of integration are needed; actually only ten are known.

If all the equations of the form (9.1.1) are added, all the terms on the right-hand side cancel out, and we have

$$\sum_{i=1}^{n} m_i\ddot{\mathbf{r}}_i = 0.$$

This integrates at once to give

$$\sum_{i=1}^{n} m_i\mathbf{r}_i = \mathbf{a}t + \mathbf{b}, \tag{9.1.2}$$

where $\mathbf{a}$ and $\mathbf{b}$ are constant vectors. This means that the center of mass of the system moves, with respect to the (inertial) system of reference, in a straight line with constant speed. We can therefore set the origin at the center of mass, when

$$\sum_{i=1}^{n} m_i\mathbf{r}_i = 0$$

and the equations (9.1.1) remain valid.

205

Multiply (9.1.1) vectorially by $\mathbf{r}_i \times$, and add the resulting n equations. Again, all the terms on the right-hand side cancel out, and we have

$$\sum_{i=1}^{n} m_i \mathbf{r}_i \times \ddot{\mathbf{r}}_i = 0,$$

or

$$\sum_{i=1}^{n} m_i \mathbf{r}_i \times \dot{\mathbf{r}}_i = \mathbf{h}, \tag{9.1.3}$$

where $\mathbf{h}$ is a constant vector. This is the integral of "areas."

The plane through the center of mass, perpendicular to $\mathbf{h}$, is called the *invariable plane* of the system. We must be careful when applying this rigorously to a physical system. The angular momentum integral is the result of the absence of external forces acting on the system, and it expresses the fact that the *total* angular momentum of the system is constant; this is made up of the angular momentum arising from orbital revolutions and from axial rotations. If all the bodies are unconnected, rigid, spherical bodies, whose concentric layers are homogeneous, then the axial rotations will remain constant, and so will the orbital angular momentum; in this case the system will have an invariable plane perpendicular to the orbital angular momentum vector. But if these conditions do not hold, then precessional movements and the effects of tidal friction result in an interchange between the orbital and rotational parts of the total angular momentum, and the invariable plane as defined by $\mathbf{h}$ in (9.1.3) will not be constant. But the conditions very nearly hold for a planetary system, and we are justified in practice in speaking of the invariable plane of the solar system: it has elements $\Omega = 107°$ and $i = 1° \, 35'$, approximately.

9.2 The Energy Integral and the Force Function

Define U, the *force function* of the system, by

$$U = k^2 \sum_{i<j=1}^{n} \frac{m_i m_j}{r_{ij}}. \tag{9.2.1}$$

Then

$$\frac{\partial U}{\partial x_i} = k^2 m_i \frac{\partial}{\partial x_i} \left\{ \sum_{j=1}^{n} \frac{m_j}{r_{ij}} \right\}$$

$$= -k^2 m_i \sum_{j=1}^{n} m_j \frac{x_i - x_j}{r_{ij}^3}.$$

Therefore equation (9.1.1) can be written

$$m_i \ddot{\mathbf{r}}_i = \nabla_i U, \tag{9.2.2}$$

where

$$\nabla_i \equiv \hat{\mathbf{i}} \frac{\partial}{\partial x_i} + \hat{\mathbf{j}} \frac{\partial}{\partial y_i} + \hat{\mathbf{k}} \frac{\partial}{\partial z_i}.$$

Suppose the system to be assembled from a state of infinite diffusion. Start with m_1 at r_1. In moving m_2 from infinity to r_2 an amount of work

$$- k^2 \frac{m_1 m_2}{r_{12}}$$

is performed. If m_3 is now moved to r_3, the additional work

$$- k^2 \frac{m_1 m_3}{r_{13}} - k^2 \frac{m_2 m_3}{r_{23}}$$

is performed. As more particles are assembled, the function $-U$ is steadily built up, so that $-U$ is the total potential energy of the system.

Now multiply (9.2.2) scalarly by $\dot{\mathbf{r}}_i \cdot$, and add all the n equations; we have

$$\sum_{i=1}^{n} m_i \dot{\mathbf{r}}_i \cdot \ddot{\mathbf{r}}_i = \sum_{i=1}^{n} \dot{\mathbf{r}}_i \cdot \nabla_i U$$

$$= \frac{dU}{dt}.$$

Integrating this, we find

$$\frac{1}{2} \sum_{i=1}^{n} m_i \dot{\mathbf{r}}_i^2 = U + \text{constant}, \tag{9.2.3}$$

which is the energy integral. Let T be the kinetic energy of the system; then

$$T = \frac{1}{2} \sum_{i=1}^{n} m_i \dot{\mathbf{r}}_i^2,$$

and the energy integral can be written

$$T = U + C. \tag{9.2.4}$$

This completes the known integrals of the problem, C being the tenth constant of integration. These integrals are merely the consequence of the absence of external forces acting on the system.

9.3   The Virial Theorem

Consider the function

$$I = \sum_{i=1}^{n} m_i \mathbf{r}_i^2.$$

Differentiating it twice with respect to the time, we find

$$\tfrac{1}{2}\ddot{I} = \sum_{i=1}^{n} m_i \dot{\mathbf{r}}_i^2 + \sum_{i=1}^{n} m_i \mathbf{r}_i \cdot \ddot{\mathbf{r}}_i$$

$$= 2T + \sum_{i=1}^{n} \mathbf{r}_i \cdot \nabla_i U.$$

Now U is a homogeneous function of all the coordinates of order -1, so that, by Euler's theorem,

$$\sum_{i=1}^{n} \mathbf{r}_i \cdot \nabla_i U = \sum_{i=1}^{n} \left\{ x_i \frac{\partial U}{\partial x_i} + y_i \frac{\partial U}{\partial y_i} + z_i \frac{\partial U}{\partial z_i} \right\}$$

$$= -U.$$

Therefore

$$\ddot{I} = 4T - 2U. \tag{9.3.1}$$

Using the energy integral, (9.2.4), this can be put into the alternative forms:

$$\ddot{I} = 2U + 4C = 2T + 2C. \tag{9.3.2}$$

(9.3.1) and (9.3.2) are forms of the *virial theorem*.

In (9.3.2) T and U are positive. If C is such as to make $2U + 4C$ or $2T + 2C$ positive, then $\ddot{I}$ is positive, and I increases without limit, so that at least one of the $\mathbf{r}_i$ must increase without limit, which is equivalent to saying that at least one of the bodies escapes from the system. For the system to hold together, or to be *stable*, it is certainly necessary that C be negative, and it must be such as to make $\ddot{I}$ negative or zero; this is, however, by no means a sufficient condition.

9.4 Transfer of the Origin: the Perturbing Forces

Suppose, as is the case with the Sun in the solar system, that one mass, m_n, say, is dominant. Let us transfer the origin to m_n, and let the position vector of m_i with respect to m_n be $\mathbf{r}_i'$. Then

$$\mathbf{r}_i = \mathbf{r}_i' + \mathbf{r}_n.$$

The r_{ij} are not affected, and we have $\partial/\partial x_i' = \partial/\partial x_i$, etc.

Now

$$U = k^2 m_n \sum_{j=1}^{n-1} \frac{m_j}{r_{nj}} + k^2 \sum_{i<j=1}^{n-1} \frac{m_i m_j}{r_{ij}}$$

$$= k^2 m_n \sum_{j=1}^{n-1} \frac{m_j}{r_{nj}} + U'.$$

So

$$\nabla_i U = \nabla_i U' - k^2 m_n m_i \frac{\mathbf{r}_i'}{r_{in}^3}. \quad (i \neq n)$$

Also, from the equation of motion of m_n, we have

$$\ddot{\mathbf{r}}_n = -k^2 \sum_{j=1}^{n-1} m_j \frac{\mathbf{r}_n - \mathbf{r}_j}{r_{nj}^3}$$

$$= k^2 \sum_{j=1}^{n-1} m_j \frac{\mathbf{r}_j'}{r_{nj}^3}.$$

The equation of motion of m_i is

$$\ddot{\mathbf{r}}'_i + \ddot{\mathbf{r}}_n = \frac{1}{m_i} \nabla_i U$$

or

$$\ddot{\mathbf{r}}'_i + k^2 \sum_{j=1}^{n-1} m_j \frac{\mathbf{r}'_i}{r^3_{nj}} = \frac{1}{m_i} \left(\nabla_i U' - k^2 m_n m_i \frac{\mathbf{r}'_i}{r^3_{in}} \right).$$

Take out the ith term in the summation on the left-hand side; we have

$$\ddot{\mathbf{r}}'_i + k^2 m_i \frac{\mathbf{r}'_i}{r^3_{in}} + k^2 \sum_{\substack{j=1 \\ (j \neq i)}}^{n-1} m_j \frac{\mathbf{r}'_j}{r^3_{nj}} = \frac{1}{m_i} \left(\nabla_i U' - k^2 m_n m_i \frac{\mathbf{r}'_i}{r^3_{in}} \right)$$

or, dropping the primes, since the transfer to the new origin is complete, and we can do so without ambiguity,

$$\ddot{\mathbf{r}}_i + k^2 (m_n + m_i) \frac{\mathbf{r}_i}{r^3_{in}} = \frac{k^2}{m_i} \nabla_i U' - k^2 \sum_{\substack{j=1 \\ (j \neq i)}}^{n-1} m_j \frac{\mathbf{r}_j}{r^3_{jn}}. \qquad (9.4.1)$$

Now let

$$R_{ij} = k^2 \left(\frac{1}{r_{ij}} - \frac{\mathbf{r}_i \cdot \mathbf{r}_j}{r^3_{jn}} \right). \qquad (9.4.2)$$

Then

$$m_j \nabla_i R_{ij} = k^2 \nabla_i \left(\frac{m_j}{r_{ij}} \right) - k^2 m_j \frac{\mathbf{r}_j}{r^3_{jn}},$$

and

$$\sum_{j=1}^{n-1} m_j \nabla_i R_{ij} = \frac{k^2}{m_i} \sum_{j=1}^{n-1} \nabla_i \left(\frac{m_i m_j}{r_{ij}} \right) - k^2 \sum_{j=1}^{n-1} m_j \frac{\mathbf{r}_j}{r^3_{jn}} \qquad (j \neq i)$$

$$= \frac{k^2}{m_i} \nabla_i U' - k^2 \sum_{j=1}^{n-1} m_j \frac{\mathbf{r}_j}{r^3_{jn}}.$$

Combining this result with (9.4.1), we have

$$\ddot{\mathbf{r}}_i + k^2 (m_n + m_i) \frac{\mathbf{r}_i}{r^3_{in}} = \sum_{j=1}^{n-1} m_j \nabla_i R_{ij}. \qquad (9.4.3)$$

The equations (9.4.3) are fundamental. If the R_{ij} are zero, we are left with the equations of motion of the two-body problem, so it is the R_{ij} which cause the departures, or perturbations, from Keplerian motion. They are called the *perturbative functions*.

(9.4.3) can be written:

$$\ddot{\mathbf{r}}_i + k^2 (m_n + m_i) \frac{\mathbf{r}_i}{r^3_{in}} = k^2 \sum_{\substack{j=1 \\ j \neq i}}^{n-1} m_j \left(\frac{\mathbf{r}_j - \mathbf{r}_i}{r^3_{ij}} - \frac{\mathbf{r}_j}{r^3_{jn}} \right). \qquad (9.4.4)$$

The first terms on the right-hand side are the *direct* attractions on m_i due to the perturbing bodies. The second terms are *indirect*, and it is tempting when working with the equations of motion to forget about these; it is a temptation that should be resisted unless the terms can definitely be shown to be negligible.

9.5 Application to the Solar System

Consider the equations of motion of a body of negligible mass, a comet, say, in the solar system. If the origin is taken at the center of the Sun and $\mathbf{r}$ is the position vector of the comet, we have

$$\ddot{\mathbf{r}} + Mk^2 \frac{\mathbf{r}}{r^3} = \sum_{i=1}^{9} m_i k^2 \left(\frac{\mathbf{r}_i - \mathbf{r}}{|\mathbf{r}_i - \mathbf{r}|^3} - \frac{\mathbf{r}_i}{r_i^3} \right), \tag{9.5.1}$$

where M is the mass of the Sun, and the summation is taken over the nine major planets, in order of increasing mean distance from the Sun.

Unless the comet moves close to another planet, the most important contribution to the right-hand side of (9.5.1) will come from Jupiter, m_5, and the effects of the other planets may be relatively small. It follows that in practice (9.5.1) may be simplified; but any simplification must be theoretically justified.

Unless the comet passes close to Pluto, we can omit $i = 9$, since both the direct and indirect terms are very small. But this is not the case for Mercury because, although the direct terms may become negligible, the indirect terms will be much greater, and they are not diminished as r increases.

The indirect term due to Mercury is

$$-m_1 k^2 \frac{\mathbf{r}_1}{r_1^3},$$

which is equal to

$$\frac{m_1}{M + m_1} \ddot{\mathbf{r}}_1 = \ddot{\bar{\mathbf{r}}}_1,$$

where $\bar{\mathbf{r}}_1$ is the center of mass of the Sun and Mercury. Hence (9.5.1) can be written:

$$\frac{d^2}{dt^2} (\mathbf{r} - \bar{\mathbf{r}}_1) + Mk^2 \frac{\mathbf{r}}{r^3} = \sum_{i=1}^{8} m_i k^2 \frac{\mathbf{r}_i - \mathbf{r}}{|\mathbf{r}_i - \mathbf{r}|^3} - \sum_{i=2}^{8} m_i k^2 \frac{\mathbf{r}_i}{r_i^3}. \tag{9.5.2}$$

Therefore the neglect of an indirect term amounts, partially, to a change in the reference system; as far as the accelerated quantities are concerned, the origin has been moved to the center of mass of the Sun and the neglected planet.

In practical work on cometary perturbations it may be convenient to neglect the four inner (terrestrial) planets, since their direct perturbations are small; their indirect perturbations are absorbed by a change of origin to the center of mass, or *barycenter*, of the Sun and the four inner planets. If this point is at $\bar{\mathbf{r}}_4$, then

$$\frac{d^2}{dt^2} (\mathbf{r} - \bar{\mathbf{r}}_4) + Mk^2 \frac{\mathbf{r}}{r^3} = \sum_{i=1}^{8} m_i k^2 \frac{\mathbf{r}_i - \mathbf{r}}{|\mathbf{r}_i - \mathbf{r}|^3} - \sum_{i=5}^{8} m_i k^2 \frac{\mathbf{r}_i}{r_i^3}. \tag{9.5.3}$$

$\bar{\mathbf{r}}_4$ is tabulated in *Planetary Coordinates* (Ref. 38); it is referred to as $\mathbf{r}_b$, and the reference system thus introduced, as S_4.

If the comet is far enough from the four inner planets for $r \gg r_i$, $i = 1, 2, 3, 4$, then

$$\frac{\mathbf{r}_i - \mathbf{r}}{|\mathbf{r}_i - \mathbf{r}|^3} \sim -\frac{\mathbf{r}}{r^3}.$$

Also $\bar{r}_4$ is always small, less than 5×10^{-6} AU, so that for large r we can take

$$\mathbf{r} - \bar{\mathbf{r}}_4 = \mathbf{r}'$$

and

$$\frac{\mathbf{r}}{r^3} \sim \frac{\mathbf{r}'}{r'^3}.$$

Let

$$M_4 = M + \sum_{i=1}^{4} m_i;$$

then (9.5.1) can be written:

$$\frac{d^2\mathbf{r}'}{dt^2} + k^2 M_4 \frac{\mathbf{r}'}{r'^3} = \sum_{i=5}^{8} m_i k^2 \left(\frac{\mathbf{r}_i' - \mathbf{r}'}{|\mathbf{r}_i' - \mathbf{r}'|^3} - \frac{\mathbf{r}_i}{r_i^3} \right). \qquad (9.5.4)$$

The device of adding the masses of the inner planets to that of the Sun is often called "throwing the planets into the Sun." It should be accompanied by a suitable change of origin.

Problems

1. Show that the angular momentum of the n-body system about a line through any origin (of an inertial system) which makes an angle θ with the normal to the invariable plane is $h' \cos \theta$, where $\mathbf{h}'$ is the constant in the integral of areas with respect to that origin.

2. Find the relation between $\mathbf{h}$ and $\mathbf{h}'$ where they are the constants of areas with respect to the center of mass of the system, and any other origin of an inertial system.

3. Prove that the planes through a fixed point O which contain the tangents to the paths of two of the n-bodies intersect the invariable plane in one line.

4. Find the invariable plane of the Earth, Moon, and Sun. Discuss the effects of precession and tidal friction on this plane.

5. Find the invariable plane of the system consisting of the Sun, Jupiter, and Saturn. To what extent does this account for the elements quoted in Section 9.1?

6. Prove that

$$\frac{1}{\sum\limits_{i=1}^{n} m_i} \frac{d^2}{dt^2} \left(\sum_{i<j=1}^{n} \sum^{n} m_i m_j r_{ij}^2 \right) = 4C + 2U.$$

7. In a system of n bodies, the force acting on m_i is $\mathbf{F}_i$. Prove that

$$\tfrac{1}{2}\ddot{I} = 2T + \sum_{i=1}^{n} m_i \mathbf{r}_i \cdot \mathbf{F}_i.$$

8. Write down the equations of motion for the n-body problem when the law of force varies inversely with the kth power of the distance. Find the force function and the integrals corresponding to those found in this chapter.

9. From the results of problem 8, find the value of k for which the equations of motion are independent. Solve the problem for this case, showing that the orbits with respect to the center of mass are ellipses, with this point as center. Show that the orbit of any body with respect to any other body is also a central ellipse, and that the same is true for the motion of any body with respect to the center of mass of any subgroup of the system. Show that all the periods are equal.

10. A comet is 15 AU from the Sun. Find numerically the possible magnitudes of the approximations introduced by (a) neglecting Pluto; (b) entirely neglecting the four inner planets; (c) adding the masses of the four inner planets to that of the Sun, without compensating for the indirect terms; (d) using the formula (9.5.4).

11. Starting with n bodies m_i at $\mathbf{r}_i$ (x_i, y_i, z_i), where the origin is at the center of mass, construct the fictitious system of masses μ_i at $\boldsymbol{\rho}_i$ (ξ_i, η_i, ζ_i), where

$$\mu_i = m_1 + m_2 + \cdots + m_i,$$

and $\boldsymbol{\rho}_i$ is the position vector of m_i with respect to the center of mass of the masses $m_1, m_2, \cdots, m_{i-1}$. There is no $\boldsymbol{\rho}_1$. Show that if T is the kinetic energy of the system,

$$2T = \sum_{i=2}^{n} m_i \frac{\mu_{i-1}}{\mu_i} (\dot{\xi}_i^2 + \dot{\eta}_i^2 + \dot{\zeta}_i^2).$$

Show that the integral of areas becomes

$$\sum_{i=2}^{n} m_i \frac{\mu_{i-1}}{\mu_i} \boldsymbol{\rho}_i \times \dot{\boldsymbol{\rho}}_i = \mathbf{h},$$

where $\mathbf{h}$ is the angular momentum of the actual system about the center of mass.

Show that the n-body problem is thus reduced to a problem of $(n-1)$ fictitious bodies, and that the total order of the differential equations of motion is reduced by six.

12. Consider the three-body problem in terms of the fictitious bodies of problem 11. Write down the angular momentum integral, and hence prove a theorem due to Jacobi that the lines of nodes, with respect to the in-

variable plane, of the instantaneous orbits of two fictitious planets coincide.

13. Prove that Jacobi's theorem of the nodes applies roughly to any two real planets and the Sun, where the invariable plane is that of these three bodies only.

Chapter 10 ** NUMERICAL PROCEDURES

10.1 Differences and Sums

In this chapter we shall describe the notation and procedures involved in some of the numerical work that occurs in celestial mechanics. No attempt has been made to make this account complete; various formulas are quoted, but no proofs are offered since the chapter is intended partly for reference. For an account of the theory the student should consult a work on finite differences. Difference notation is not universal; here we shall use that given in *Interpolation and Allied Tables*, published by H.M. Nautical Almanac Office (Ref. 37). This is a small but invaluable volume containing details of many numerical procedures and hints on using them, as well as suitable tables.

Suppose some function, $f(x)$, to be tabulated at equal intervals, h, of the independent variable x. If x_0 is some suitable tabular point, then we have a table of values $f(x_0 + ph)$ for integral values of p; this may be written $f(x_p)$, or simply f_p. The argument is $(x_0 + ph)$, but this can be written without ambiguity as p.

If we subtract f_p from f_{p+1}, we shall have formed the *first difference*, $\delta_{p+\frac{1}{2}}$. It is written to the right of the column of values of f_p and between the values of f_p and f_{p+1} (see Table 10.1). If we form a column of first differences in this way, and difference this column, we form the second differences. Thus

$$\delta_{p+\frac{1}{2}} - \delta_{p-\frac{1}{2}} = \delta_p^2.$$

Here the superscript denotes the number of the difference, and the subscript shows the position with respect to the argument. This differencing can be carried out indefinitely, in principle. A formal scheme is shown in Table 10.1.

Table 10.1 can be modified by inserting arithmetical means of the entries standing immediately above and below a space. These *half-differences* will always be preceded by "μ." Thus

$$\mu\delta f_p = \tfrac{1}{2}(\delta_{p+\frac{1}{2}} + \delta_{p-\frac{1}{2}}).$$

This is shown in Table 10.2.

214

Table 10.1

Argument	Function	1st	2nd	3rd	4th
-2	f_{-2}		δ^2_{-2}		δ^4_{-2}
		$\delta_{-1\frac{1}{2}}$		$\delta^3_{-1\frac{1}{2}}$	
-1	f_{-1}		δ^2_{-1}		δ^4_{-1}
		$\delta_{-\frac{1}{2}}$		$\delta^3_{-\frac{1}{2}}$	
0	f_0		δ^2_0		δ^4_0 etc.
		$\delta_{\frac{1}{2}}$		$\delta^3_{\frac{1}{2}}$	
$+1$	f_1		δ^2_1		δ^4_1
		$\delta_{1\frac{1}{2}}$		$\delta^3_{1\frac{1}{2}}$	
$+2$	f_2		δ^2_2		δ^4_2

This table is assumed to be part of a more extensive one. If we start with only the five values tabulated, then only one fourth difference, δ^4_0, can be found, and the difference table ends there.

Table 10.2

Argument	Function	1st	2nd	3rd	4th
-1	f_{-1}	$[\mu\delta_{-1}]$	δ^2_{-1}	$[\mu\delta^3_{-1}]$	δ^4_{-1}
	$[\mu f_{-\frac{1}{2}}]$	$\delta_{-\frac{1}{2}}$	$[\mu\delta^2_{-\frac{1}{2}}]$	$\delta^3_{-\frac{1}{2}}$	$[\mu\delta^4_{-\frac{1}{2}}]$
0	f_0	$[\mu\delta_0]$	δ^2_0	$[\mu\delta^3_0]$	δ^4_0 etc.
	$[\mu f_{\frac{1}{2}}]$	$\delta_{\frac{1}{2}}$	$[\mu\delta^2_{\frac{1}{2}}]$	$\delta^3_{\frac{1}{2}}$	$[\mu\delta^4_{\frac{1}{2}}]$
$+1$	f_1	$[\mu\delta_1]$	δ^2_1	$[\mu\delta^3_1]$	δ^4_1

The use of differencing in checking certain calculations will be described in Section 10.6.

We can regard the tabulated values, f_p, as being the first differences of another function, which we shall call the *first sum* of f_p. The first sums can be regarded in their turn as the differences of the *second sums*, and so on. We then have the scheme shown in Table 10.3, page 216.

In forming a sum there is uncertainty to the extent of an additive constant. There is an analogy here between summing and integrating, and also between differencing and differentiating. In fact the δ's can be regarded as operators that obey the ordinary laws of algebra.

10.2 Interpolation

The tables of the preceding section refer to values of $f(x_0 + ph)$ for integral values of p; but once an adequate table has been constructed, it can be used for finding the value of f for any value of p that is included comfortably within the range of the table. This is known as *interpolation*. In the following work we shall assume $0 \leqslant p < 1$.

Table 10.3

Argument	Sums			Function	Differences			
	2nd	1st		*Function*	1st	2nd	3rd	4th
-2	δ_{-2}^{-2}			f_{-2}		δ_{-2}^2		δ_{-2}^4
		$\delta_{-1\frac{1}{2}}^{-1}$			$\delta_{-1\frac{1}{2}}$		$\delta_{-1\frac{1}{2}}^3$	
-1	δ_{-1}^{-2}			f_{-1}		δ_{-1}^2		δ_{-1}^4
		$\delta_{-\frac{1}{2}}^{-1}$			$\delta_{-\frac{1}{2}}$		$\delta_{-\frac{1}{2}}^3$	
0	δ_0^{-2}			f_0		δ_0^2		δ_0^4 etc.
		$\delta_{\frac{1}{2}}^{-1}$			$\delta_{\frac{1}{2}}$		$\delta_{\frac{1}{2}}^3$	
1	δ_1^{-2}			f_1		δ_1^2		δ_1^4
		$\delta_{1\frac{1}{2}}^{-1}$			$\delta_{1\frac{1}{2}}$		$\delta_{1\frac{1}{2}}^3$	
2	δ_2^{-2}			f_2		δ_2^2		δ_2^4

We notice that if the second differences are negligible or zero (and there need be no distinction in numerical work), then

$$f_p = f_0 + p\delta_{\frac{1}{2}}. \tag{10.2.1}$$

In most books of tables the interval of tabulation, h, is chosen to be so small that second differences are usually negligible; but this cannot normally be done in a practical calculation. We might suspect that f_p would in general be given by a formula involving successive differences in a way that depends on p. This is the case; two such relations, out of many, will be described here. The first is Bessel's formula:

$$f_p = f_0 + p\delta_{\frac{1}{2}} + B_2(\delta_0^2 + \delta_1^2) + B_3\delta_{\frac{1}{2}}^3 + B_4(\delta_0^4 + \delta_1^4) + \cdots \tag{10.2.2}$$

where the B's, or *Bessel interpolation coefficients*, are functions of p. For instance,

$$B_2 = \tfrac{1}{4}p(p-1), \quad B_3 = \tfrac{1}{12}p(p-1)(2p-1), \quad B_4 = \tfrac{1}{48}p(p^2-1)(p-2), \quad \text{etc.}$$

These functions are tabulated in standard references.

The second relation is Everett's formula:

$$f_p = (1-p)f_0 + pf_1 + E_2\,\delta_0^2 + F_2\,\delta_1^2 + E_4\,\delta_0^4 + F_4\,\delta_1^4 + \cdots \tag{10.2.3}$$

The Everett coefficients are related to the Bessel coefficients by

$$E + F = 2B,$$

and we also have $E(p) = F(1-p)$ and $E(1-p) = F(p)$.

We shall illustrate the use of these formulas by taking a table of $\sin x$ to six places of decimals where $h = 5°$. This is given in Table 10.4, with differences up to the sixth. When differencing a table, the differences should be taken up to the stage where they become small and irregular (this is discussed further in Section 10.6); this is the case for the fifth and sixth differences. Since the interpolation coefficients become very small anyway for these differences, they will not contribute anything in the interpolation.

Table 10.4

$x°$	$\sin x$	δ	δ^2	δ^3	δ^4	δ^5	δ^6
0	0.000 000						
		+87 156					
5	+0.087 156		− 664				
		86 492		− 657			
10	173 648		1321		+ 8		
		85 171		649		+ 8	
15	258 819		1970		16		− 4
		83 201		633		4	
20	342 020		2603		20		− 1
		80 598		613		3	
25	422 618		3216		23		+ 6
		77 382		590		+ 9	
30	500 000		3806		32		−12
		73 576		558		− 3	
35	573 576		4364		29		+14
		69 212		529		+11	
40	642 788		4893		40		− 9
		64 319		489		+ 2	
45	707 107		5382		42		− 3
		58 937		447		− 1	
50	766 044		5829		41		+11
		53 108		406		+10	
55	819 152		6235		51		−14
		46 873		355		− 4	
60	866 025		6590		47		+11
		40 283		308		+ 7	
65	906 308		6898		54		− 6
		33 385		254		+ 1	
70	939 693		7152		55		− 1
		26 233		199		0	
75	965 926		7351		55		+ 2
		18 882		144		+ 2	
80	984 808		7495		+57		
		11 387		− 87			
85	996 195		−7582				
		+ 3 805					
90	+1.000 000						

Decimal points can be omitted without ambiguity in this case, with the understanding that quantities are in units of the sixth place.

Let us use this table to find the value of $\sin 41°$; then $x_0 = 40°$ and $p = 0.200\ 000$. First we shall use the Everett formula. From tables we find

$$E_2 = -0.048, \qquad F_2 = -0.032,$$
$$E_4 = +0.008, \qquad F_4 = +0.006;$$

further coefficients are not needed. We then find

$$
\begin{aligned}
(1 - p)f_0 &= +0.514\ 230 \\
pf_1 &= +\ \ \ \ 141\ 421 \\
E_2\delta_0^2 &= +\ \ \ \ \ \ \ \ \ \ 235 \\
F_2\delta_1^2 &= +\ \ \ \ \ \ \ \ \ \ 172 \\
E_4\delta_0^4 &= \ \ \ \ \ \ \ \ \ \ \ \ \ \ 0 \\
F_4\delta_1^4 &= \ \ \ \ \ \ \ \ \ \ \ \ \ \ 0 \\
\hline
f_p &= +0.656\ 058.
\end{aligned}
$$

The appropriate Bessel coefficients are

$$B_2 = -0.040, \quad B_3 = +0.008, \quad B_4 = +0.007.$$

We find

$$
\begin{aligned}
f_0 &= +0.642\ 788 \\
p\delta_{\frac{1}{2}} &= +\ \ \ \ 12\ 864 \\
B_2(\delta_0^2 + \delta_1^2) &= +\ \ \ \ \ \ \ \ 411 \\
B_3\delta_{\frac{1}{2}}^3 &= -\ \ \ \ \ \ \ \ \ \ \ \ 4 \\
B_4(\delta_0^4 + \delta_1^4) &= +\ \ \ \ \ \ \ \ \ \ \ \ 1 \\
\hline
f_p &= +0.656\ 060.
\end{aligned}
$$

The actual answer, correct to six places, is $+0.656\ 059$, so that the agreement is good, considering the number of calculations performed.

If the fourth differences are small (less than 1000), the term in B_4 may be neglected if the second differences are modified so that

$$\delta^2{}_{\text{mod}} = \delta^2 - 0.184\ \delta^4. \tag{10.2.4}$$

The fourth differences are said to have been *thrown back*. A similar device can be used in Everett's formula. There are more complicated throwbacks involving higher differences; the student will find these described in the standard references.

If in our example we had required the value of $\sin 86°$, on the basis of Table 10.4 alone, it would have been necessary to guess some of the differences. This can be done with reasonable confidence, since the run of differences is smooth; we can reasonably assume that the fourth differences will remain at about $+57$, and so build up the lower differences. If our guess of the fourth differences was wrong by 10, the error in the product $B_4\delta^4$ would be less than one, and so would not affect the accuracy of the answer.

If we build up extra differences in this way, it is possible to add extra values to the table. Let us assume that the next fourth difference is $+57$. Then, extra third, second, and first differences of -30, -7612, and -3807, respectively, can be added to the table of differences, so that we can deduce that $\sin 95° = +0.996\ 193$, giving an error of two only. This process is known as *extrapolation*.

We can also use Table 10.4 to find the argument for a given value of $\sin x$. This is known as *inverse interpolation*. It requires successive approximations, as, unfortunately, there is no direct formula that can be used.

10.3 Differentiation

If all the second differences in a table were zero, the function would be an arithmetical series, and its differential coefficient would be given exactly by

$$h\frac{df}{dx} = hf' = \frac{df}{dp} = \delta_{\frac{1}{2}}. \tag{10.3.1}$$

This corresponds to the case (10.2.1) considered in the preceding section, and so we would expect in general to find f' given by a series involving higher differences. The student should note the appearance of h on the left-hand side of (10.3.1); it must never be forgotten.

If the Bessel interpolation coefficients are expressed in terms of p, then (10.2.2) can be differentiated any number of times to give appropriate formulas for successive differential coefficients. We have, for instance,

$$hf'_p = \delta_{\frac{1}{2}} + \tfrac{1}{4}(2p - 1)(\delta_0^2 + \delta_1^2) + B'_3\delta_{\frac{1}{2}}^3 + B'_4(\delta_0^4 + \delta_1^4) + \cdots \tag{10.3.2}$$

The B'_n are tabulated in the standard references. As in the case of interpolation, there are alternative formulas.

Often only the derivatives at tabular or half-tabular points are required. The coefficients can then be given definite numerical values. For tabular points we have

$$hf'_0 = \mu\delta_0 - \tfrac{1}{6}\mu\delta_0^3 + \tfrac{1}{30}\mu\delta_0^5 - \tfrac{1}{140}\mu\delta\,_0^7 + \cdots \tag{10.3.3}$$

and

$$h^2f''_0 = \delta_0^2 - \tfrac{1}{12}\delta_0^4 + \tfrac{1}{90}\delta_0^6 + \cdots \tag{10.3.4}$$

As an illustration let us find the differential coefficient of $\sin 40°$ from Table 10.4. Expressed in radians, h is $0.087\ 2665$. We find

$$\mu\delta_0 = +66\ 766,$$

and

$$\tfrac{1}{6}\mu\delta_0^3 = +85,$$

from which we find

$$\sin'40° = +0.066\ 681 \text{ divided by } 0.087\ 266$$

$$= +0.766\ 06.$$

This compares with the correct figure, 0.766 04.

The formulas for the derivatives at half-tabular points are

$$hf'_{\frac{1}{2}} = \delta_{\frac{1}{2}} - \tfrac{1}{24}\delta^3_{\frac{1}{2}} + \tfrac{3}{640}\delta^5_{\frac{1}{2}} - \cdots \tag{10.3.5}$$

and

$$h^2 f''_{\frac{1}{2}} = \mu\delta^2_{\frac{1}{2}} - \tfrac{5}{24}\mu\delta^4_{\frac{1}{2}} + \tfrac{259}{5760}\mu\delta^6_{\frac{1}{2}} - \cdots \tag{10.3.6}$$

10.4 Integration

The analogy between sums and integrals (or the direct integration of Bessel's interpolation formula) leads us to expect a formula of the type

$$\int^p f_p\, dp = \delta^{-1}_{\frac{1}{4}} + A^1_0(f_0 + f_1) + A^1_1\delta_{\frac{1}{4}} + A^1_2(\delta^2_0 + \delta^2_1) + \cdots \tag{10.4.1}$$

for the integral of f_p. This is the case, and the A's are tabulated in standard references. A similar formula holds for double integrals; these involve the second sums. We note that

$$\int f(x)\, dx = h\int f_p\, dp.$$

For our purposes we shall need only to evaluate integrals at tabular points, for which $p = 0$. Then we have

$$h^{-1}\int^0 f(x)\, dx = \int^0 f_p\, dp$$
$$= \mu\delta^{-1}_0 - \tfrac{1}{12}\mu\delta_0 + \tfrac{11}{720}\mu\delta^3_0 - \tfrac{191}{60480}\mu\delta^5_0 + \cdots \tag{10.4.2}$$

and

$$h^{-2}\int\int^0 f(x)\, dx = \int\int^0 f_p\, dp^2$$
$$= \delta^{-2}_0 + \tfrac{1}{12}f_0 - \delta^2_0\tfrac{1}{240} + \tfrac{31}{60480}\delta^4_0 - \cdots \tag{10.4.3}$$

These expressions will be needed later when we consider the numerical solution of differential equations.

The notation $\int^p$ is confusing because an integral must have two limits for it to have a definite value. Specifying only the upper limit results in uncertainty to the extent of an added constant; but this is related in (10.4.1) to the uncertainty in forming the first sums. We can express a definite integral as

$$\int^p_q f\, dp = \int^p_C f\, dp - \int^q_C f\, dp,$$

where C is arbitrary. Then let us omit the C altogether and apply (10.4.1) to each integral. The final answer for the definite integral will not be influenced by the choice of arbitrary constant when forming the first sums, as this will disappear in the subtraction.

When solving a differential equation, the sums must be known definitely; in this case they are found by using the initial conditions. Suppose we are required to calculate y from

$$\frac{dy}{dx} = \sin x,$$

subject to the initial condition that when $x = 45°$, $y = -0.707\ 107$. Using Table 10.4, let $x_0 = 45°$; then from (10.4.2) we find

$$-0.707\ 107 = h(\mu\delta_0^{-1} - 0.005\ 143),$$

from which

$$\mu\delta_0^{-1} = -8.097\ 707,$$

where the final digit is unreliable. Then since

$$\delta_{\frac{1}{2}}^{-1} - \delta_{-\frac{1}{2}}^{-1} = +0.707\ 107,$$

we find

$$\delta_{\frac{1}{2}}^{-1} = -7.744\ 154.$$

Using this value, the complete column of first sums can be entered into Table 10.4, and the application of (10.4.2) will yield values of $-\cos x$. The student should verify that this is, in fact, the case.

Definite integrals are often evaluated numerically by using values of the function to be integrated at tabular points, instead of its sums and differences. There are many suitable formulas; here we shall quote only one, known as the *repeated Simpson rule*. Let the function $y = f(x)$ be integrated from $x_0 = a$ to $x_n = b$, and suppose y to be tabulated for all the x_i, such that $y_i = f(x_i)$, $i = 1, 2, 3, \cdots n$. We assume that n is even. Then

$$\int_a^b y\ dx = \frac{b-a}{3n}(y_0 + 4y_1 + 2y_2 + 4y_3 + 2y_4 + \ldots + 2y_{n-2} + 4y_{n-1} + y_n)$$

$$(10.4.4)$$

This formula should be used only if the third differences of the y_i are approximately constant.

10.5   Differential Equations

The numerical solution of ordinary differential equations can be performed in literally dozens of ways. Our purpose here is to develop sufficient understanding for the student to appreciate some standard methods for the calculation of special perturbations.

The situation to be faced when solving a differential equation numerically has been described by Herget in terms of the problem of filling in quantities on an initially blank sheet of paper, where only one quantity (the starting value) may be known; for the others we have to enter and use tentative values and proceed by successive approximations. Once the integration has been started, we can proceed, step by step, to build up the solution, using methods to be described shortly. To start the solution, we might solve the equation

$$h \frac{dx}{dt} = f(x,t), \qquad (10.5.1)$$

say, in a series that converges rapidly over a small range of t; this series is then used to find a run of values from which the numerical solution proceeds. This is not convenient in celestial mechanics, since it is impractical to find such series expansions. Suppose we want to find the perturbations of a cometary orbit due to the actions of the planets; as long as these are not too violent at the time of the start of the integration, we can use the ephemeris of the un-perturbed orbit as a start. This will enable us to set up a table like Table 10.5, from which the integration proceeds. The arbitrary constants involved in the sums are determined by the initial conditions.

Table 10.5 shows initial starting values schematically for the equation (10.5.1). x_0 is the starting value and the x^a are approximate and may have to be modified as the solution proceeds.

Table 10.5

t	x	x^a	δ^{-1}	f	δ	δ^2	δ^3	δ^4
0	x_0			f_0		δ_0^2		δ_0^4
			$\delta_{\frac{1}{2}}^{-1}$		$\delta_{\frac{1}{2}}$		$\delta_{\frac{1}{2}}^3$	
1		x_1^a		f_1		δ_1^2		
			$\delta_{1\frac{1}{2}}^{-1}$		$\delta_{1\frac{1}{2}}$			
2		x_2^a		f_2				
			$\delta_{2\frac{1}{2}}^{-1}$					

We assume that the interval chosen is such that the differences after the fourth are negligible. The extra terms that are necessary when higher differences are involved should be clear. In practice, higher differences should be used.

x_1 can be found from

$$x_1 = \mu \delta_1^{-1} - \tfrac{1}{12} \mu \delta_1 + \tfrac{11}{720} \mu \delta_1^3. \qquad (10.5.2)$$

Here $\delta_{1\frac{1}{2}}^3$ must be extrapolated, but unless this extrapolation is very wrong, x_1 will not be badly affected. For suppose it is wrong by 20; then $\mu \delta_1^3$ will be wrong by 10 and $(\tfrac{11}{720})\mu \delta_1^3$ by 0.1, which will not affect x_1 at all. This illustrates the rather satisfying process of convergence in much of this work. The extrapolation in Table 10.5 might be accomplished by assuming $\delta_1^{4a} = \delta_0^4$, and we could then build up extra values to give the quantities in Table 10.6.

We might now find an approximate value for x_3 from

$$x_3^a = \mu \delta_3^{-1} - \tfrac{1}{12} \mu \delta_3 + \tfrac{11}{720} \mu \delta_3^3, \qquad (10.5.3)$$

where some more judicious extrapolation would be needed; from this, a better value of f_3 can be found, and the approximate differences improved. (It might also be necessary to improve the value of x_1.) For our purposes f will not be too sensitive to small errors in x, and this value of f_3 may be final. But any of these steps may have to be revised as the solution is built up.

Table 10.6

t	x	x^a	δ^{-1}	f	δ	δ^2	δ^3	δ^4
0	x_0			f_0		δ_0^2		δ_0^4
			$\delta_{\frac{1}{2}}^{-1}$		$\delta_{\frac{1}{2}}$		$\delta_{\frac{1}{2}}^3$	
1	x_1	x_1^a		f_1		δ_1^2		δ_1^{4a}
			$\delta_{1\frac{1}{2}}^{-1}$		$\delta_{1\frac{1}{2}}$		$\delta_{1\frac{1}{2}}^{3a}$	
2		x_2^a		f_2		δ_2^{2a}		
			$\delta_{2\frac{1}{2}}^{-1}$		$\delta_{2\frac{1}{2}}^{2a}$			
3				f_3^a				
			$\delta_{3\frac{1}{2}}^{-1a}$					

We have now arrived at a situation similar to that in Table 10.5, but one step further on; we are ready to find x_2, and so on. If the x's differ so much from the corresponding x^a's that the values of the f's are affected, the table will have to be revised. This may happen in the early stages of an integration, but should not happen later unless the interval of tabulation is too great. At all events, tentative results should be entered in soft pencil, and ink used only for the final results.

In practice x_3^a is usually found not from (10.5.3) but from the extrapolation formula

$$x_3^a = x_1 + 2f_2 + \tfrac{1}{3}\delta_2^2 - \tfrac{1}{90}\delta_2^4. \tag{10.5.4}$$

Now consider the second-order differential equation

$$h^2 \frac{d^2x}{dt^2} = f(x,t). \tag{10.5.5}$$

Here we tabulate the second sums, and a starting table will be of the form given in Table 10.7.

Table 10.7

t	x	x^a	δ^{-2}	δ^{-1}	f	δ	δ^2	δ^3	δ^4
0	x_0		δ_0^{-2}		f_0		δ_0^2		δ_0^4
				$\delta_{\frac{1}{2}}^{-1}$		$\delta_{\frac{1}{2}}$		$\delta_{\frac{1}{2}}^3$	
1		x_1^a	δ_1^{-2}		f_1		δ_1^2		
				$\delta_{1\frac{1}{2}}^{-1}$		$\delta_{1\frac{1}{2}}$			
2		x_2^a	δ_2^{-2}		f_2				
				$\delta_{2\frac{1}{2}}^{-1}$					
3			δ_3^{-2}						

Now we have

$$x_1 = \delta_1^{-2} + \tfrac{1}{12} f_1 - \tfrac{1}{240} \delta_1^2 + \tfrac{31}{60480} \delta_1^4. \tag{10.5.6}$$

As before, provided the fourth differences are small and steady (or higher differences, if these are required; but the table should extend to an even difference), we can build up the tentative values for δ_1^4, $\delta_{1\frac{1}{2}}^3$, δ_2^2, $\delta_{2\frac{1}{2}}$, and f_3. From these we can find a tentative value of δ_3^2, and hence of x_3^a, using

$$x_3^a = \delta_3^{-2} + \tfrac{1}{12} f_3 - \tfrac{1}{240} \delta_3^2. \tag{10.5.7}$$

x_3^a is used to find f_3 more accurately, a value that will probably be final. The added differences can now be corrected in ink, and $\delta_{3\frac{1}{2}}^{-1}$ and δ_4^{-2} added. We can now proceed to the next step.

In perturbation problems we have to solve three simultaneous equations of the form

$$\ddot{x} = X(x,y,z,t), \quad \ddot{y} = Y(x,y,z,t), \quad \ddot{z} = Z(x,y,z,t).$$

The method is the same as that for a single equation, except that integrations on three sheets of paper proceed together. We find tentative values x^a, y^a, z^a and use these to correct the extrapolated values of X, Y, and Z.

10.6 Errors

The most important parts of this section deal with errors that are unavoidable. This may come as a surprise to some students grounded in arithmetic where errors are, very properly, considered to be the result of reprehensible human failure. We shall briefly discuss this latter kind of error first, and (more important) mention some precautions for avoiding it.

Wherever possible, the results of a calculation should be checked. A good example of this occurs in the calculation of P_x, P_y, P_z, and Q_x, Q_y, Q_z when computing an aphemeris. Here the computer should apply the checks

$$P_x^2 + P_y^2 + P_z^2 = 1 = Q_x^2 + Q_y^2 + Q_z^2, \quad P_x Q_x + P_y Q_y + P_z Q_z = 0.$$

Another example (which is more of a check on the accumulation of accidental errors) concerns the integration of equations where the energy integral is known; this is not used in the calculation but can be used as a check at any stage during the numerical integration of the equations of motion.

Whenever some sort of table is constructed, as in the calculation of an ephemeris, the figures should be differenced. Differences should be taken to a point where they become small; if this is not possible, then there is probably a mistake in the table. (A fuller discussion of this is given below.)

The layout of the work should be planned before starting, and if some sort of a table is involved, the work should be set out in rows and columns; in this way any column of figures can be easily differenced on a blank sheet of paper placed immediately to its right. The work will be easier to follow if the rows are spaced in groups, say, of five. If the student does not appreciate this point, he should look at the layout of a good volume of tables. Plenty of space should be allowed between rows and columns. Mistakes should be corrected alongside the errors; never alter a figure. Do not try to economize on paper.

If possible, the computer should have some idea beforehand of the sort of answer to be expected. This can be illustrated in the computation of an ephemeris. A rough sketch of the orbits of the comet and the Earth will show the region of the sky in which a comet should appear at some time. An error, of sign, for instance, could result in the computer putting the comet into the wrong quadrant of the celestial sphere, and a mistake of this kind would easily be recognized. Similarly, a computer should be suspicious of the sort of result where a minor planet, say, is apparently found to be moving in a hyperbolic orbit.

If numbers are used to many significant figures, it is helpful in reading them if the figures are grouped; for instance a seven-figure number might be written

123 4567.

The layout of the work often enables the decimal point to be omitted, but it must always be quite clear where the decimal point should be. Losing touch with the decimal point is a fruitful source of error; the student is advised to be particularly careful when taking square roots.

Signs must always be clear and never be forgotten. It may not be necessary to attach a sign to every number, but there should be suitable reminders, as in the example on the right.

It is safest to write down every stage of a calculation; then the calculation is much easier to check (as it must be checked). Simple operations, such as division by two, can be performed mentally, but it is in the simpler operations that mistakes are most likely to occur, through overconfidence.

Errors often occur when a number is copied, from a calculating machine, say, to paper (in this case the figure should be read back from paper to calculating machine as a check). Frequent mistakes involve repeated figures, or the reversal of a pair of figures, 45 for 54, for instance.

$+10$
9
8
7
$+6$
$+5$
4
3
2
$+1$
0
-1
2
3
4
-5

Care should be taken over the signs of trigonometric functions and the quadrants of angles. If the computer has a choice of trigonometric functions, he should choose those that behave most reasonably in the context; for example, the cotangent of an angle near 90° can be determined more accurately from tables than the tangent.

A mistake is not a crime, although it may become one if it is not corrected. But in the long run the most serious sources of error are those that are unavoidable. As an obvious example, the data may not be accurate. The computer can do little about this, but he should normally avoid quoting more significant figures in his answer than are justified by the data. Many methods of numerical solution are only approximate; the computer should be aware when this is the case and should know roughly just how inaccurate the methods can become, that he may guard against the results becoming meaningless. For example, in computing cometary perturbations we might find the deviations from the Keplerian orbit which is instantaneously described by the comet at the start of the computation; the elements of this orbit could be used to calculate the perturbing forces at each step of the integration. But if the perturbations were to become large, the predictions given by these elements would be so much in error that the calculated perturbing forces would be unreliable. The computer should notice when this happens, and should alter the reference orbit to another that is more up to date.

Probably the most fruitful source of error is the fact that in numerical work virtually no figure is accurate. A number correct to six places of decimals might be

$$0.987\ 654.$$

Correct to seven places it might be

$$0.987\ 6543.$$

So the first number is in error by 0.3 in the final figure. Now suppose we multiply each number by two; we obtain

$$1.975\ 308 \quad \text{and} \quad 1.975\ 3086.$$

If we round off the second number to six-figure accuracy, it becomes

$$1.975\ 309.$$

This disagrees with, but is more accurate than the first number, which was found by working throughout to six figures; but if we are working to six figures from the start, the error in the first number cannot be avoided. Hence the result of *one* operation can be to produce an error, and the greater the number of operations involved, the greater the number of errors that can unavoidably creep in. The computer must face the fact that at the end of a long calculation several of the figures may have lost any meaning. One precaution against this is to use more figures in the calculation than are needed in the answer. If the answer is required to five-figure accuracy, say, the calculation may be performed with seven figures and the final results rounded off to five figures. The student may have some doubts as to what to do when the figure to be rounded off is 5. In fact it probably will not matter if 0.12345 is rounded off to 0.1234 or to 0.1235, but it can save trouble to have an automatic rule such as to make the last figure even after rounding off. (At least if it is later divided by two there will be no further quandary.)

In solving a differential equation, the results of an early error of this sort can be considerable, since at each step it will be added again to the answer. It follows that we should use the minimum number of steps and have an interval that is as large as possible. There is a limit to this because, if the interval is too large, the approximations fail to converge satisfactorily. But if, during the solution, the low differences become small, then the interval should be increased. Instructions for changing the interval are given in most references. To consider this in a different way, suppose the equation

$$\ddot{x} = f(x,t)$$

to have the general solution

$$x = ax_1(t) + bx_2(t),$$

where a and b are arbitrary constants. Numerically the equation will be solved subject to certain initial conditions that determine a and b. But if an error is introduced, the solution found may be

$$x = (a + da)x_1(t) + (b + db)x_2(t).$$

It can happen that the initial conditions put $b = 0$, and that the function $x_2(t)$ is divergent in the time interval considered.

It is inevitable that in any table where we are not dealing wholly with rational numbers the final figure of any number may be in error by $\pm\frac{1}{2}$. To see the effect that this can have on the differences of the table, consider the differences of the sequence $+\frac{1}{2}$, $-\frac{1}{2}$, $+\frac{1}{2}$, $-\frac{1}{2}$, etc. These are given in Table 10.8. The magnitude of δ^n is 2^{n-1}. So, if we calculated a table and found that the sixth differences fluctuated between $+32$ and -32, this would not signify any avoidable error; for instance, the sixth differences in Table 10.4 are perfectly healthy. But a larger fluctuation would signify an avoidable error.

Table 10.8

	δ	δ^2	δ^3	δ^4	δ^5	δ^6
$+\frac{1}{2}$		-2		$+8$		-32
	-1		$+4$		-16	
$-\frac{1}{2}$		$+2$		-8		$+32$
	$+1$		-4		$+16$	
$+\frac{1}{2}$		-2		$+8$		-32 etc.
	-1		$+4$		-16	
$-\frac{1}{2}$		$+2$		-8		
	$+1$		-4			
$+\frac{1}{2}$		-2				
	-1					
$-\frac{1}{2}$						

To find the effect of a mistake on the differences, suppose that one tabular value is in error by one, and difference the sequence 0, 0, 0, 1, 0, 0, 0.

Table 10.9

δ	δ^2	δ^3	δ^4	δ^5	δ^6
0	0		0		+ 1
		0		+ 1	
0	0		+1		− 6
		+1		− 5	
0	+1		− 4		+15
	+1	− 3		+10	
+1	− 2		+ 6		− 20 etc.
	− 1	+ 3		− 10	
0	+1		− 4		+15
		− 1		+ 5	
0	0		+1		− 6
		0		− 1	
0	0		0		+ 1

At each stage the numbers occuring in δ^n are the binomial coefficients in the expansion of $(1 - x)^n$. Consider only the even differences; the largest number always occurs opposite the error. Suppose that we differenced a table which, apart from the error of one in a value, would yield negligible sixth differences; the error would become obvious as soon as the sixth differences were written down. Not only this, but the number that was wrong could be spotted (this is easiest if the differencing extends to an even difference), as could the magnitude and sign of the error. The student will appreciate this if he introduces a deliberate error into Table 10.4.

Problems

1. How will the differences of a table be affected if the tabular interval h is doubled? Check your answer by comparing Table 10.4 with the differences of the table giving $\sin 0$, $\sin 10°$, $\sin 20°$, etc.

2. Use the table found in problem 1 to interpolate the values of $\sin 5°$, $\sin 15°$, etc. (Find the interpolation coefficients from the formulas in the text. B_6, E_6, and F_6 are all equal to -0.00244 for $p = 0.5$.)

3. Find polynomial expressions in p for the first four Everett interpolation coefficients.

4. Consider the ratio B_4/B_2. Hence justify the numerical coefficient 0.184 in the throwback of fourth to second differences.

5. From a suitable table of x^5 (tabulated for integral x), find the value of $(6.5)^5$ by interpolation. Also find, by numerical differentiation and integration, the values of 6^6 and 6^4.

6. From a table of the function
$$y = (2x - 1)^3(1.423\ 856x + 9.745\ 963)$$
for integral values of x, find numerically the values of y, y', and y'' when $x = \frac{1}{2}$.

7. Solve the equation
$$\ddot{x} = -g$$
numerically with the initial conditions $x = 10^4$ cm, $\dot{x} = 0$, when $t = 0$. (g is the attraction due to gravity at the surface of the Earth.) From the solution find the time when $x = 0$. At each tabular point find the value of $\dot{x}$, and hence check that the energy integral is satisfied throughout the integration. Finally check your answers with the known analytical solutions.

8. Solve the equation
$$\dot{x} = \cos t$$
numerically with the initial condition $x = 0$ when $t = 0$. Show that the solution can be used to find the value of π.

9. Solve the equation
$$\ddot{x} = -x$$
numerically with the initial conditions $x = 0$, $\dot{x} = 1$ when $t = 0$. Solve the equation, using different numbers of significant figures, and compare the results with one another and with a table of $\sin t$.

10. Solve the equations
$$\dot{x} - y = 1,$$
$$\dot{y} + x = 1,$$
numerically with the initial conditions $x = 1$, $y = 0$ when $t = 0$.

Chapter 11 ** PERTURBATIONS

11.1 Introduction

The equation of motion of a perturbed orbit is of the form

$$\ddot{\mathbf{r}} + \mu \frac{\mathbf{r}}{r^3} = \mathbf{F}. \tag{11.1.1}$$

In Chapter Nine the perturbing force $\mathbf{F}$ was derived from the action of other bodies, but it could equally well arise from other causes such as atmospheric drag or the fact that the attracting body was not perfectly spherical. For example, when considering the motion of a close artificial satellite of the Earth, we are mainly concerned with the consequences of atmospheric friction and the oblateness of the Earth.

If the right-hand side of (11.1.1) is zero, the motion is Keplerian; the deviations from Keplerian motion are perturbations. The purpose of this chapter is to explain to the student some of the fundamental principles involved in the consideration of perturbations. For practical work the student is particularly urged to consult *Planetary Coordinates* (Ref. 38), in which there are numerous worked examples, and Refs. 26 and 27.

As an example of a perturbed orbit, consider the hypothetical case of a body of mass m moving in the Newtonian field of a mass M and also subject to a small tangential resistance

$$R = \frac{cV}{r^2}$$

per unit mass, where V is the orbital speed and r is the distance from the center of M. If ds is the element of arc length, R can be resolved radially and transversely as

$$-R\frac{dr}{ds} \quad \text{and} \quad -Rr\frac{d\theta}{ds},$$

(see Figure 11.1), or, since $V = ds/dt$,

$$-c\frac{1}{r^2}\frac{dr}{dt} \quad \text{and} \quad -c\frac{1}{r}\frac{d\theta}{dt}.$$

The motion takes place in a plane, and the equations of motion in that plane are

$$\ddot{r} - r\dot{\theta}^2 = -\frac{\mu}{r^2} - c\frac{\dot{r}}{r^2} \tag{11.1.2}$$

and

$$\frac{d}{dt}(r^2\dot{\theta}) = -c\dot{\theta}, \tag{11.1.3}$$

where

$$\mu = (M + m)k^2.$$

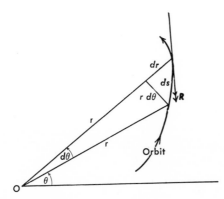

Figure 11.1

Let $H = r^2\dot{\theta}$. Because of the perturbing force, this is not constant, but, integrating (11.1.3),

$$H = h - c\theta, \tag{11.1.4}$$

where h is a constant of integration.

Let $r = 1/u$; then, as in Section 4.3,

$$\ddot{r} = -Hu^2\frac{d}{d\theta}\left(H\frac{du}{d\theta}\right)$$

and (11.1.2) becomes

$$\frac{d^2u}{d\theta^2} + u = \frac{\mu}{H^2}.$$

Using (11.1.4) we can expand H^{-2} in powers of c, and since the resisting force is small, c is a small quantity whose square may be neglected. Then

$$\frac{d^2u}{d\theta^2} + u = \frac{\mu}{h^2}\left(1 + 2\frac{c}{h}\theta\right). \tag{11.1.5}$$

The solution of this equation is easily verified to be

$$u = \frac{1}{p}\left(1 + e\cos(\theta - \omega) + 2\frac{c}{h}\theta\right), \tag{11.1.6}$$

where e and ω are constants of integration, and $p = h^2/\mu$ is also constant. We assume that e is less than one.

To interpret this solution, suppose that at some point P_1, where the position and velocity are given by u_1, θ_1, $(du/dt)_1$, and $(d\theta/dt)_1$, the perturbing force suddenly ceases; then m will move in an ellipse defined by these initial values. This is called the *osculating ellipse* at P_1; it is the Keplerian orbit having simultaneously the same position and velocity as the true orbit.

Let the osculating orbit at P_1 have equation

$$u = \frac{1}{p_1}[1 + e_1 \cos(\theta - \omega_1)]. \tag{11.1.7}$$

(Note: We must not assume it to be $u = \dfrac{1}{p}[1 + e\cos(\theta - \omega)]$.)

The angular momentum h_1 must be equal to the value of $(r^2\dot\theta)_1$, or, from (11.1.4),

$$h_1 = h - c\theta_1.$$

Hence

$$\begin{aligned}
p_1 &= \frac{h_1^2}{\mu} = \frac{(h - c\theta_1)^2}{\mu} \\
&= p\left(1 - \frac{c}{h}\theta_1\right)^2 \\
&= p\left(1 - 2\frac{c}{h}\theta_1\right),
\end{aligned} \tag{11.1.8}$$

where c^2 has been neglected.

At P_1, u and $du/d\theta$ must be the same both for (11.1.6) and (11.1.7), so that

$$\frac{1}{p_1}[1 + e_1\cos(\theta_1 - \omega_1)] = \frac{1}{p}\left[1 + e\cos(\theta_1 - \omega) + 2\frac{c}{h}\theta_1\right]$$

and

$$\frac{1}{p_1}[-e_1\sin(\theta_1 - \omega_1)] = \frac{1}{p}\left[-e\sin(\theta_1 - \omega) + 2\frac{c}{h}\right].$$

Using (11.1.8) and neglecting c^2, we find

$$e_1\cos(\theta_1 - \omega_1) = e\cos(\theta_1 - \omega) - 2\frac{c}{h}e\theta_1\cos(\theta_1 - \omega)$$

and

$$e_1\sin(\theta_1 - \omega_1) = e\sin(\theta_1 - \omega) - 2\frac{c}{h} - 2\frac{c}{h}e\theta_1\sin(\theta_1 - \omega).$$

Multiply the first of these by $\cos(\theta_1 - \omega)$ and the second by $\sin(\theta_1 - \omega)$, and add. Then multiply the first by $\sin(\theta_1 - \omega)$ and the second by $\cos(\theta_1 - \omega)$

and subtract. We find

$$e_1 \cos(\omega_1 - \omega) = e - 2\frac{c}{h}e\theta_1 - 2\frac{c}{h}\sin(\theta_1 - \omega)$$

and

$$e_1 \sin(\omega_1 - \omega) = 2\frac{c}{h}e\cos(\theta_1 - \omega).$$

Now let

$$e_1 - e = \delta e_1 \quad \text{and} \quad \omega_1 - \omega = \delta \omega_1.$$

Then, still neglecting c^2,

$$\delta e_1 = -2\frac{c}{h}[e\theta_1 + \sin(\theta_1 - \omega)] \tag{11.1.9}$$

and

$$\delta \omega_1 = 2\frac{c}{h}\cos(\theta_1 - \omega). \tag{11.1.10}$$

e_1 and ω_1 are two of the *osculating elements* at P_1. From (11.1.9) we see that the variation in e_1, as P_1 varies in the true orbit, consists of two parts; the first represents a steady decrease to a circular orbit, while the second is periodic and contributes nothing in the long run. A steady monotonic change is called a *secular perturbation*. The other terms are *periodic perturbations*; since their cumulative effect is zero, they can often be ignored, but the secular perturbations, however small, are bound to become important over a long enough period of time. From (11.1.10) we see that ω_1 suffers only periodic perturbations.

Let Δp_1, Δa_1, and Δn_1 now be defined as the perturbations in these elements *over one revolution*; the periodic components cancel out and only the secular parts remain. From (11.1.8),

$$\frac{\Delta p_1}{p_1} = -4\pi\frac{c}{h}$$

(neglecting c^2), and from (11.1.9),

$$\frac{\Delta e_1}{e_1} = -4\pi\frac{c}{h} = \frac{\Delta p_1}{p_1}.$$

Also $p_1 = a_1(1 - e_1^2)$, so

$$\frac{\Delta a_1}{a_1} = \frac{\Delta p_1}{p_1} + \frac{2e_1 \Delta e_1}{1 - e_1^2}$$

$$= -4\pi\frac{c}{h}\frac{1 + e_1^2}{1 - e_1^2}. \tag{11.1.11}$$

Also, since $n_1 = \sqrt{\mu}\,a_1^{-3/2}$,

$$\frac{\Delta n_1}{n_1} = -\frac{3}{2}\frac{\Delta a_1}{a_1}$$

$$= 6\pi\frac{c}{h}\frac{1 + e_1^2}{1 - e_1^2}. \tag{11.1.12}$$

So a_1 decreases secularly, and there is a corresponding increase in the mean motion; in addition, these quantities will fluctuate periodically about the secular trend.

This form of resistance would be unlikely to be encountered in practice, but the equations have been considered in some detail in order to demonstrate some of the important considerations involved in perturbations. The solution found is a closed analytical solution, correct to the order of magnitude required (we could, without much difficulty, extend the solutions to the order c^2). We can find the perturbations and the character of the orbit at any future time simply by substituting the appropriate value of t into the equations; the same would apply if we had found a solution in the form of a series. This is the method of *general* or *absolute perturbations*. In our example the solution was simple because the perturbing force was deliberately chosen; but normally this can only be expressed as an infinite series of great complexity, and the method of general perturbations involves considerable labor and analysis.

Another approach to perturbations is to integrate the equations of motion, or adaptations of these, by a numerical procedure in order to find out what will happen over some limited time interval. This is the method of *special perturbations*. It has some obvious practical advantages in that no complicated analytical work is involved and that, anyway, the general form of the solution for all time may be of no interest (as, for instance, in the case of an interplanetary rocket). Much of this chapter will be devoted to methods of considering special perturbations, but the student should remember that if a general solution can be found, it will probably be superior to a numerical integration.

In the example the solution described the changes in the osculating elements in time. This type of method is called the *variation of the elements*, or the *variation of the arbitrary constants* (since the elements are the arbitrary constants of the two-body problem). Alternatively we can work in terms of the coordinates; since there are six elements but only three coordinates, we have fewer unknowns, but the solution may give no immediate insight into what is happening to the orbit in a geometrical sense; however, this information may not be required. We shall start by considering some of the methods of special perturbations in which the coordinates are used, and will go on to consider the variation of the elements.

11.2   Cowell's Method

The equations of motion of the two-body problem,

$$\ddot{x} + \mu \frac{x}{r^3} = 0, \quad \text{etc.,}$$

could be solved numerically, using the methods of Chapter Ten, provided the initial conditions were specified. Three equations would be integrated simultaneously; corresponding extrapolations would be made in each equation to find rough values of x, y, z, and r, and therefore x/r^3, etc., which would then be used to find better values of the coordinates. But since the two-body problem has been solved analytically, this procedure would be a waste of time (and not so accurate as a direct substitution). Also, as we remarked before, the solution would provide no immediate information about the nature of the orbit.

But the analytical solution of the equations

$$\ddot{x} + \mu \frac{x}{r^3} = F_x, \quad \text{etc.,}$$

is not, in general, known. Apart from the errors inherent in any numerical integration, the equations can be solved as accurately as required by the method of Section 10.5. This is known as *Cowell's method*. Other approaches to the perturbation problem refer to some reference orbit, as we shall see, but Cowell's method is direct. In fact an alternative name, often used, is the *direct integration method*, but this can include methods of numerical integration other than that used in Cowell's method: any suitable numerical method can, of course, be used to solve the equations. Full details of Cowell's method together with worked examples are given by Herget and in *Planetary Coordinates*.

Any method of direct integration has the disadvantage that when the motion becomes rapid (near perihelion) or perhaps when the perturbations become severe, smaller intervals of integration and therefore more calculations are necessary, and the errors will be correspondingly increased. For some parts of the work it may be more convenient to change to another method, such as Encke's (see Section 11.3), which involves more labor at each step of the integration but which allows a longer interval to be used.

All the remarks of Section 9.5 about the neglect of some planets in calculating perturbations in the solar system and "throwing the planets into the Sun" are relevant in the direct integration methods and also in Encke's method. Full practical details are given in *Planetary Coordinates*.

11.3 Encke's Method

Consider the disturbed motion given by

$$\ddot{\mathbf{r}} + \mu \frac{\mathbf{r}}{r^3} = \mathbf{F}. \tag{11.3.1}$$

The equation of undisturbed motion is

$$\ddot{\boldsymbol{\rho}} + \mu \frac{\boldsymbol{\rho}}{\rho^3} = 0. \tag{11.3.2}$$

Let

$$\Delta\mathbf{r} = \mathbf{r} - \boldsymbol{\rho}, \tag{11.3.3}$$

then

$$\frac{d^2}{dt^2} \Delta\mathbf{r} = \mathbf{F} + \mu \left(\frac{\boldsymbol{\rho}}{\rho^3} - \frac{\mathbf{r}}{r^3} \right). \tag{11.3.4}$$

Let the solution of (11.3.2) apply to the osculating orbit at some epoch that will be the start of the integration; this will be used as a *reference orbit*. Since this solution is fully known, the terms in ρ in (11.3.4) are known, so that the three equations which it comprises can be integrated numerically to give $\Delta\mathbf{r}$ (the deviation from the reference orbit) as a function of time.

The term

$$\frac{\boldsymbol{\rho}}{\rho^3} - \frac{\mathbf{r}}{r^3}$$

is small, but its separate components are not, and it is inconvenient to calculate the difference between two nearly equal quantities; to avoid this the equations are transformed as follows. Let

$$\frac{r^2}{\rho^2} = 1 + 2q$$

and

$$\frac{\rho^3}{r^3} = (1 + 2q)^{-3/2}$$

$$= 1 - fq.$$

Then

$$q = \frac{r^2 - \rho^2}{2\rho^2}$$

$$= \frac{1}{\rho^2} \{(\xi + \tfrac{1}{2}\Delta x)\Delta x + (\eta + \tfrac{1}{2}\Delta y)\Delta y + (\zeta + \tfrac{1}{2}\Delta z)\Delta z\}, \qquad (11.3.5)$$

where $\boldsymbol{\rho} = (\xi, \eta, \zeta)$. f is a function of q (a small quantity) and is tabulated in many references. It is given by the series

$$f = 3\left(1 - \frac{5}{2}q + \frac{5\cdot 7}{2\cdot 3}q^2 - \frac{5\cdot 7\cdot 9}{2\cdot 3\cdot 4}q^3 + \cdots\right). \qquad (11.3.6)$$

With these substitutions (11.3.4) becomes

$$\frac{d^2}{dt^2}\Delta\mathbf{r} = \mathbf{F} + \frac{\mu}{\rho^3}\{\boldsymbol{\rho} - \mathbf{r}(1 - fq)\}$$

or

$$\frac{d^2}{dt^2}\Delta\mathbf{r} = \mathbf{F} + h\mathbf{r}fq - h\,\Delta\mathbf{r}, \qquad (11.3.7)$$

where $h = \mu/\rho^3$.

The advantage of Encke's method is that, as perturbations are usually small, $\Delta\mathbf{r}$ and its derivatives are small, and consequently a larger integration interval is possible than in Cowell's method. Near perihelion, when the integration intervals have to be diminished in Cowell's method, Encke's method is unaffected. Against this is the fact that each step of Encke's method takes longer. Also, as the perturbations accumulate, $\Delta\mathbf{r}$ goes on increasing and the equations may become unmanageable. In this case a new and more up-to-date set of osculating elements must be found, and the integration proceeds with these. This method has been successfully used to calculate orbits from the Earth to the Moon; the osculating elements refer to the time of burn-out of a rocket, and the Moon is considered throughout as the perturbing body.

11.4   The Osculating Orbit

In this section we shall consider the accuracy of the osculating orbit for making short-term predictions, and shall show how the orders of magnitude of the perturbations from the osculating orbit can be found.

Let the position and velocity at time t_0 in the orbit, which is described under the equations of motion

$$\ddot{\mathbf{r}} + \mu\frac{\mathbf{r}}{r^3} = \mathbf{F}, \tag{11.4.1}$$

be $\mathbf{r}_0$ and $\dot{\mathbf{r}}_0$. The osculating orbit at t_0 is the solution of

$$\ddot{\boldsymbol{\rho}} + \mu\frac{\boldsymbol{\rho}}{\rho^3} = 0 \tag{11.4.2}$$

having the initial conditions $\boldsymbol{\rho} = \mathbf{r}_0$ and $\dot{\boldsymbol{\rho}} = \dot{\mathbf{r}}_0$ at $t = t_0$. The functions $\mathbf{r}$ and $\boldsymbol{\rho}$ can be expanded in Taylor series about this position as

$$\mathbf{r}(t_0 + \Delta t) = \mathbf{r}_0 + \Delta t\,\dot{\mathbf{r}}_0 + \tfrac{1}{2}(\Delta t)^2\ddot{\mathbf{r}}_0 + \cdots$$

and

$$\boldsymbol{\rho}(t_0 + \Delta t) = \boldsymbol{\rho}_0 + \Delta t\,\dot{\boldsymbol{\rho}}_0 + \tfrac{1}{2}(\Delta t)^2\ddot{\boldsymbol{\rho}}_0 + \cdots$$

where $\ddot{\mathbf{r}}_0$ means that $\ddot{\mathbf{r}}$ is evaluated at $t = t_0$. Subtracting these equations and applying the initial conditions, we find

$$\Delta\mathbf{r} = \mathbf{r} - \boldsymbol{\rho} = \tfrac{1}{2}(\Delta t)^2(\ddot{\mathbf{r}}_0 - \ddot{\boldsymbol{\rho}}_0) + O\{(\Delta t)^3\}.$$

Suppose that Δt is small enough for its cube to be neglected; then, substituting from the equations of motion, we find

$$\Delta\mathbf{r} = \tfrac{1}{2}(\Delta t)^2\mathbf{F}_0. \tag{11.4.3}$$

We shall use this formula to estimate the extent of perturbations by Jupiter on Mars. Here

$$\mathbf{F} = m'k^2\left\{\frac{\mathbf{r}' - \mathbf{r}}{|\mathbf{r}' - \mathbf{r}|^3} - \frac{\mathbf{r}'}{r'^3}\right\}, \tag{11.4.4}$$

where m' is the mass of Jupiter and $\mathbf{r}'$ its position vector with respect to the Sun. Let a be the semimajor axis of Mars' orbit; then

$$\mu = 4\pi^2\frac{a^3}{P^2}, \tag{11.4.5}$$

where P is the period of Mars and $\mu = k^2(M + m)$; M and m are masses of the Sun and Mars, respectively. Putting

$$(\Delta t)^2 = \left(\frac{\Delta t}{P}\right)^2 P^2$$

$$= \left(\frac{\Delta t}{P}\right)^2 4\pi^2 \frac{a^3}{(M + m)k^2},$$

(11.4.3) can be written

$$\Delta \mathbf{r} = 2\pi^2 a^3 \frac{m'}{M + m} \left(\frac{\Delta t}{P}\right)^2 \left\{ \frac{\mathbf{r}' - \mathbf{r}}{|\mathbf{r}' - \mathbf{r}|^3} - \frac{\mathbf{r}'}{r'^3} \right\}. \tag{11.4.6}$$

It should be noted that the perturbations depend on the ratio of the masses of the perturbing body and the Sun.

Consider the perturbations near the time of a conjunction of Mars and Jupiter, as observed from the Sun, when we would expect them to be most severe. Neglecting the relative inclination of the two orbits, let the x-axis point along the line of conjunction, and let the conjunction take place at time t_0. Taking the coordinates of Mars and Jupiter at that time as $(1.52, 0, 0)$ and $(5.21, 0, 0)$, where the unit of length is the astronomical unit, and putting

$$\frac{m'}{M + m} = \frac{1}{1047},$$

we find

$$\Delta x = 2.44 \times 10^{-3} \left(\frac{\Delta t}{P}\right)^2 \text{ AU.}$$

Take

$$\frac{\Delta t}{P} = 0.1,$$

so that we are considering the perturbation over 0.188 years; then

$$\Delta x = 2.44 \times 10^{-5} \text{ AU}$$
$$= 3650 \text{ km.}$$

Whether or not this is serious may depend on the job in hand. For example, if Mars is the target for a rocket, the osculating orbit may not give a sufficiently accurate prediction of its position. But it should be noted that the numerical results were derived from approximate distances for Mars and Jupiter; if these were changed by 3650 km, the result would not be altered. Hence, when predicting perturbing forces, the osculating elements may be good enough as long as departures from them are not too severe and as long as we do not approach too closely to the perturbing body.

11.5   The Effects of Small Impulses on the Elements

Suppose a body moving in a Keplerian orbit to be acted on by a force $\mathbf{F}$

per unit mass for a time dt. This impulse will alter the elements of the orbit in a way which we shall now investigate.

Resolve $\mathbf{F}$ along $\hat{\mathbf{r}}$, $\hat{\mathbf{h}}$, and $\hat{\mathbf{h}} \times \hat{\mathbf{r}}$ so that

$$\mathbf{F} = R\hat{\mathbf{r}} + N\hat{\mathbf{h}} + B\hat{\mathbf{h}} \times \hat{\mathbf{r}}. \tag{11.5.1}$$

The moment of $\mathbf{F}\,dt$ gives the change of angular momentum, so

$$d\mathbf{h} = \mathbf{r} \times \mathbf{F}\,dt$$
$$= (rN\,dt)\hat{\mathbf{r}} \times \hat{\mathbf{h}} + (rB\,dt)\hat{\mathbf{h}}.$$

But

$$d\mathbf{h} = h\,d\hat{\mathbf{h}} + \hat{\mathbf{h}}\,dh,$$

so, since $d\hat{\mathbf{h}}$ is perpendicular to $\hat{\mathbf{h}}$, we have

$$dh = rB\,dt \tag{11.5.2}$$

and

$$d\hat{\mathbf{h}} = \frac{rN\,dt}{h}\,\hat{\mathbf{r}} \times \hat{\mathbf{h}}. \tag{11.5.3}$$

Resolve all vectors along axes x, y, z, where $\hat{\mathbf{x}}$ points toward the vernal equinox and $\hat{\mathbf{z}}$ toward the north pole of the ecliptic. Then

$$\hat{\mathbf{h}} = (\sin \Omega \sin i, -\cos \Omega \sin i, \cos i). \tag{11.5.4}$$

From (11.5.3) and (11.5.4) we see that N is the only component of F that affects Ω and i. Multiply (11.5.3) scalarly by $\hat{\mathbf{z}}\cdot$; we find

$$\hat{\mathbf{z}}\cdot d\hat{\mathbf{h}} = \frac{rN\,dt}{h}\,\hat{\mathbf{z}}\cdot(\hat{\mathbf{r}} \times \hat{\mathbf{h}})$$

or

$$-\sin i\,di = -\frac{rN\,dt}{h}\,\hat{\mathbf{r}}\cdot(\hat{\mathbf{z}} \times \hat{\mathbf{h}}).$$

Now $\hat{\mathbf{z}} \times \hat{\mathbf{h}}$ has magnitude $\sin i$ and the direction of the ascending node; so, since $\hat{\mathbf{r}}$ makes an angle u with the ascending node,

$$di = \frac{N\,dt}{h}\,r \cos u. \tag{11.5.5}$$

Next multiply (11.5.3) by $\hat{\mathbf{h}} \times$ and then by $\hat{\mathbf{z}}\cdot$; we find

$$\hat{\mathbf{z}}\cdot(\hat{\mathbf{h}} \times d\hat{\mathbf{h}}) = \frac{rN\,dt}{h}\,\hat{\mathbf{z}}\cdot\hat{\mathbf{r}}.$$

Now $\hat{\mathbf{z}}\cdot\hat{\mathbf{r}}$ is the sine of the celestial latitude of the body; in the notation of Figure 11.2, page 240, this is $\sin PP'$, which is equal to $\sin u \sin i$. The left-hand side can be evaluated by differentiating (11.5.4). We find, eventually,

$$\sin^2 i \, d\Omega = \frac{rN \, dt}{h} \sin u \sin i$$

or

$$d\Omega = \frac{N \, dt}{h} r \sin u \operatorname{cosec} i. \tag{11.5.6}$$

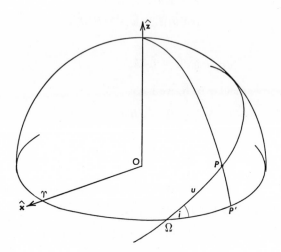

Figure 11.2

$N \, dt$ does not affect h; nor, since it is perpendicular to the velocity, does it affect the linear momentum. Therefore it has no effect on the other elements except indirectly on ω, since this angle is measured from the ascending node. The change in ω caused *solely* by a change $d\Omega$ in the node is

$$d\omega = -\cos i \, d\Omega. \tag{11.5.7}$$

If $\tilde{\omega}$ is used, then

$$d\tilde{\omega} = (1 - \cos i) d\Omega$$
$$= 2 \sin^2 \tfrac{1}{2}i \, d\Omega. \tag{11.5.8}$$

We can now ignore N and evaluate the effects of R and B. Consider the equations for Keplerian motion:

$$e \cos v = \frac{h^2}{\mu r} - 1,$$

$$e \sin v = \frac{h}{\mu} \dot{r}.$$

Since r is not instantaneously altered by the impulse, changes in the motion must obey

$$d(e \cos v) = \frac{2h\,dh}{\mu r},$$

and

$$\left.\begin{array}{c} \\ d(e \sin v) = \dot{r}\,\frac{dh}{\mu} + \frac{h}{\mu}\,d\dot{r}. \end{array}\right] \tag{11.5.9}$$

From the equation of linear momentum we have

$$d\dot{r} = R\,dt.$$

Now

$$v = u - \omega,$$

and as neither R nor B alters the node, u is not instantaneously changed, so that

$$dv = -d\omega.$$

Applying this condition and (11.5.2) to the equations (11.5.9), we find

$$de \cos v + d\omega\, e \sin v = \frac{2h}{\mu r}\, rB\,dt$$

and

$$de \sin v - d\omega\, e \cos v = \frac{\dot{r}}{\mu}\, rB\,dt + \frac{h}{\mu}\, R\,dt.$$

Solving these for de and $d\omega$, we find

$$de = \frac{h}{\mu}\, R\,dt \sin v + \left(\frac{2h}{\mu}\cos v + \frac{r\dot{r}}{\mu}\sin v\right)B\,dt$$

and

$$e\,d\omega = -\frac{h}{\mu}\, R\,dt \cos v + \left(\frac{2h}{\mu}\sin v - \frac{r\dot{r}}{\mu}\cos v\right)B\,dt.$$

Using the familiar formulas for Keplerian motion, these can be simplified to give

$$de = \frac{na^2}{\mu}\sqrt{1 - e^2}\,\{R\,dt \sin v + B\,dt(\cos v + \cos E)\}, \tag{11.5.10}$$

and

$$d\omega = \frac{na^2}{\mu e}\sqrt{1 - e^2}\left\{-R\,dt \cos v + B\,dt\left(1 + \frac{r}{p}\right)\sin v\right\}. \tag{11.5.11}$$

Next we find da from the relation

$$a(1 - e^2) = \frac{h^2}{\mu},$$

so that

$$da(1 - e^2) = 2ae\,de + \frac{2h\,dh}{\mu}.$$

Substituting for de and dh and simplifying, we find

$$da = \frac{2na^2}{\mu}\left\{ R\,dt\frac{ae}{\sqrt{1-e^2}}\sin v + B\,dt\frac{a^2}{r}\sqrt{1-e^2}\right\}. \qquad (11.5.12)$$

These formulas have been found for isolated impulses. From their form they can be generalized for any forces acting continuously on the body. Then the elements become variables in the differential equations:

$$\frac{d\Omega}{dt} = \frac{nar}{\mu\sqrt{1-e^2}} N\sin u \operatorname{cosec} i,$$

$$\frac{di}{dt} = \frac{nar}{\mu\sqrt{1-e^2}} N\cos u,$$

$$\frac{de}{dt} = \frac{na^2}{\mu}\sqrt{1-e^2}\{R\sin v + B(\cos v + \cos E)\},$$

$$\frac{d\tilde\omega}{dt} = \frac{na^2}{\mu e}\sqrt{1-e^2}\left\{-R\cos v + B\left(1 + \frac{r}{p}\right)\sin v\right\}$$

$$+ 2\sin^2\tfrac{1}{2}i\frac{d\Omega}{dt},$$

or
$$\frac{d\omega}{dt} = \frac{na^2}{\mu e}\sqrt{1-e^2}\left\{-R\cos v + B\left(1 + \frac{r}{p}\right)\sin v\right\}$$

$$- \cos i\frac{d\Omega}{dt},$$ $(11.5.13)$

or
$$\frac{da}{dt} = \frac{2na^2}{\mu}\left\{R\,\frac{ae}{\sqrt{1-e^2}}\sin v + B\frac{a^2\sqrt{1-e^2}}{r}\right\},$$

or
$$\frac{dn}{dt} = -\frac{3}{2}\frac{n}{a}\frac{da}{dt}.$$

These equations omit the element T or associated elements; these will be discussed in the following section. The equations constitute one form of *Lagrange's planetary equations*; their application will be discussed later and, in particular, will be illustrated in the following chapter.

11.6   The Equation for ϵ

Continuing along the lines of the preceding section, we can find the equation for the variation of T by differentiating

$$r = a(1 - e \cos E)$$

to find dE/dt and then differentiating

$$n(t - T) = E - e \sin E.$$

Instead of solving for dT, we shall find the variation in the element ϵ, so we use Kepler's equation in the form:

$$nt + \epsilon - \tilde{\omega} = E - e \sin E. \tag{11.6.1}$$

Here $nt + \epsilon = l$, the mean longitude.

Differentiating (11.6.1), we find

$$n + t\frac{dn}{dt} + \frac{d\epsilon}{dt} - \frac{d\tilde{\omega}}{dt} = (1 - e \cos E)\frac{dE}{dt} - \sin E \frac{de}{dt}. \tag{11.6.2}$$

Having substituted for dn/dt, $d\tilde{\omega}/dt$, dE/dt, and de/dt, we have an expression for $d\epsilon/dt$ in which the coefficients of some terms contain t. If we intend to use these equations over long intervals of time, this will lead to the appearance of disagreeably large quantities.

This difficulty is avoided by the introduction of a new variable, ϵ_1, defined by

$$nt + \epsilon = \int n \, dt + \epsilon_1. \tag{11.6.3}$$

Differentiating this, we have

$$n + t\frac{dn}{dt} + \frac{d\epsilon}{dt} = n + \frac{d\epsilon_1}{dt}.$$

The left-hand side of (11.6.2) becomes

$$n + \frac{d\epsilon_1}{dt} - \frac{d\tilde{\omega}}{dt},$$

and there are now no embarrassing coefficients in the equation for $d\epsilon_1/dt$.

It will be seen that when working with ϵ_1, we are able to assume that n in the mean anomaly is constant. This is confusing at first, but the advantages will appear more clearly when we consider Lagrange's equations in a different form in Section 11.9.

The derivation of the equation for the variation of ϵ_1 is straightforward; the result is

$$\frac{d\epsilon_1}{dt} = -\frac{2nar}{\mu} R + (1 - \sqrt{1 - e^2})\frac{d\tilde{\omega}}{dt} + 2\sqrt{1 - e^2} \sin^2 \tfrac{1}{2}i \frac{d\Omega}{dt}. \tag{11.6.4}$$

11.7 Modifications when the Components of the Perturbing Force Are Tangential and Normal. Drag-Perturbed Orbits

Instead of R and B, consider components T along the tangent to the orbit, and S perpendicular to T and in the instantaneous plane of the orbit, pointing away from the origin. (The appearances of N are not affected, and it can be ignored.)

To find the effects of T and S, it is possible to proceed from first principles. The change in the speed is

$$dV = T\,dt;$$

differentiating the energy equation

$$V^2 = \mu\left(\frac{2}{r} - \frac{1}{a}\right)$$

we find

$$2V\,dV = \mu\frac{da}{a^2},$$

so that

$$\frac{da}{dt} = \frac{2Va^2}{\mu}\,T.$$

And so on.

Alternatively, we can proceed directly from equations (11.5.13) by resolving R and B in the new directions. If χ is the angle between the radius vector and tangent, then

$$\left.\begin{aligned} R &= T\cos\chi + S\sin\chi, \\ B &= T\sin\chi - S\cos\chi. \end{aligned}\right] \qquad (11.7.1)$$

To find $\sin\chi$ and $\cos\chi$, consider Figure 11.3. Let P and Q be neighboring

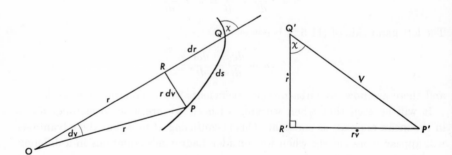

Figure 11.3

positions on the path, and let the perpendicular from P on to OQ meet OQ at R. Then $PQ = ds$, $QR = dr$, and $RP = r\,dv$. The sides of the triangle PQR are therefore proportional to V, $\dot{r}$, and $r\dot{v} = h/r$. Then

$$\cos\chi : \sin\chi : 1 = \dot{r} : \frac{h}{r} : V$$

and, substituting for $\dot{r}$, we find

$$\sin \chi = \frac{h}{rV}, \quad \cos \chi = \frac{e\mu \sin v}{hV}.$$

An immediate application of these results concerns orbits that are perturbed by drag. If we neglect the effects of the Earth's rotation on the upper atmosphere, the orbit of a close satellite of the Earth will be subject to a negative tangential force, or a drag. This will not affect the plane of the orbit, and here we shall consider only the equations for the variation in a, e, and ω. Including only the terms in T, we find

$$\frac{da}{dt} = \frac{2\,Va^2}{\mu}\,T, \tag{11.7.2}$$

$$\frac{d\omega}{dt} = \frac{2\sin v}{eV}\,T, \tag{11.7.3}$$

$$\frac{de}{dt} = 2\,\frac{\cos v + e}{V}\,T. \tag{11.7.4}$$

Since T is negative, a is secularly decreased for any law of resistance, but the form of this law will affect what happens to e and ω. Consider the example of Section 11.1 for which $T = -c(V/r^2)$. Changing the independent variable from t to v, (11.7.3) and (11.7.4) become

$$\frac{d\omega}{dv} = -c\,\frac{2\sin v}{eh}, \quad \frac{de}{dv} = -\frac{2c}{h}(\cos v + e),$$

and these can be integrated immediately, provided that the elements appearing on the right-hand sides are held constant.

For a satellite moving close to the Earth's surface, the law of resistance is

$$mT = -\tfrac{1}{2}C_D A\rho V^2, \tag{11.7.5}$$

where A is the cross-sectional area, C_D is the (dimensionless) aerodynamic drag coefficient, with value of the order of one, and ρ is the atmospheric density. m is the mass of the satellite and appears because T in the formulas is a force per unit mass. The equation for the variation of a is

$$\frac{da}{dt} = -\frac{C_D A\rho a^2}{\mu m}\,V^3.$$

Now

$$V^2 = \mu\left(\frac{2}{r} - \frac{1}{a}\right)$$

$$= \frac{\mu}{a}\,\frac{1 + e\cos E}{1 - e\cos E},$$

and

$$dt = \frac{1}{n} dE(1 - e \cos E)$$

$$= \frac{a^{3/2}}{\sqrt{\mu}} dE(1 - e \cos E).$$

Hence

$$\frac{da}{dE} = -\frac{C_D A \rho a^2}{m} \frac{(1 + e \cos E)^{3/2}}{(1 - e \cos E)^{1/2}}.$$

If Δa is the perturbation over one revolution,

$$\Delta a = -\frac{C_D A a^2}{m} \int_0^{2\pi} \rho \frac{(1 + e \cos E)^{3/2}}{(1 - e \cos E)^{1/2}} dE, \qquad (11.7.6)$$

a result due to Sterne.

In the same way,

$$\Delta e = -\frac{C_D A a (1 - e^2)}{m} \int_0^{\pi} \rho \cos E \frac{(1 + e \cos E)^{1/2}}{(1 - e \cos E)^{1/2}} dE, \qquad (11.7.7)$$

and

$$\Delta \omega = 0.$$

11.8   Hansen's Method

Earlier we considered approaches to the problem of perturbations which involved rectangular coordinates. It is possible to use polar coordinates, and the fundamental method in which these are used is due to Hansen. We have left mention of this until now because Hansen's method combines the variation of coordinates with the variation of the elements. Only the general idea involving the reference orbit will be described here. The student will find accounts in several references; a recent one is given by Musen in the Astronomical Journal. (Ref. 41.)

The motion of the osculating plane of the orbit is governed by the component of force N, perpendicular to this plane. Hansen devised a method of finding special perturbations in which the motion of the osculating plane is found from the equations of the variation of the elements, involving N, and the motion in the osculating plane is considered as a two-dimensional perturbation problem of the coordinates. The reference orbit is a Keplerian ellipse fixed in the plane of the osculating orbit. Suppose this to be described by a fictitious planet, with position vector $\mathbf{r}_1(t)$; then the perturbations are the deviations between this and the true orbit $\mathbf{r}(t)$. Now both orbits take place in the same plane, so that the directions $\hat{\mathbf{r}}$ and $\hat{\mathbf{r}}_1$ can be the same but not for the same instant; then we have

$$\hat{\mathbf{r}}(t) = \hat{\mathbf{r}}_1(t_1).$$

Define ν by

$$r(t) = (1 + \nu)r_1(t_1),$$

then ν and $(t - t_1)$, the perturbation in the time, are sufficient to determine the perturbations.

11.9 The Equations in Terms of $\partial\Re/\partial a$, etc.

When calculating the disturbing force $\mathbf{F}$, we start off with a set of elements for the perturbed body and a knowledge of the disturbance, whether it be the action of other planets, atmospheric drag, or the effect of the Earth's equatorial bulge, etc. The set of elements is used to calculate the position of the perturbed body at some time; since the disturbing force will depend on position and time, this calculated position is used to find $\mathbf{F}$; therefore $\mathbf{F}$ can be considered as a function of the elements and time. For numerical work it will probably be convenient to resolve $\mathbf{F}$ into R, B, and N, but analytically there are advantages in expressing it in terms of the elements.

Suppose $\mathbf{F}$ to arise from a force function $\Re$. Instead of working with $\mathbf{F}$ and its components, it is possible to work in terms of $\Re$ and its partial derivatives with respect to the elements. First we shall find the relations between these partial derivatives and R, B, and N.

Let the force $\mathbf{F}$ change its point of application by small distances δr, δb, and δn in the directions of R, B, and N. Then it is said to have performed the virtual work

$$\delta W = R\,\delta r + B\,\delta b + N\,\delta n. \tag{11.9.1}$$

Now consider $\Re$ as a function of the elements, and interpret the change in the point of application as being due to changes in the elements (the time being kept constant). We shall suppose that the elements used to calculate the position are Ω, $\tilde{\omega}$, i, a, e, and the mean longitude $l = nt + \epsilon$. A change in l given by a change in the elements is $\delta l = t\,\delta n + \delta\epsilon = \delta\epsilon_1$. Then

$$\delta W = \frac{\partial\Re}{\partial a}\,\delta a + \frac{\partial\Re}{\partial e}\,\delta e + \frac{\partial\Re}{\partial(nt + \epsilon)}\,\delta\epsilon_1 + \frac{\partial\Re}{\partial\tilde{\omega}}\,\delta\tilde{\omega} + \frac{\partial\Re}{\partial\Omega}\,\delta\Omega + \frac{\partial\Re}{\partial i}\,\delta i. \tag{11.9.2}$$

Before we can equate these two expressions, we must find what changes in the elements correspond to the changes in position, δr, δb, and δn. Consider the relations between the changes δr, δb, and δn, and those in the position P of the body as given by changes in r, Ω, i, and u. δr obviously presents no difficulties. From Figure 11.4a, page 248, we see that

$$\delta b = \delta\Omega \cos i + \delta u. \tag{11.9.3}$$

To find the effect of δn, we see that if Ω remains constant (Figure 11.4b), and i changes, P moves to P', and $PP' = \delta n$. So, in this case,

$$\delta n_{(\Omega \text{ constant})} = \sin u\,\delta i.$$

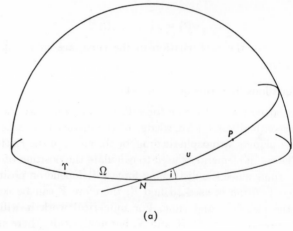

(a)

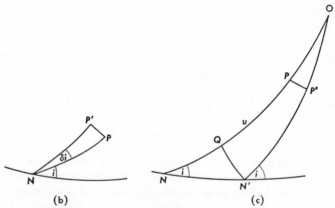

(b)   (c)

Figure 11.4

(We must remember that we are dealing with spherical triangles.) Now let i stay constant, and vary Ω; the effect of this is not seen so directly. Let the node shift from N to N' (Figure 11.4c), and let P shift to P'' so that $PP'' = \delta n$. The great circles NP and $N'P''$ will meet in a point O where $N'O = 90°$. Let Q lie on the arc NP such that $N'Q$ is an arc of the great circle of which O is a pole; then

$$PP'' = N'Q \cos u.$$

Also from the triangle $NN'Q$, since $NN' = \delta\Omega$, we have

$$N'Q = \sin i\, \delta\Omega.$$

But we notice that a positive $\delta\Omega$ leads to a negative δn, so that

$$\delta n_{(i \text{ constant})} = -\sin i \cos u\, \delta\Omega.$$

Finally we have, in general,

$$\delta n = \sin u \, \delta i - \sin i \cos u \, \delta \Omega. \qquad (11.9.4)$$

Now

$$r = a(1 - e \cos E) \quad \text{and} \quad M = E - e \sin E,$$

so that

$$\delta r = \frac{r}{a} \delta a - a \cos E \, \delta e + ae \sin E \, \delta E$$

and

$$\delta E = \frac{a}{r} \delta M + \frac{a}{r} \sin E \, \delta e. \qquad (11.9.5)$$

Therefore

$$\delta r = \frac{r}{a} \delta a + \frac{a^2 e \sin E}{r} \delta M + a \left(- \cos E + \frac{ae}{r} \sin^2 E \right) \delta e$$

$$= \frac{r}{a} \delta a + \frac{ae \sin v}{\sqrt{1 - e^2}} \delta M + a \frac{- \cos E + e}{1 - e \cos E} \delta e$$

$$= \frac{r}{a} \delta a + \frac{ae \sin v}{\sqrt{1 - e^2}} \delta M - a \cos v \, \delta e.$$

Now

$$\delta M = \delta \epsilon_1 - \delta \tilde{\omega}$$

so we have finally

$$\delta r = \frac{r}{a} \delta a + \frac{ae \sin v}{\sqrt{1 - e^2}} (\delta \epsilon_1 - \delta \tilde{\omega}) - a \cos v \, \delta e. \qquad (11.9.6)$$

Since

$$u = v + \tilde{\omega} - \Omega.$$

$$\delta u = \delta v + \delta \tilde{\omega} - \delta \Omega.$$

Consider the equation

$$\tan \frac{v}{2} = \sqrt{\frac{1 + e}{1 - e}} \tan \frac{E}{2}.$$

Take logs and differentiate; we find

$$\frac{\delta v}{\sin v} = \frac{\delta e}{1 - e^2} + \frac{\delta E}{\sin E}$$

$$= \left(\frac{1}{1 - e^2} + \frac{a}{r} \right) \delta e + \frac{a}{r \sin E} \delta M,$$

from (11.9.5). Now

$$r \sin v = a\sqrt{1 - e^2} \sin E,$$

so

$$\delta u = \delta\tilde{\omega} - \delta\Omega + \sin v\left(\frac{1}{1 - e^2} + \frac{a}{r}\right)\delta e + \frac{a^2}{r^2}\sqrt{1 - e^2}(\delta\epsilon_1 - \delta\tilde{\omega}).$$

Then from (11.9.3) we have

$$\delta b = \sin v\left(\frac{1}{1 - e^2} + \frac{a}{r}\right)\delta e + \frac{a^2}{r^2}\sqrt{1 - e^2}\,\delta\epsilon_1$$

$$+ \left(1 - \frac{a^2}{r^2}\sqrt{1 - e^2}\right)\delta\tilde{\omega} - (1 - \cos i)\,\delta\Omega. \quad (11.9.7)$$

Equations (11.9.4), (11.9.6), and (11.9.7) are now substituted into (11.9.1), and this expression for δW is equated with that of (11.9.2). The variations in the elements are independent, so that we can then equate their coefficients to zero; the six resulting equations give the values of $\delta\Re/\delta a, \cdots \delta\Re/\delta i$ in terms of R, N, and B. Before writing them down, we notice that since ϵ never occurs except in the form $(nt + \epsilon)$,

$$\frac{\partial\Re}{\partial(nt + \epsilon)} = \frac{\partial\Re}{\partial\epsilon}.$$

Also, provided we work with $d\epsilon_1/dt$, $\partial\Re/\partial a$ is taken with reference to a only as it occurs explicitly and not as it occurs through n; this means that in differentiating with respect to a, we treat n in the mean longitude as constant. We find

$$\left.\begin{array}{l}
\dfrac{\partial\Re}{\partial a} = R\dfrac{r}{a}, \\[2ex]
\dfrac{\partial\Re}{\partial e} = -Ra\cos v + Ba\left(\dfrac{r}{p} + 1\right)\sin v, \\[2ex]
\dfrac{\partial\Re}{\partial\epsilon} = R\dfrac{ae}{\sqrt{1 - e^2}}\sin v + B\dfrac{a^2}{r}\sqrt{1 - e^2}, \\[2ex]
\dfrac{\partial\Re}{\partial\tilde{\omega}} = -R\dfrac{ae}{\sqrt{1 - e^2}}\sin v - B\dfrac{a^2}{r}\sqrt{1 - e^2} + Br, \\[2ex]
\dfrac{\partial\Re}{\partial\Omega} = -Br\sin^2\tfrac{1}{2}i - Nr\sin i\cos u, \\[2ex]
\dfrac{\partial\Re}{\partial i} = Nr\sin u.
\end{array}\right\} \quad (11.9.8)$$

These equations can now be substituted into (11.5.13) and (11.6.4). The substitutions are straightforward, although the equation in (11.5.13) for

de/dt requires some rearrangement. The results are

$$\frac{da}{dt} = 2\,\frac{na^2}{\mu}\frac{\partial\mathfrak{R}}{\partial\epsilon},$$

$$\frac{de}{dt} = \frac{na(1 - e^2)}{\mu e}\frac{\partial\mathfrak{R}}{\partial\epsilon} - \frac{na\sqrt{1 - e^2}}{\mu e}\left(\frac{\partial\mathfrak{R}}{\partial\epsilon} + \frac{\partial\mathfrak{R}}{\partial\tilde{\omega}}\right),$$

$$\frac{d\tilde{\omega}}{dt} = \frac{na\sqrt{1 - e^2}}{\mu e}\frac{\partial\mathfrak{R}}{\partial e} + \frac{na}{\mu\sqrt{1 - e^2}}\tan\tfrac{1}{2}i\,\frac{\partial\mathfrak{R}}{\partial i},$$

or

$$\frac{d\omega}{dt} = \frac{na\sqrt{1 - e^2}}{\mu e}\frac{\partial\mathfrak{R}}{\partial e} - \frac{na}{\mu\sqrt{1 - e^2}}\cot i\,\frac{\partial\mathfrak{R}}{\partial i},$$

$$\frac{d\epsilon_1}{dt} = -\frac{2na^2}{\mu}\frac{\partial\mathfrak{R}}{\partial a} + \frac{na\sqrt{1 - e^2}}{\mu e}(1 - \sqrt{1 - e^2})\frac{\partial\mathfrak{R}}{\partial e}$$

$$+ \frac{na}{\mu\sqrt{1 - e^2}}\tan\tfrac{1}{2}i\,\frac{\partial\mathfrak{R}}{\partial i},$$

$$\frac{d\Omega}{dt} = \frac{na}{\mu\sqrt{1 - e^2}}\csc i\,\frac{\partial\mathfrak{R}}{\partial i},$$

$$\frac{di}{dt} = -\frac{na}{\mu\sqrt{1 - e^2}}\left\{\csc i\,\frac{\partial\mathfrak{R}}{\partial\Omega} + \tan\tfrac{1}{2}i\left(\frac{\partial\mathfrak{R}}{\partial\epsilon} + \frac{\partial\mathfrak{R}}{\partial\tilde{\omega}}\right)\right\},$$

or

$$\frac{di}{dt} = -\frac{na}{\mu\sqrt{1 - e^2}}\left\{\csc i\,\frac{\partial\mathfrak{R}}{\partial\Omega} - \cot i\,\frac{\partial\mathfrak{R}}{\partial\omega}\right\}.$$

(11.9.9)

It is normal to expand $\mathfrak{R}$ as a Fourier series of cosines in which the mean anomaly, nt, and multiples of this appear, among other terms, in the arguments. (See Section 11.12.) In this case the partial differentiation $\partial\mathfrak{R}/\partial a$ will produce factors

$$t\!\left(\frac{dn}{da}\right)$$

outside the trigonometric functions (now sines). It is to avoid these coefficients, which could become too large and unwieldy, that we find the variation in ϵ_1; accordingly when differentiating with respect to a, n is considered constant whenever it appears in the argument of a term in the expansion of $\mathfrak{R}$.

It is a normal procedure in texts on celestial mechanics to derive the equations (11.9.9) first by analytical methods (which are outside the scope of this present text); for this approach the student should consult the texts by Smart or Plummer. Also, the equations (11.9.8) can be derived differently; the method used here, which the author prefers, is taken from Brown's *Lunar Theory* (Ref. 39).

11.10 Substitutions for Small e or i

In the solar system, e and i are often small, so that some of the denominators in the equations for the variation of the elements become small. This difficulty is avoided by the following substitutions.

If e is small, let

$$h_1 = e \sin \tilde{\omega}, \qquad k_1 = e \cos \tilde{\omega},$$

when the equations for e and $\tilde{\omega}$ are replaced by

$$
\begin{aligned}
\frac{dh_1}{dt} &= \frac{an}{\mu} \sqrt{1 - e^2} \frac{\partial \Re}{\partial k_1} + \frac{an}{\mu} \frac{k_1}{\sqrt{1 - e^2}} \tan \tfrac{1}{2}i \frac{\partial \Re}{\partial i} \\
&\qquad\qquad - \frac{anh_1}{\mu} \frac{\sqrt{1 - e^2}}{(1 + \sqrt{1 - e^2}} \frac{\partial \Re}{\partial \epsilon}, \\
\frac{dk_1}{dt} &= - \frac{an}{\mu} \sqrt{1 - e^2} \frac{\partial \Re}{\partial h_1} - \frac{an}{\mu} \frac{h_1}{\sqrt{1 - e^2}} \tan \tfrac{1}{2}i \frac{\partial \Re}{\partial i} \\
&\qquad\qquad - \frac{ank_1}{\mu} \frac{\sqrt{1 - e^2}}{(1 + \sqrt{1 - e^2})} \frac{\partial \Re}{\partial \epsilon}.
\end{aligned}
\tag{11.10.1}
$$

If i is small, let

$$h_2 = \sin i \sin \Omega, \qquad k_2 = \sin i \cos \Omega,$$

when the equations for i and Ω are replaced by

$$
\begin{aligned}
\frac{dh_2}{dt} &= \frac{an \cos i}{\mu \sqrt{1 - e^2}} \frac{\partial \Re}{\partial k_2} - \frac{an}{\mu} \frac{h_2 \cos i}{\sqrt{1 - e^2}(1 + \cos i)}\left(\frac{\partial \Re}{\partial \tilde{\omega}} + \frac{\partial \Re}{\partial \epsilon}\right), \\
\frac{dk_2}{dt} &= - \frac{an \cos i}{\mu \sqrt{1 - e^2}} \frac{\partial \Re}{\partial h_2} - \frac{an}{\mu} \frac{k_2 \cos i}{\sqrt{1 - e^2}(1 + \cos i)}\left(\frac{\partial \Re}{\partial \tilde{\omega}} + \frac{\partial \Re}{\partial \epsilon}\right).
\end{aligned}
\tag{11.10.2}
$$

The verification of these is left as an exercise for the student.

11.11 The General Approach to the Solution of Lagrange's Planetary Equations

Before considering any application of the planetary equations, we shall consider quite generally the approach to their solution. This approach is, almost inevitably, one involving successive approximations.

All the quantities in the planetary equations vary, but with the exception of the time, they vary slowly. Suppose the perturbations to be caused by a planet; the perturbing forces will contain a factor that is the ratio of the mass of the perturbing planet to the mass of the Sun; in the solar system this is 10^{-3}, at most. However the perturbations are caused, $\Re$ will have some small coefficient, α, say, as a factor, and the right-hand sides of the planetary equations will be small, of the order of α. We might expect the solution for an element, a, say, to be of the form

$$a = a_0 + \delta_1 a_0 + \delta_2 a_0 + \delta_3 a_0 + \cdots \tag{11.11.1}$$

where a_0 is constant and $\delta_1 a_0$, $\delta_2 a_0$, etc., are functions of the time of the order of α, α^2, etc. To find $\delta_1 a_0$, it is sufficient to assume that all the elements occurring on the right-hand sides of the planetary equations are constant, the only variable being the time as it occurs explicitly. Then we find

$$a = a_0 + \delta_1 a_0, \tag{11.11.2}$$

which is said to be the *first-order solution* for a.

To find $\delta_2 a_0$, the first-order solutions for all the elements are substituted into the right-hand sides of the planetary equations, and terms in α^2 are retained. The terms in α will be exactly the same as the terms from which the first-order solutions were found; with the inclusion of terms in α^2, we find the second-order solution:

$$a = a_0 + \delta_1 a_0 + \delta_2 a_0, \tag{11.11.3}$$

with similar expressions for the other elements. We can continue, formally, to any order of accuracy, building up the series (11.11.1). Since α is usually very small, a solution of low order will probably suffice.

To put the situation more explicitly, let the elements be A_1, A_2, $\cdots$ A_6, and let the equation for A_m be

$$\frac{dA_m}{dt} = \alpha F_m(A_1, A_2, \cdots A_6) \equiv \alpha F_m(A_i). \tag{11.11.4}$$

Then each side can be expanded:

$$\frac{dA_{m0}}{dt} + \frac{d(\delta_1 A_{m0})}{dt} + \frac{d(\delta_2 A_{m0})}{dt} + \cdots$$
$$= \alpha \left\{ F_m(A_{i0}) + \sum_{i=1}^{6} \left(\frac{\partial F_m}{\partial A_i} \right)_0 \delta A_{i0} + \cdots \right\} \tag{11.11.5}$$

where

$$A_m = A_{m0} + \delta A_{m0}$$
$$= A_{m0} + \delta_1 A_{m0} + \delta_2 A_{m0} + \cdots \tag{11.11.6}$$

Since A_{m0} is constant, the first term on the left-hand side of (11.11.5) would not normally appear.

The equations for the first-order solution are found from the terms in (11.11.5) of the order of α; they are

$$\frac{d(\delta_1 A_{m0})}{dt} = \alpha F_m(A_{i0}). \tag{11.11.7}$$

The equations for the second-order solution (of the order of α^2) are

$$\frac{d(\delta_2 A_{m0})}{dt} = \alpha \sum_{i=1}^{6} \left(\frac{\partial F_m}{\partial A_i} \right)_0 \delta_1 A_{i0}, \tag{11.11.8}$$

and so on.

11.12   The Disturbing Function

In this section we shall consider the type of expression obtained when the disturbing function $\Re$ is expressed in terms of the elements of the disturbed and disturbing body, in this case a planet. Fuller treatments of this matter are given in various texts, but a complete treatment would require a text of its own. Here we are concerned with the nature of the function, and shall consider it only very generally. The results will be used in the following section.

Suppose a planet of mass m to be perturbed by another planet of mass m'. The disturbing function is, from Section 9.4,

$$\Re = m'\left(\frac{1}{\Delta} - \frac{r\cos S}{r'^2}\right), \tag{11.12.1}$$

where $\mathbf{r}$ and $\mathbf{r}'$ are the radius vectors of the two planets with respect to the Sun, S is the angle between them, and

$$\Delta^2 = r^2 + r'^2 - 2rr'\cos S.$$

The unit of time is chosen to make $k = 1$.

Let us suppose, for a start, that the planets move in the same plane in circular orbits, and that $a' > a$. Then

$$\begin{aligned}
\Re &= \frac{m'}{(a^2 + a'^2 - 2aa'\cos S)^{1/2}} - \frac{m'a\cos S}{a'^2}\\[4pt]
&= \frac{m'}{a'}\left[1 - 2\frac{a}{a'}\cos S + \left(\frac{a}{a'}\right)^2\right]^{-1/2} - \frac{m'}{a'}\left(\frac{a}{a'}\right)\cos S\\[4pt]
&= \frac{m'}{a'}\left\{1 - \frac{1}{2}\left(\frac{a}{a'}\right)^2 + \frac{3}{8}\left[2\left(\frac{a}{a'}\right)\cos S - \left(\frac{a}{a'}\right)^2\right]^2 + \cdots\right\}.
\end{aligned}$$

The powers of $\cos S$ are expressed in terms of cosines of multiples of S; we then have a series of the form

$$\Re = \sum_i C_i \cos i\,S. \tag{11.12.2}$$

The coefficients C_i are expanded in powers of a/a'; the number of terms needed depends naturally on the smallness of a/a'.

For the example above, S is simply the difference between the anomalies. Now suppose that the orbits are still circular but that they no longer lie in the same plane; then S will also depend on the mutual inclination of the two orbits. Let this be i; then if u and u' are measured from the node,

$$\cos S = \cos u\cos u' + \cos i\sin u\sin u'$$

$$= \cos^2\frac{i}{2}\cos(u - u') + \sin^2\frac{i}{2}\cos(u + u').$$

$\Re$ now takes the form

$$\Re = \sum_{jj'} C_{jj'}\cos(ju + j'u'). \tag{11.12.3}$$

The $C_{jj'}$ now depend on i as well as on a and a'; if the ecliptic is taken as the plane of reference, they will depend on i, i', a, and a'.

Now let us introduce elliptic orbits. Instead of u and u', we write $\tilde{\omega} - \Omega + v$ and $\tilde{\omega}' - \Omega' + v'$. The C's now involve r and r', and these, as well as v and v', can be expanded in Fourier series in the mean anomalies M and M', in which the coefficients involve powers of the eccentricities (which, with luck, will be small). Terms such as $\cos(ju + j'u')$ can be expanded in Fourier series such that the arguments involve the angles M, $\tilde{\omega}$, Ω, and M', $\tilde{\omega}'$, Ω', and the coefficients involve a, e, a', and e'. The C's have been similarly expanded, except that here the coefficients involve i and i' in addition. Finally the whole expression can be put into the form

$$\Re = \sum C \cos D, \tag{11.12.4}$$

where

$$C = A e^{q_1} e'^{q_2} (\tan i)^{q_3} (\tan i')^{q_4}, \tag{11.12.5}$$

A being a function of a and a', homogeneous and of degree -1, and

$$D = p(M + \tilde{\omega} - M' - \tilde{\omega}') + p_1 M + p_2 M' + p_3(M + \tilde{\omega} - \Omega) \\ + p_4(M' + \tilde{\omega}' - \Omega'). \tag{11.12.6}$$

The q's and p's are integers; some of the p's can be negative. There are restrictions on their possible values, as follows:

$$q_i - |p_i|, \quad \text{where } i = 1, 2, 3, 4,$$

are even positive integers, or zero, and $(p_3 + p_4)$ and therefore $(q_3 + q_4)$ are always even. A series of the type (11.12.4) with these restrictions is called a *D'Alembert series*.

The argument D can be written:

$$D = qM + q'M' - j_1\tilde{\omega} - j_2\tilde{\omega}' - j_3\Omega - j_4\Omega'.$$

It follows that

$$p_1 = q + j_1, \quad p_2 = q' + j_2, \quad p_3 = j_3, \quad p_4 = j_4.$$

In the new form the restrictions become

$$q_1 - |q + j_1|, \quad q_2 - |q' + j_2|, \quad q_i - |j_i| \quad \text{where } i = 3, 4,$$

are even positive integers, or zero, and $(j_3 + j_4)$ and therefore $(q_3 + q_4)$ are always even.

These restrictions are not much of a comfort. The series are very complicated, and at this stage it is unrewarding to consider them further. But even from such a general expression as (11.12.4) it is possible to find out something about the general character of the first-order solutions of the planetary equations.

11.13   General Discussion of the First-Order Solution of the Planetary Equations

Consider the disturbing function in the form (11.12.4) where now

$$D = q\left(\int n\, dt + \epsilon_1\right) + q'\left(\int n'\, dt + \epsilon_1'\right) - j_1\tilde{\omega} - j_2\tilde{\omega}' - j_3\Omega - j_4\Omega'.$$

$$(11.13.1)$$

When differentiating partially with respect to a, n is kept constant. Two cases must be considered which can make a D independent of the time:

(i) $$q = q' = 0.$$

This will happen for one term, D_0.

(ii) $$qn + q'n' = 0 \quad \textit{for some values of } q, q'.$$

This can only happen exceptionally; also, since all the quantities are slowly varying, it can only happen instantaneously. In practice we are concerned with the case

$$qn + q'n' \textit{ is small for some values of } q, q'.$$

Let A_1 be one of $\tilde{\omega}$, ϵ_1, and Ω, and consider the equations for dA_1/dt from (11.9.9). The partial differentiations on the right-hand sides will affect only the C's, so we shall have equations of the form

$$\frac{dA_1}{dt} = \sum C_1 \cos D + C_{10} \cos D_0,$$

where the summation excludes $q = q' = 0$. Since we are interested here only in the first-order solutions, all quantities but t are constant, and these equations can be integrated term by term (assuming suitable convergence of the series) to give

$$A_1 = \sum C_1 \frac{1}{qn + q'n'} \sin D + t\, C_{10} \cos D_0 + \text{constant.} \quad (11.13.2)$$

Let A_2 be one of e and i. Now the partial differentiations affect only the D's, so that

$$\frac{dA_2}{dt} = \sum C_2 \sin D + C_{20} \sin D_0$$

and, on integration, we find

$$A_2 = -\sum C_2 \frac{1}{qn + q'n'} \cos D + t\, C_{20} \sin D_0 + \text{constant.} \quad (11.13.3)$$

Finally consider the equation for a. This contains no term that is independent of the time (as long as $qn + q'n' \neq 0$) because D_0 does not contain ϵ. Hence

$$\frac{da}{dt} = \sum C_3(q + q') \sin D$$

so that

$$a = -\sum C_3 \frac{q + q'}{qn + q'n'} \cos D + \text{constant.} \quad (11.13.4)$$

Accordingly, every perturbation except that of a contains a secular term as well as periodic terms. In fact it can be shown that a has no secular perturbation of the second order (Poisson's theorem); this is important when considering the stability of the solar system over long periods of time.

The solutions found are only of the first order; second-order solutions will introduce terms in t^2 into the perturbations of all elements except a. Higher order solutions lead to the appearance of higher powers of t. As they stand, the first-order solutions will clearly not be valid for large t, but the fact that the general solution involves a power series in t suggests that the terms in t in (11.13.2) and (11.13.3) are merely the first terms in series for functions, such as sine functions, which remain bounded for all t, and might oscillate. This can be shown to be the case (for the disturbing function considered here) for the elements i and e. For example, the eccentricity of the Earth's orbit is gradually being diminished by planetary perturbations at the present time, but in about 24,000 years it will start to increase.

It remains to consider the case when $nq + n'q'$ is small. When it is zero, all the elements have additional secular terms, but since n and n' are not constant, this is of academic interest only. But when it is small for some pair of values q and q' (there may be several such pairs which are significant), a denominator in each solution becomes small, so that the corresponding periodic term has large amplitude. The period of such a term is

$$\frac{2\pi}{nq + n'q'},$$

which is large; these terms are known as *long period inequalities*.

Given any n and n', $nq + n'q'$ can be made arbitrarily small by suitable q and q'; but to achieve this at least one of the latter may have to be made very large, and, looking back at the general derivation of the perturbing function, we see that this implies a very small C. Hence we are interested in the possibility of small $nq + n'q'$ when q and q' are not too large numerically. This happens in some minor planet orbits, but the values of a that would make n for a minor planet commensurable with n for Jupiter are not popular, presumably because of the resulting perturbations from Jupiter, which become vicious since they are always applied to the same parts of the orbit of the minor planet. Similarly, gaps are observed in Saturn's rings, where particles would be in resonance with the inner satellites of Saturn.

The most famous case of a long period inequality occurs in the mutual perturbations of Jupiter and Saturn. For the two planets we have $n = 299''.13$ and $n' = 120''.45$. If $q = -2$ and $q' = 5$, then

$$qn + q'n' = 3''.99.$$

The resulting period is about 900 years. We also have

$$-29n + 72n' = 2''.37,$$

but this is not so important, since the q's are too large for the corresponding C's to be of much consequence.

The expression for the mean longitude l involves

$$\int n \, dt = \rho, \quad \text{say.}$$

Substituting for n, we have

$$\rho = \sqrt{\mu} \int a^{-3/2} \, dt$$

so that

$$\frac{d^2\rho}{dt^2} = -\frac{3}{2} \sqrt{\mu} \, a^{-5/2} \frac{da}{dt}$$

$$= -\frac{3}{a^2} \frac{\partial \Re}{\partial \epsilon},$$

from (11.9.9). Hence

$$\rho = -3 \iint \frac{1}{a^2} \frac{\partial \Re}{\partial \epsilon} \, dt \, dt. \tag{11.13.5}$$

The double integration means that instead of $nq + n'q'$ appearing in a denominator, we have $(nq + n'q')^2$. Hence the most noticeable effect of a long period inequality is in the mean longitude. Jupiter and Saturn are perturbed by $21'$ and $49'$, respectively, in this way. The correct explanation of this was first given by Laplace.

11.14   Secular Perturbations

From the preceding section we see that the secular terms found in the first-order solution arise from the constant term in the disturbing function, when the latter is expanded in a Fourier series in the mean anomalies of the disturbed and disturbing planets. We may find this term from the integral

$$\frac{1}{4\pi^2} \int_0^{2\pi} \int_0^{2\pi} \Re \, dM \, dM'$$

since all but the constant term vanishes.

In this section we shall consider an important interpretation of the equations for secular perturbations, which is due to Gauss. As an example, consider the secular variation in i; the equation for the first-order perturbation of i is of the form

$$\frac{di}{dt} = A_{00} + \sum_{\substack{j \neq 0 \\ j' \neq 0}} A_{jj'} \cos(jM + j'M' + q) \tag{11.14.1}$$

so that

$$i - i_0 = A_{00}t + \sum_{\substack{j \neq 0 \\ j' \neq 0}} A_{jj'} \frac{\sin(jM + j'M' + q)}{jn + j'n'}, \tag{11.14.2}$$

so it is the term A_{00} in which we are interested. Multiply both sides of (11.14.1) by $dM\,dM'$, and integrate from 0 to 2π for each anomaly; we find

$$\int_0^{2\pi}\int_0^{2\pi}\frac{di}{dt}\,dM\,dM' = \int_0^{2\pi}\int_0^{2\pi} A_{00}\,dM\,dM' = 4\pi^2 A_{00},$$

so that

$$A_{00} = \frac{1}{4\pi^2}\int_0^{2\pi}\int_0^{2\pi}\frac{di}{dt}\,dM\,dM'. \tag{11.14.3}$$

Using the equation for di/dt from (11.5.13), we find

$$A_{00} = \frac{na}{\mu\sqrt{1-e^2}}\frac{1}{4\pi^2}\int_0^{2\pi}\int_0^{2\pi} r\cos u\,N\,dM\,dM'$$

and, since $\mu = a^3n^2$, this can be written:

$$A_{00} = \frac{1}{2\pi na^2\sqrt{1-e^2}}\int_0^{2\pi} r\cos u\left\{\frac{1}{2\pi}\int_0^{2\pi} N\,dM'\right\}dM.$$

Define N_0 by

$$N_0 = \frac{1}{2\pi}\int_0^{2\pi} N\,dM' \tag{11.14.4}$$

with similar expressions for R_0 and B_0. Then

$$A_{00} = \frac{1}{2\pi na^2\sqrt{1-e^2}}\int_0^{2\pi} N_0\,r\cos u\,dM. \tag{11.14.5}$$

Consider a definite point P in the orbit of m, the perturbed body, and the value of N that is exerted at P by m', the perturbing body. If we consider the average of this value over a complete orbit of m', we find it to be

$$\frac{\displaystyle\int_0^{2\pi} N\,dM'}{\displaystyle\int_0^{2\pi} dM'} = \frac{1}{2\pi}\int_0^{2\pi} N\,dM' = N_0.$$

Now consider the elliptic orbit of m' as a thin wire, of which the line density of an element of length ds' is proportional to the time dt spent by m' in traversing ds' in its orbit. The density can be written

$$\rho = \frac{c}{2\pi}\frac{dM'}{ds'},$$

where c is some constant. Then the total mass of the wire is

$$\int \rho\,ds' = \frac{c}{2\pi}\int_0^{2\pi} dM' = c.$$

Now suppose the mass m' to be distributed over the wire in this way; then

$c = m'$. The value of the normal force exerted by the wire at P will be

$$\int_0^{2\pi} \rho \left(\frac{N}{m'}\right) ds' = \int_0^{2\pi} \frac{m'}{2\pi} \frac{dM'}{ds'} \frac{N'}{m'} ds' = N_0,$$

since N/m' is the normal force per unit mass of the disturbing planet.

Hence the configuration obtained by spreading out the mass of the disturbing planet m' around its orbit, in such a way that the mass of an element is proportional to the time spent by m' in that element in its orbit, will reproduce the secular perturbations suffered by another planet through the action of m'.

This is the basis of Gauss' method for the calculation of secular perturbations. For further details the student should consult the texts by Smart and Plummer. The simplification introduced is that the mean anomaly of the disturbing planet can be dispensed with in the equations; but expressions must be evolved for finding the forces exerted by the "loaded" elliptic wires. The method was not translated into practical form by Gauss. This was accomplished later, in particular by Hill.

11.15 The Motion of a Satellite in the Field of an Oblate Planet

We shall assume that a satellite of negligible mass moves around a primary that is slightly distorted from a sphere, but which has symmetry about an axis. Atmospheric drag is entirely neglected. From (5.6.9) the potential of the primary can be expressed as

$$V = -\frac{\mu}{r} \left\{ 1 - \frac{1}{r^2} J_2 \frac{1}{2} (3 \sin^2 \delta - 1) - \frac{1}{r^3} J_3 \frac{1}{2} (5 \sin^3 \delta - 3 \sin \delta) - \cdots \right\}$$

$$(11.15.1)$$

where $\mu = MG$, M being the mass of the primary, and δ is the declination measured from the equator of the primary. For an oblate planet, J_2 is positive.

Initially we shall neglect all the small coefficients except J_2. The disturbing function is then

$$\Re = - \frac{\mu}{2r^3} J_2 (3 \sin^2 \delta - 1). \qquad (11.15.2)$$

But

$$\sin \delta = \sin i \sin u$$
$$= \sin i \sin(\omega + v),$$

so

$$\Re = - \frac{\mu}{2r^3} J_2 (3 \sin^2 i \sin^2(\omega + v) - 1). \qquad (11.15.3)$$

If r and v are expressed in terms of the elements and mean anomaly by suitable series, then $\Re$ is in a form that is ready for the application of the formulas (11.9.9).

Students requiring a complete treatment of the problem using the planetary equations should consult an article by Kozai in the *Astronomical Journal* (Ref. 42). Here we shall find the first-order secular perturbations and discuss those of long and short period.

To find the secular perturbations, we remember that the part of $\Re$ responsible for these is given by the constant term in the Fourier expansion of $\Re$ in terms of M. Hence

$$\Re_s = \frac{1}{2\pi} \int_0^{2\pi} \Re \, dM.$$

Using the following relations (which the student should confirm):

$$\frac{1}{2\pi} \int_0^{2\pi} \frac{1}{r^3} \, dM = \frac{1}{a^3(1 - e^2)^{3/2}}$$

and

$$\frac{1}{2\pi} \int_0^{2\pi} \frac{1}{r^3} \cos 2(\omega + v) \, dM = 0,$$

we find

$$\Re_s = -\frac{\mu J_2}{2a^3(1 - e^2)^{3/2}} \left(\frac{3}{2} \sin^2 i - 1 \right). \tag{11.15.4}$$

We see immediately from this that a, e, and i suffer no secular perturbations. Instead of working with ϵ_1, we shall find the perturbation in the mean anomaly,

$$M = \epsilon_1 + \int n \, dt - \tilde{\omega}.$$

Then we have

$$\frac{dM}{dt} = n - \frac{na}{\mu} \frac{1 - e^2}{e} \frac{\partial \Re}{\partial e} - \frac{2na^2}{\mu} \frac{\partial \Re}{\partial a}, \tag{11.15.5}$$

where n, the first term on the right-hand side, must be considered a variable even in first-order work; this assumes that the perturbations in a are known, but, as far as secular perturbations are concerned, these are zero.

Using the expression for $\Re_s$, we find the secular perturbations from

$$d\omega_s = -\frac{3nJ_2}{2a^2(1 - e^2)^2} \left(\frac{5}{2} \sin^2 i - 2 \right) dt,$$

$$d\Omega_s = -\frac{3nJ_2}{2a^2(1 - e^2)^2} \cos i \, dt, \tag{11.15.6}$$

$$dM_s = n \, dt \left\{ 1 - \frac{3J_2}{2a^2(1 - e^2)^{3/2}} \left(\frac{3}{2} \sin^2 i - 1 \right) \right\}.$$

Hence for an oblate planet, the nodes regress. The line of apsides advances or regresses, depending on whether i is less than or greater than the critical value given by $\sin i = 2/\sqrt{5}$. The perturbation in M can be interpreted as a perturbation of the period; i.e., we can allow for it by using a slightly different or *perturbed* value of n. Observations of an artificial satellite made over a long enough period will yield the secular perturbations, particularly that of the node, and if they are interpreted according to equations (11.15.6), they will lead to a first-order estimate of J_2 for the Earth.

That part of $\Re$ remaining after $\Re_s$ has been subtracted is

$$\Re_p = -\frac{\mu J_2}{2}\left(\frac{3}{2}\sin^2 i - 1\right)\left(\frac{1}{r^3} - \frac{1}{a^3(1 - e^2)^{3/2}}\right) + \frac{3\mu J_2}{4r^3}\sin^2 i \cos 2(\omega + v).$$

$$(11.15.7)$$

This will produce periodic perturbations, and to illustrate its application we shall find the short period perturbations in i, which (the student should be warned) is the simplest case. The expansions of r and v involve a, e, and M but not ω, so that $\partial \Re_p/\partial\omega$ can be written down directly from (11.15.7). The equation for i is

$$\frac{di_p}{dt} = \frac{na}{\mu\sqrt{1 - e^2}}\operatorname{cosec} i \frac{\partial \Re_p}{\partial\omega}$$

$$= -\frac{3naJ_2}{4\sqrt{1 - e^2}}\sin 2i \frac{\sin 2(\omega + v)}{r^3}.$$

To integrate this, change from dt to dv, using

$$r^2\frac{dv}{dt} = na^2\sqrt{1 - e^2},$$

and then put

$$\frac{1}{r} = \frac{1 + e \cos v}{a(1 - e^2)}.$$

We find

$$di_p = -\frac{3J_2}{4a^2(1 - e^2)^2}\sin 2i(1 + e \cos v)\sin 2(\omega + v)\, dv$$

$$= -\frac{3J_2}{4a^2(1 - e^2)^2}\sin 2i\left\{\sin(2\omega + 2v) + \frac{e}{2}\sin(2\omega + 3v) + \frac{e}{2}\sin(2\omega + v)\right\}dv.$$

Then

$$\Delta i_p = \int di_p$$

$$= \frac{3J_2}{8a^2(1 - e^2)^2}\sin 2i\left\{\cos(2\omega + 2v) + \frac{e}{3}\cos(2\omega + 3v) + e \cos(2\omega + v)\right\}.$$

$$(11.15.8)$$

Now the mean value of Δi_p taken over one revolution is not zero; in fact we find

$$\overline{\Delta i_p} = -\frac{J_2}{8a^2(1 - e^2)^2}\sin 2i \cos 2\omega \frac{(1 - \sqrt{1 - e^2})^2}{e^2}(1 + 2\sqrt{1 - e^2}).$$

$$(11.15.9)$$

It is about this mean value that i fluctuates with short period. But we have seen that ω has a secular variation, so that the trigonometric terms that include ω in the argument contribute long period perturbations of i. (11.15.9) shows *some* of the long period perturbations in i of the first order; a complete solution would take more space than we can afford here.

Now consider the consequences of including the third harmonic, with coefficient J_3, in the disturbing function. The additional term in $\Re$ is

$$\Re_3 = -\frac{\mu J_3}{2r^4} \sin i \, \sin(v + \omega)\{5 \sin^2 i \, \sin^2(v + \omega) - 3\}.$$

This produces long and short periodic perturbations but no secular perturbation. The short period perturbations result from the variation of M around the orbit; they are of order J_3, so they are very small and difficult to observe. But we can reasonably hope that some of the long period perturbations, resulting from the secular variation of ω, may have amplitudes large enough to be observed. For these perturbations we are concerned with the changes of ω and not of M; therefore we can take the mean value of the disturbing function with respect to M. The term in $\Re$ due to the third harmonic can be written:

$$\Re_3 = -\frac{\mu J_3}{8r^4} \sin i \, \{3(5 \sin^2 i - 4) \sin(v + \omega) - 5 \sin^2 i \, \sin(3v + 3\omega)\},$$

and using the following mean values with respect to M:

$$\overline{\left(\frac{a}{r}\right)^4 \cos v} = e(1 - e^2)^{-5/2}$$

$$\overline{\left(\frac{a}{r}\right)^4 \sin v} = \overline{\left(\frac{a}{r}\right)^4 \cos 3v} = \overline{\left(\frac{a}{r}\right)^4 \sin 3v} = 0,$$

we find the mean value of this term to be

$$\overline{\Re_3} = -\frac{3\mu J_3}{2a^4} \sin i \left(\frac{5}{4} \sin^2 i - 1\right) \frac{e}{(1 - e^2)^{5/2}} \sin \omega. \qquad (11.15.10)$$

The equation for the corresponding long-period perturbation of i is

$$\frac{di_3}{dt} = \frac{na}{\mu\sqrt{1 - e^2}} \cot i \cdot \frac{\partial \overline{\Re_3}}{\partial \omega}$$

$$= -\frac{3nJ_3}{2a^3} \frac{e}{(1 - e^2)^3} \cos i \left(\frac{5}{4} \sin^2 i - 1\right) \cos \omega.$$

To integrate this, we put

$$\frac{di_3}{dt} = \frac{di_3}{d\omega}\frac{d\omega}{dt} = -\frac{3nJ_2}{a^2(1 - e^2)^2} \left(\frac{5}{4} \sin^2 i - 1\right) \frac{di_3}{d\omega},$$

from (11.15.6). Then

$$di_3 = \frac{J_3}{2J_2} \frac{e}{a(1-e^2)} \cos i \cos \omega \, d\omega$$

and

$$\Delta i_3 = \int di_3$$

$$= \frac{J_3}{2J_2} \frac{e}{a(1-e^2)} \cos i \sin \omega. \qquad (11.15.11)$$

It is from perturbations of this kind, and notably from a long period perturbation in the eccentricity, that J_3 has been found.

The division of the right-hand sides of the planetary equations by $d\omega/dt$ when finding long period perturbations has two important consequences. If we consider only the second harmonic in the disturbing function and form the equations for the second-order solution, (11.11.8), then the right-hand sides contain the factor J_2^2. But a division by $d\omega/dt$ will leave only J_2. Therefore some of the long period perturbations of order J_2 come from the second-order solution of the planetary equations. In addition the factor $(\frac{5}{4} \sin^2 i - 1)$ may be left in the denominators of some perturbations, which means that the results are not valid for $i = \sin^{-1}(2/\sqrt{5})$, and are not reliable for inclinations close to this critical value.

11.16 The Computation of the Variations of the Elements

Equations of the form (11.5.13) can be integrated numerically. Considered formally, we have six simultaneous first-order differential equations; the values found for the elements at each step are used to find the position of the perturbed body, and from this the components of the perturbing force for the next step, and so on. The labor here is obviously considerable, and, provided the perturbations do not become too large, it is possible to use the osculating elements for the epoch of the start of the computation to find the positions and components of force at the later times. When these osculating elements become noticeably out of date, a new set for a later epoch can be used, when the orbit is said to have been *rectified*. It should be remarked that when one set of elements is used, the most serious error is likely to arise in the mean anomaly, since here we are multiplying n (and the errors in n accruing from the neglect of its perturbation) by the time. Hence the variation in M due to perturbations in n must be considered at each step.

There are many alternative procedures for the computation. Details of five (including worked examples) are given in *Planetary Coordinates* (Ref. 38), and Herget (Ref. 27) gives a numerical example. Here we shall discuss only the general problem of determining the perturbation in the mean anomaly. From the definition

$$M = M_0 + n(t - t_0), \qquad (11.16.1)$$

where M_0, the value of the mean anomaly at time t_0, is itself a function of the time. At time $t + dt$, M has been increased by dM, where

$$dM = dM_0 + dn(t - t_0) + n\,dt. \tag{11.16.2}$$

Let n have the value n_0 at t_0; then at time t,

$$n = n_0 + \Delta n$$
$$= n_0 + \int_{t_0}^{t} \frac{dn}{dt}\,dt. \tag{11.16.3}$$

Hence

$$\frac{dM}{dt} = \frac{dM_0}{dt} + (t - t_0)\frac{dn}{dt} + n_0 + \int_{t_0}^{t} \frac{dn}{dt}\,dt.$$

Multiplying through by dt, and integrating between t_0 and t, we find

$$\Delta M = \Delta M_0 + n_0(t - t_0) + \int_{t_0}^{t} (t - t_0)\frac{dn}{dt}\,dt + \int\int_{t_0}^{t} \frac{dn}{dt}\,dt^2, \tag{11.16.4}$$

where

$$\Delta M = \int_{t_0}^{t} \frac{dM}{dt}\,dt$$

and

$$\Delta M_0 = \int_{t_0}^{t} \frac{dM_0}{dt}\,dt.$$

The value of M at any instant is $M_{00} + \Delta M$, where M_{00} is the value of M_0 at t_0.

Now suppose that by assuming n to be constant in the differential equations, we find a perturbation dM_{01}; then

$$dM_{01} = dM - n\,dt,$$

so

$$dM_{01} + n\,dt = dM_0 + n\,dt + dn(t - t_0). \tag{11.16.5}$$

Then

$$\Delta M_{01} = \int_{t_0}^{t} \frac{dM_{01}}{dt}\,dt$$
$$= \Delta M_0 + \int_{t_0}^{t} (t - t_0)\frac{dn}{dt}\,dt.$$

Hence we have, from (11.16.4),

$$M = M_{00} + \Delta M_{01} + n_0(t - t_0) + \int\int_{t_0}^{t} \frac{dn}{dt}\,dt^2. \tag{11.16.6}$$

This is the expression normally used. An alternative form, due to Laplace, which avoids the double integration, can be derived as follows: Integrating by parts, we have

$$\int_{t_0}^{t} (t - t_0) \frac{dn}{dt} \, dt = (t - t_0) \int_{t_0}^{t} \frac{dn}{dt} \, dt - \int\int_{t_0}^{t} \frac{dn}{dt} \, dt^2.$$

Accordingly, (11.16.4) becomes

$$\Delta M = \Delta M_0 + n_0(t - t_0) + (t - t_0) \int_{t_0}^{t} \frac{dn}{dt} \, dt, \qquad (11.16.7)$$

an equation that can also be deduced from first principles.

Watson (Ref. 31, pp. 530–532) compares these formulas in a numerical example, obtaining results that differ appreciably. He attributes this difference to the factor $(t - t_0)$ of the integral in (11.16.7), and reasons that the formula (11.16.6) is to be preferred. However, Herrick (Ref. 45) has recently shown that the difference is apparently due to a numerical error on the part of Watson, and that the two formulas are equally accurate.

In this work it is usual to treat the time as the independent variable. In a recent modification (Ref. 46) Merton uses the mean anomaly as the independent variable; he points out that inaccurate values for the mean motion have led to unsatisfactory results in the former method, but that this weakness can be overcome by making the time one of the perturbed elements, and the mean anomaly, the independent variable. The modifications to the differential equations are straightforward; each is multiplied by dt/dM. The perturbation in the time can be derived as follows: Differentiating (11.16.1) with respect to M, we find

$$1 = \frac{dM_0}{dM} + (t - t_0) \frac{dn}{dM} + n \frac{dt}{dM},$$

or, from (11.16.5),

$$1 = \frac{dM_{01}}{dM} + n \frac{dt}{dM}.$$

Hence

$$\frac{dt}{dM} = \frac{1}{n} \left(1 - \frac{dM_{01}}{dM} \right)$$

and

$$t = t_0 + \int_{M_0}^{M} \frac{dt}{dM} \, dM. \qquad (11.16.8)$$

A complete description of this method and a list of formulas for computation will be found in the original paper and in *Planetary Coordinates*.

In another important modification (Ref. 43) Herrick introduces the parameters

$$a_x = eP_x, \quad a_y = eP_y, \quad a_z = eP_z,$$
$$b_x = e\sqrt{p}Q_x, \quad b_y = e\sqrt{p}Q_y, \quad b_z = e\sqrt{p}Q_z,$$
$$u = r\dot{r},$$
$$w = r - p.$$

The perturbations are found in rectangular coordinates, and these are related to those in u and w and hence to the a's and b's and to perturbations in M and n. The relevant formulas and a specimen calculation are given in *Planetary Coordinates*.

11.17   The Activity Sphere

If a comet passes very close to a perturbing body such as Jupiter, the perturbing force may become so great that inconveniently small time intervals have to be used between steps in the computation of the perturbations. In this case it may be easier to consider the comet as moving in an orbit about Jupiter, perturbed by the Sun from the motion required by the inverse square law (hyperbolic in this case). This contingency is remote in astronomy, but in astronautics the close approach to a planet may very well be the prime purpose of a mission.

We shall discuss the situation in the following way: A rocket R of negligible mass approaches close to a planet P of mass m. Both rocket and planet are subject to the Newtonian field of the Sun S of mass M. Let

$$\mathbf{SR} = \mathbf{r}, \quad \mathbf{SP} = \mathbf{r}_1 \quad \text{and} \quad \mathbf{PR} = \boldsymbol{\rho}.$$

Then

$$\mathbf{r} = \mathbf{r}_1 + \boldsymbol{\rho}.$$

Treating the planet as the perturbing body, we have

$$\ddot{\mathbf{r}} + Mk^2 \frac{\mathbf{r}}{r^3} = mk^2 \left(-\frac{\boldsymbol{\rho}}{\rho^3} - \frac{\mathbf{r}_1}{r_1^3} \right) \tag{11.17.1}$$

or

$$\ddot{\mathbf{r}} + \mathbf{F}_1 = \mathbf{F}_1', \tag{11.17.2}$$

say, where $\mathbf{F}_1'$ is the perturbing force.

Treating the Sun as the perturbing body, we have

$$\ddot{\boldsymbol{\rho}} + mk^2 \frac{\boldsymbol{\rho}}{\rho^3} = Mk^2 \left(-\frac{\mathbf{r}}{r^3} + \frac{\mathbf{r}_1}{r_1^3} \right) \tag{11.17.3}$$

or

$$\ddot{\boldsymbol{\rho}} + \mathbf{F}_2 = \mathbf{F}_2'. \tag{11.17.4}$$

At great distances from P, (11.17.1) is obviously superior to (11.17.3). But as the rocket approaches P, F_1' becomes large and F_2' diminishes; if we reach a stage when the ratio $F'_1 : F_1$ is greater than $F'_2 : F_2$, then (11.17.1) loses its advantage over (11.17.3). Hence, for

$$\frac{F_1}{F_2} > \frac{F'_1}{F'_2}$$

we use (11.17.1), and for

$$\frac{F_1}{F_2} < \frac{F'_1}{F'_2}$$

we use (11.17.3).

The limit

$$\frac{F_1}{F_2} = \frac{F'_1}{F'_2}$$

can be shown to define, very nearly, a locus that is a sphere of radius

$$r_{\text{act}} = r_1 \left(\frac{m}{M} \right)^{2/5}. \tag{11.17.6}$$

This is known as the *activity sphere* of the planet.

11.18 General Methods

The word "perturbation" normally has a much more general meaning than that applied here (i.e., the deviation from Keplerian motion). For instance, when considering the stability of the positions of equilibrium in the restricted three-body problem, we considered *perturbations* of the motion about these positions. In this section we shall consider, only very generally, some other examples of perturbed equations; these examples arise in the following two problems:

(i) Let **x** represent the vector with components $(x_1, x_2, \cdots, x_n)$, and suppose that the solution to the n equations

$$\dot{x}_i = f_i(\mathbf{x}, t) \quad (i = 1, 2, \cdots, n) \tag{11.18.1}$$

is known for the initial conditions $\mathbf{x} = \mathring{\mathbf{x}}$ at $t = t_0$. How can this solution be used to find the solution for the slightly different initial conditions $\mathbf{x} = \mathring{\mathbf{x}} + \delta\mathring{\mathbf{x}}$ at $t = t_0$?

(ii) How can the solution to (11.18.1) be used to solve the equations

$$\dot{x}_i = f_i(\mathbf{x}, t) + g_i(\mathbf{x}, t), \tag{11.18.2}$$

where, over an appropriate range of time, $|f| \gg |g|$?

Consider problem (i). For economy of space we shall work with only two unknowns, x_1 and x_2; the generalization for n unknowns is straightforward. The equations to be solved are

$$\dot{x}_1 = f_1(x_1, x_2, t) \quad \text{and} \quad \dot{x}_2 = f_2(x_1, x_2, t). \tag{11.18.3}$$

The solution with the initial conditions

$$x_1 = \mathring{x}_1 \quad \text{and} \quad x_2 = \mathring{x}_2 \quad \text{at } t = t_0$$

is known to be, say,

$$x_1 = x_1(t) \quad \text{and} \quad x_2 = x_2(t). \tag{11.18.4}$$

We require the solution

$$x_1 = x_1(t) + \delta x_1(t) \quad \text{and} \quad x_2 = x_2(t) + \delta x_2(t)$$

which has the initial conditions

$$x_1 = \mathring{x}_1 + \delta \mathring{x}_1 \quad \text{and} \quad x_2 = \mathring{x}_2 + \delta \mathring{x}_2 \quad \text{at } t = t_0.$$

As long as the differences remain small, we can expand each side of the equations (11.18.3) in Taylor series; neglecting $(\delta x)^2$, the equation for x_1 becomes

$$\dot{x}_1 + \delta\dot{x}_1 = f_1(x_1,x_2,t) + \frac{\partial f_1}{\partial x_1}\,\delta x_1 + \frac{\partial f_1}{\partial x_2},\,\delta x_2,$$

where

$$\delta\dot{x}_1 = \frac{d}{dt}\,(\delta x_1).$$

Remembering that $x_1(t)$ and $x_2(t)$ satisfy the differential equations, we find

$$\delta\dot{x}_1 = \frac{\partial f_1}{\partial x_1}\,\delta x_1 + \frac{\partial f_1}{\partial x_2}\,\delta x_2$$

and

$$\delta\dot{x}_2 = \frac{\partial f_1}{\partial x_1}\,\delta x_1 + \frac{\partial f_2}{\partial x_2}\,\delta x_2. \tag{11.18.5}$$

These equations are the *first variation* of the given system. The quantities $\partial f_i/\partial x_j$ are evaluated from the solution (11.18.4). These equations can be solved numerically for any given set of initial conditions, but an important modification enables the solution to be found once and for all for any set of initial conditions.

Consider the equations

$$\delta\dot{y}_1 = -\delta y_1 \frac{\partial f_1}{\partial x_1} - \delta y_2 \frac{\partial f_2}{\partial x_1}$$

and

$$\delta\dot{y}_2 = -\delta y_1 \frac{\partial f_1}{\partial x_2} - \delta y_2 \frac{\partial f_2}{\partial x_2}. \tag{11.18.6}$$

They are said to be *adjoint* to the equations (11.18.5). In matrix notation the equations (11.18.5) can be written in the form

$$\dot{\mathbf{x}} = \mathbf{A}\mathbf{x}, \tag{11.18.7}$$

where $\mathbf{x}$ is a column matrix and $\mathbf{A}$ is a two-by-two matrix. The adjoint equations are then

$$\dot{\mathbf{y}} = -\mathbf{y}\mathbf{A}, \qquad (11.18.8)$$

where $\mathbf{y}$ is a row matrix. Now, if we multiply the first equation by $\mathbf{y}$, and then multiply $\mathbf{x}$ by the second equation, and add, the terms on the right-hand side cancel out, and we have

$$\mathbf{y}\dot{\mathbf{x}} + \dot{\mathbf{y}}\mathbf{x} = 0,$$

so that

$$\mathbf{y}\mathbf{x} = \sum y_i x_i = \text{constant}. \qquad (11.18.9)$$

Let us return to equations (11.18.6). We find (probably numerically) the following sets of solutions:

$$\delta y_{11} \text{ and } \delta y_{21}, \text{ where at } t = t_0, \delta y_{11} = 1 \text{ and } \delta y_{21} = 0,$$

and

$$\delta y_{12} \text{ and } \delta y_{22}, \text{ where at } t = t_0, \delta y_{12} = 0 \text{ and } \delta y_{22} = 1.$$

Applying (11.18.9), and using the initial conditions to find the constant in each case, we find

$$\delta y_{11} \, \delta x_1 + \delta y_{21} \, \delta x_2 = \delta \dot{x}_1$$

and

$$\delta y_{12} \, \delta x_1 + \delta y_{22} \, \delta x_2 = \delta \dot{x}_2. \qquad (11.18.10)$$

Therefore, once the adjoint equations have been solved, subject to these initial conditions, the functions δx_1 and δx_2 can be rapidly found subject to any initial conditions, $\delta \dot{x}_1$ and $\delta \dot{x}_2$.

The adjoint equations have many uses. They can be used to find the cumulative errors in numerical integration, and in this context they are developed by Kopal in his *Numerical Analysis* (Ref. 47). The perturbations $\delta \dot{x}_i$ need not be applied at the beginning of a solution (a trajectory, say) but can be applied to the end or at any intermediate point. They are used in ballistics in calculating the effects of wind, etc. (the adjoint equations for a trajectory are solved, and then corrections can be rapidly applied according to conditions); an account of this is given by Bliss (Ref. 48). Or if a rocket bound, say, for the Moon is found to have strayed a little from its predicted path *and predicted velocity*, the effects of this on the future of the trajectory can be calculated, as can the necessary counter measures.

It is important to remember that *anything* arising in an equation can be perturbed; this includes not only position, velocity, and the time but also assumed physical constants (the astronomical unit, say). In addition, the equations of motion can be perturbed by including effects of gravitational anomalies or atmospheric drag. Where equations such as (11.18.1) are perturbed, we shall arrive at equations of the form (11.18.2). The functions $g_i(\mathbf{x},t)$ may or may not be known explicitly; they may, for instance, include uncertainties in gravitational anomalies close to the surface of the Earth, and in this case the *observed* motion of a projectile furnishes the perturbed *solution*, from which the nature of the g_i must be found.

The student may be confused over equations (11.18.1) being considered as equations of motion, where accelerations are to be expected. But if the velocity v is considered as a variable in motion in one dimension subject to a force F, then we have $\dot{x} = v$ and $\dot{v} = F$ as the equations of motion. In this case we have two first-order differential equations in two variables and the time; these can be called x_1, x_2, and t.

If **x** is the solution of (11.18.1), and $\mathbf{x} + \delta\mathbf{x}$ the solution of (11.18.2), then as long as $|\delta\mathbf{x}|$ remains small, we find

$$\delta\dot{x}_i = \sum_{j=1}^{n} \frac{\partial f_i}{\partial x_j} \delta x_j + g_i(\mathbf{x},t). \tag{11.18.11}$$

As before, the quantities $\partial f_i/\partial x_j$ are evaluated from the solution of (11.18.1), and, to this order of accuracy, this solution may also be used in the evaluation of the g_i. The equations (11.18.11) can be written in the form

$$\dot{\mathbf{x}} = \mathbf{Ax} + \mathbf{b}. \tag{11.18.12}$$

This is fundamental; but we shall not discuss it further here, except to remark that it will normally have to be integrated numerically.

We shall finish by discussing very briefly two important approaches to problem (ii). The first is that of Lagrange.

Let equations (11.18.1) have the general solution

$$x_i = X_i[c_1, c_2, \cdots, c_n, t] \equiv X_i[\mathbf{c},t],$$

where the c's are the arbitrary constants of integration. Let this solution be substituted into (11.18.2), where now the c's become functions of the time. We have

$$x_i = X_i[\mathbf{c}(t),t]$$

and

$$\dot{x}_i = \frac{\partial X_i}{\partial t} + \sum_{j=1}^{n} \frac{\partial X_i}{\partial c_j} \dot{c}_j.$$

Equating this to

$$f_i(\mathbf{x},t) + g_i(\mathbf{x},t),$$

and applying (11.18.1), we find

$$\sum_{j=1}^{n} \frac{\partial X_i}{\partial c_j} \dot{c}_j = g_i(\mathbf{x},t). \tag{11.18.13}$$

This is the method of the "variation of arbitrary constants."

Another approach, due to Poisson, assumes that the equations (11.18.1) have been solved by finding the n integrals

$$a_i(\mathbf{x},t) = c_i. \tag{11.18.14}$$

If these are solved for the x_i, we find, as before,

$$x_i = X_i[\mathbf{c}, t] \tag{11.18.15}$$

and the conditions for this are the identities

$$a_i(\mathbf{X}[\mathbf{c}, t], t) \equiv c_i. \tag{11.18.16}$$

As before, this solution is substituted into equation (11.18.2), where the c's are now functions of the time. Differentiating the identities (11.18.16) with respect to t, we find

$$\frac{d}{dt} c_i(t) = \frac{\partial}{\partial t} a_i(\mathbf{X}[\mathbf{c}(t), t], t) + \sum_{j=1}^{n} \frac{\partial}{\partial x_j} a_i(\mathbf{X}[\mathbf{c}(t), t], t) \frac{dx_j}{dt}.$$

But $\mathbf{x}$ is now to satisfy (11.18.2); so,

$$\frac{d}{dt} c_i(t) = \frac{\partial}{\partial t} a_i(\mathbf{X}[\mathbf{c}(t), t], t) + \sum_{j=1}^{n} \frac{\partial}{\partial x_j} a_i(\mathbf{X}[\mathbf{c}(t), t], t)\{f_j(\mathbf{x}, t) + g_j(\mathbf{x}, t)\}. \tag{11.18.17}$$

Now, in the solution to (11.18.1), the c's are constants, and

$$0 = \frac{\partial}{\partial t} a_i(\mathbf{X}[\mathbf{c}, t], t) + \sum_{j=1}^{n} \frac{\partial}{\partial x_j} a_i(\mathbf{X}[\mathbf{c}, t], t) f_j(\mathbf{x}, t). \tag{11.18.18}$$

This is true for arbitrary $\mathbf{c}$, so it will be true for $\mathbf{c}(t)$. Hence we can substitute $\mathbf{c}(t)$ for $\mathbf{c}$ in (11.18.18) and subtract the result from (11.18.17), leaving

$$\frac{d}{dt} c_i(t) = \sum_{j=1}^{n} \frac{\partial a_i}{\partial x_j} g_j, \tag{11.18.19}$$

where the terms on the right-hand side are evaluated by using the solutions (11.18.15). This form is similar to that of equations (11.9.9).

The equations (11.18.19) and (11.18.13) are clearly related. Full details of the relations between them, and of the applications of these methods in celestial mechanics, are given in the texts by Smart and Plummer.

Problems

1. Find the periodic perturbations in a for the case of elliptic motion perturbed by a resisting force cV/r^2.

2. Consider the modification due to the theory of relativity produced in the equation of the orbit in an inverse square field. (See Section 4.7.) Use the methods of Section 11.1 to interpret the solution, considering the variations from Keplerian motion as perturbations. Hence find the resulting secular and periodic perturbations in the elements.

3. Justify the series (11.3.6).

4. Assuming that Jupiter remains fixed during one complete revolution of Mars, find, by dividing up the orbit of Mars into ten sections, and using the methods of Section 11.4, the perturbations in the coordinates of Mars for the cases when the line of apsides points toward Jupiter and perihelion

is (a) pointing toward Jupiter and (b) pointing away from Jupiter, and
(c) when the line of apsides is at right angles to the line joining the Sun
and Jupiter.

5. Investigate by the methods of Section 11.4 the perturbations in the coordinates of each planet taken separately, which are inflicted by each of
the other planets taken separately.

6. Solve problem 4, using a rough integration according to Encke's method.

7. Find the separate effects of the components R, N, and B on the speed
of the perturbed body; hence derive the equation for the variation of a.

8. Find, from first principles, the full equations for the variation of the
elements in terms of T and S (see Section 11.7). Check these by the use
of equations (11.5.13) and (11.7.1).

9. Verify equation (11.6.4).

10. Find the equations for the variation of T and ϵ (*not* ϵ_1).

11. Investigate motion in an inverse square field with a small tangential
resistance proportional to $V^{\alpha}r^{\beta}$. Find, in particular, the condition for the
eccentricity to be increased, and discuss the possibility of this occurring
in practice. Investigate also the motion of the line of apsides, and consider
the possibility that some of the advance of Mercury's line of apsides is
due to the presence of resisting material in the solar system. Finally
consider the possible consequences of the existence of continuous, all-
pervasive luminiferous ether that is capable of exerting resistance to
motion.

12. Evaluate qualitatively the effect of the rotation of the Earth's atmosphere
on the orbit of a close artificial satellite. (Note: It will produce more than
just a tangential drag.)

13. Assuming the law of resistance to be given by (11.7.5), show that the
perturbations in the perigee and apogee distances are given respectively by

$$\Delta r_p = -\frac{C_D A a^2}{m}(1-e)\int_0^\pi \rho\left(\frac{1+e\cos E}{1-e\cos E}\right)^{1/2}(1-\cos E)\,dE$$

and

$$\Delta r_a = -\frac{C_D A a^2}{m}(1+e)\int_0^\pi \rho\left(\frac{1+e\cos E}{1-e\cos E}\right)^{1/2}(1+\cos E)\,dE.$$

14. Find an expression for the loss of energy per unit mass of the satellite
during a revolution when the law of resistance is given by (11.7.5). Consider some possible numerical values.

15. Prove that

$$\frac{\partial \Re}{\partial \tilde{\omega}} + \frac{\partial \Re}{\partial \epsilon} = Br$$

and

$$\frac{\partial \Re}{\partial \tilde{\omega}} + \frac{\partial \Re}{\partial \epsilon} + \frac{\partial \Re}{\partial \Omega} = Br\cos i - Nr\sin i\cos u.$$

16. Verify equations (11.10.1) and (11.10.2).

17. Evaluate the first-order effects of the perturbations by the planets on the line of apsides of Mercury. Calculate the predicted angular motion in one century.

18. The perturbations of the plane of the Earth's orbit around the Sun are produced mainly by Jupiter (large mass) and Venus (large inclination). Find these effects to the first order.

19. The system of minor planets thins out in the regions where the periods of circular orbits would be commensurate with the period of Jupiter. Calculate the likely distances of these gaps from the Sun.

20. Investigate the possibility that the gaps in Saturn's rings are caused by the action of the satellites of Saturn, and if this is reasonable, find which satellites are responsible. (Use data from Appendix C.)

21. Prove equation (11.15.5).

22. Find the perturbations of the period of a satellite of an oblate planet, using the equation for dM/dt.

   The mass of a homogeneous spheroidal planet is found from observations of the period and mean distance of a satellite revolving in the equatorial plane of the planet, on the assumption that the planet is spherical. Find the error involved in terms of the oblateness of the planet.

23. Find the nodical period of a satellite of an oblate planet.

24. Find the relation between the sidereal and anomalistic (perigee to perigee) periods of a satellite of an oblate planet.

25. Find the mean value, with respect to the time, of the radial attraction experienced by a satellite of an oblate planet with field given by (11.15.1), neglecting J_3, etc. Hence find the perturbation of the period.

26. Verify equation (11.15.9).

27. Given the following elements for satellite 1957 $\beta 1$, for December, 1957, find J_2 and hence the ratio $(C - A)/C$ for the Earth. What will be the theoretical rate of change of the line of apsides? Find the anomalistic, nodical, and sidereal periods, and the perturbation in the period.

   $a = 1.1311$ Earth radii,

   $e = 0.0868$,

   $i = 65°.3$,

   rate of change of right ascension of ascending node $= -2°.75$ per day.

28. Find the amplitude of the short term oscillations of i for 1957 $\beta 1$, given that $\omega = 42°.8$.

29. Prove that the third harmonic in the Earth's field gives rise to no secular perturbations.

30. Find the secular perturbations produced by the fourth harmonic in the Earth's field.

31. Find the long period perturbation in the eccentricity of a satellite in the

Earth's field which is of order J_3/J_2. If the ratio is 2.5×10^{-3}, consider the possibility of observing the effect of this perturbation on the perigee distance.

32. Consider the application of the formulas of Section 11.10 to satellite orbits with small e or i.

33. The line of apsides of the fifth satellite of Jupiter (181,500 km from the center of Jupiter; assume its orbit to be equatorial and nearly circular) advances through $900°$ per year. Supposing Jupiter to be a spheroid composed of homogeneous incompressible fluid, of density 1.34 and total mass 1/1047 solar masses; find the shape of Jupiter which would account for this apsidal motion, and also find the uniform angular velocity which would account for this shape. Discuss your answer in relation to the actual figures for Jupiter.

34. That part of the motion of Mercury's line of apsides left unexplained by Newton's law of gravitation amounts to $43''$ per century. Assume that this is caused by the oblateness of the Sun, and that this oblateness is the result of the rotation of an incompressible fluid mass of density 1.41. Find the oblateness and the angular velocity of rotation. Comment on the feasibility of the actual rotation of the Sun providing an appreciable portion of this $43''$.

35. Two equal stars of mass M, composed of homogeneous incompressible fluid of density ρ, revolve around each other in nearly circular orbits; the axis of rotation of each is perpendicular to the orbital plane, and the angular velocity of rotation of each is equal to the mean motion in the orbit. The distortion of the stars may be considered only to the first order of small quantities, but should include both tidal and rotational effects. Assuming that the fluid is not viscous, find the perturbations.

36. Let the stars in problem 35 suddenly become solid; how will the perturbations be affected?

37. Consider qualitatively the perturbations of problem 35 when the fluid is viscous.

38. Suppose the orbit of a comet passes near Jupiter's orbit at one of its nodes; under what conditions will the inclination of the comet's orbit be decreased? Show that if the major axis remains constant while the inclination is decreased, then the eccentricity is increased.

39. Investigate qualitatively the effect of the gradual accretion of meteoric matter by a planet on the major axis of its orbit.

40. A planet is perturbed by the action of another planet more distant from the Sun. Assuming that both move in circular orbits in the same plane, describe the perturbations that would be observed from a third planet, the orbit of which lies within the other two. Show how the perturbing force could be deduced from these observations, and that, if the distance of the outer planet is assumed, then its direction and mass can be found.

(This is a highly oversimplified introduction to the theory involved in the discovery of Neptune, when the deviations of Uranus from a Keplerian orbit were used by Leverrier and Adams to predict where a new planet was to be found, in addition to its orbit and mass. They assumed the distance of Neptune to be given by Bode's law.)

41. Consider qualitatively the perturbations that would be produced on the orbits of the planets in the solar system if the entire system were to pass through an interstellar cloud of uniform density with relative velocity (a) in the plane of the ecliptic and (b) at right angles to the plane of the ecliptic. Could perturbations of this kind, over a very long period, help to account for some of the regularities of the solar system, or would they tend to destroy them?

42. Consider qualitatively the perturbations that would be produced on the orbits of the planets in the solar system by a distant passing star, where the star moves (a) in the ecliptic and (b) at right angles to the ecliptic. What would be the cumulative effects of such encounters, where the directions of motion of the passing stars are oriented at random?

43. Find the perturbations that would be produced on the orbits of the planets as the result of a steady loss of mass by the Sun.

44. Investigate the first-order secular perturbations of the orbit of a satellite revolving around a primary that is in the form of an ellipsoid with three *slightly* unequal axes. Apply your results to a satellite revolving close to the surface of the Moon.

45. Suppose the perturbations inflicted by Jupiter on a comet's orbit are to be investigated by the method of the variation of the elements of the orbit. Consider the problem of expressing, at any time, the coordinates of the comet and of Jupiter with respect to axes, with the x-axis pointing toward perihelion of the osculating orbit, and the z-axis pointing toward $\hat{h}$. Write down the components R, N, and B in terms of the coordinates defined by these axes.

46. Prove that the limiting formula (11.17.5) very nearly defines a sphere with radius given by (11.17.6).

47. Find the radii of the activity spheres of all the major planets, and of the Moon (where the Earth and Moon replace the Sun and planet).

48. A body subject to no forces moves in a straight line with uniform speed. The elements of this orbit are the constants defining the position of the line, the speed, the direction of motion in the line, and the position at time T. Show that they can be expressed in terms of six independent constants, and that it is permissible in the problem of two bodies to regard one body as always moving with respect to the other in a straight line whose position continually changes. Find the expressions for these line elements in terms of the time in the case of elliptic motion.

49. Show from general considerations based on problem 48 that the methods of the variation of coordinates and the variation of arbitrary constants are essentially the same, differing only in the variables used in defining the coordinates and velocities of the bodies.

50. Show that the equation $\mathbf{x} = \mathbf{A}(t)\mathbf{x}$ can be solved in the successive approximations

$$\mathbf{x}_1 = \mathring{\mathbf{x}} + \mathbf{A}_1\mathring{\mathbf{x}}, \quad \text{where } \mathbf{A}_1 = \int_{t_0}^{t} \mathbf{A}\, dt,$$

$$\mathbf{x}_2 = \mathring{\mathbf{x}} + \mathbf{A}_1\mathring{\mathbf{x}} + \mathbf{A}_2\mathring{\mathbf{x}}, \quad \text{where } \mathbf{A}_2 = \int_{t_0}^{t} \mathbf{A}\mathbf{A}_1\, dt,$$

and find an expression for $\mathbf{x}_n$.

51. Let $\mathbf{X}$ be the matrix with columns consisting of n independent solutions of

$$\dot{\mathbf{x}} = \mathbf{A}(t)\mathbf{x}.$$

Show that $\dot{\mathbf{X}} = \mathbf{A}\mathbf{X}$, and that the general solution is $\mathbf{X}\mathbf{a}$, where $\mathbf{a}$ is an arbitrary vector.

52. In the notation of the previous two problems, show that

$$\mathbf{X}(t) = \sum_{i=0}^{\infty} \mathbf{A}_i(t),$$

assuming suitable convergence.

53. Consider the equation

$$\dot{\mathbf{x}} = \mathbf{A}(t)\mathbf{x} + \mathbf{b}(t).$$

Show by Lagrange's or Poisson's method of the variation of parameters, or otherwise, that a particular solution is

$$\mathbf{x} = \mathbf{X}\mathring{\mathbf{x}} + \mathbf{X}\int_{t_0}^{t} \mathbf{X}^{-1}\mathbf{b}\, dt.$$

Hence find the general solution.

54. Apply the methods discussed in the problems above to the equation

$$\dot{\mathbf{x}} = \mathbf{x}.$$

55. Integrate the equation of motion

$$\ddot{x} = -x + \alpha x^2, \quad |\alpha| \ll 1,$$

   (a) by Lagrange's method of variation of parameters,
   (b) by Poisson's method of variation of parameters,
   (c) by expansion in powers of α, a constant.

56. $\mathbf{X} = \mathbf{A}\mathbf{X}$ and $\mathbf{Y} = \mathbf{Y}\mathbf{A}$ are adjoint equations. Prove that $\mathbf{Y}\mathbf{X}$ is a constant matrix.

57. Write down the procedure for using the adjoint equations for n variables, using matrix notation when possible.

Chapter 12 ** THE MOTION OF THE MOON

12.1 Introduction

Roughly speaking, we can say that the Moon revolves around the Earth in an elliptic orbit with eccentricity 0.0549 and semimajor axis 0.002570 astronomical units, or 384,400 kilometers. The plane of the orbit is inclined to the ecliptic at an angle of 5° 9′, but the node is regressing around the ecliptic, taking 18.60 years for a complete revolution. In the plane of the orbit the line of apsides advances, taking 8.85 years for a complete revolution. But if this information were used in the computation of an ephemeris of the Moon, the results would be hopelessly inadequate. In addition to the secular motions of the apsides and nodes, each element has considerable periodic variations; the position of the node can vary about its average motion by $\pm 1°\,40′$, and that of the line of apsides by $\pm 12°\,20′$. The eccentricity varies by ± 0.0117. The inclination varies by $\pm 9′$. Our ephemeris could be out by several degrees.

An adequate account of even any one lunar theory is outside the scope of this text. Instead we shall give a descriptive account based largely on the use of equations (11.5.13) for the variation of the elements. (Equations (11.9.9) were used by Poisson to investigate the motion of the Moon, but not to any great purpose.) To represent the Moon's motion adequately, solutions of a high order of approximation are needed; these require a prodigious amount of labor anyway, but the amount of work required in using the method of the variation of the elements would be prohibitive. But if this approach is almost useless for the development of an accurate lunar theory, it offers quick descriptions of the principal perturbations involved, and of their orders of magnitude.

The principal part of the problem of the lunar motion is to find the solution to the particular instance of the three-body problem presented by the system of the Earth, the Moon, and the Sun. A refined theory also includes the effects of the Earth's equatorial bulge, and of perturbations by the other planets. Here we shall consider only some first-order effects of the perturbations by the Sun on the motion of the Moon around the Earth. We shall adopt the provincial attitude of considering the Earth to be the most important body, and of referring to the orbit of the Sun about the Earth.

12.2   The Perturbing Forces

In the notation of Figure 12.1, where E, M, and S are the Earth, Moon, and Sun, respectively, the perturbing function due to the action of the Sun is

$$R = k^2 \left[\frac{1}{\rho} - \frac{\mathbf{R} \cdot \mathbf{r}}{R^3} \right]$$

and the perturbing force is

$$\mathbf{F} = Sk^2 \left[\frac{\boldsymbol{\rho}}{\rho^3} - \frac{\mathbf{R}}{R^3} \right]$$

$$= Sk^2 \left[\frac{\mathbf{R} - \mathbf{r}}{\rho^3} - \frac{\mathbf{R}}{R^3} \right]$$

$$= Sk^2 \left[-\frac{\mathbf{r}}{\rho^3} + \mathbf{R} \left(\frac{1}{\rho^3} - \frac{1}{R^3} \right) \right], \qquad (12.2.1)$$

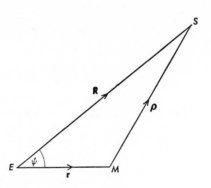

Figure 12.1

where S is the mass of the Sun. This must be resolved in the usual directions to find the components F_r, F_b, and F_n.

Take a set of axes with directions $\hat{\mathbf{x}}$, $\hat{\mathbf{y}}$, $\hat{\mathbf{z}}$, where $\hat{\mathbf{x}}$ points toward the vernal equinox and $\hat{\mathbf{z}}$ toward the north pole of the ecliptic; also take a set with directions $\hat{\mathbf{f}}$, $\hat{\mathbf{g}}$, $\hat{\mathbf{h}}$, where $\hat{\mathbf{f}}$ points toward the ascending node N of the Moon's orbit, and $\hat{\mathbf{h}}$ is perpendicular to the plane of the orbit, in the usual sense. Then

$$\hat{\mathbf{r}} = \hat{\mathbf{f}} \cos u + \hat{\mathbf{g}} \sin u,$$

and

$$\hat{\mathbf{R}} = \hat{\mathbf{f}} \cos U + (\hat{\mathbf{z}} \times \hat{\mathbf{f}}) \sin U, \qquad (12.2.2)$$

where $\angle NEM = u$ and $\angle NES = U$. (See Figure 12.2.)

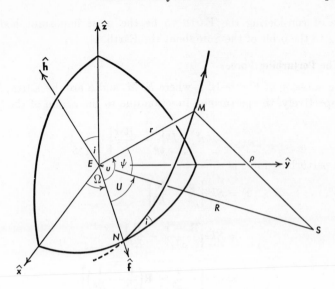

Figure 12.2

Now $(\hat{\mathbf{z}} \times \hat{\mathbf{f}})$ is a unit vector lying in the ecliptic, perpendicular to the ascending node, so that we have

$$\hat{\mathbf{z}} \times \hat{\mathbf{f}} = \hat{\mathbf{g}} \cos i - \hat{\mathbf{h}} \sin i.$$

Then

$$\hat{\mathbf{R}} = \hat{\mathbf{f}} \cos U + \sin U (\hat{\mathbf{g}} \cos i - \hat{\mathbf{h}} \sin i). \tag{12.2.3}$$

The directions of F_r, F_b, and F_n are $\hat{\mathbf{r}}$, $(\hat{\mathbf{h}} \times \hat{\mathbf{r}})$, and $\hat{\mathbf{h}}$, so that multiplying (12.1.1) scalarly by each of these in turn, and using (12.2.2), we find

$$F_r = Sk^2 \left[-\frac{r}{\rho^3} + R(\cos U \cos u + \sin U \sin u \cos i) \left(\frac{1}{\rho^3} - \frac{1}{R^3} \right) \right], \tag{12.2.4}$$

$$F_b = Sk^2 \left[\qquad R(-\cos U \sin u + \sin U \cos u \cos i) \left(\frac{1}{\rho^3} - \frac{1}{R^3} \right) \right], \tag{12.2.5}$$

$$F_n = Sk^2 \left[\qquad\qquad -R \sin U \sin i \left(\frac{1}{\rho^3} - \frac{1}{R^3} \right) \right]. \tag{12.2.6}$$

ψ is the angle SEM, so that, from (12.2.1),

$$F_r = Sk^2 \left[-\frac{r}{\rho^3} + R \cos \psi \left(\frac{1}{\rho^3} - \frac{1}{R^3} \right) \right], \tag{12.2.7}$$

and

$$\cos \psi = \cos U \cos u + \sin U \sin u \cos i. \tag{12.2.8}$$

Now

$$\rho^2 = R^2 + r^2 - 2rR \cos \psi;$$

hence

$$\frac{1}{\rho^3} = \frac{1}{R^3} \left[1 - 2\frac{r}{R} \cos \psi + \left(\frac{r}{R}\right)^2 \right]^{-3/2}$$

$$= \frac{1}{R^3} \left[1 + 3\frac{r}{R} \cos \psi \right], \qquad (12.2.9)$$

where terms in $(r/R)^2$ have been neglected. Since r/R is approximately equal to 2.6×10^{-3}, this neglect is well justified because we are dealing only in orders of magnitude. But this is equivalent to putting

$$R = \rho + r \cos \psi, \qquad (12.2.10)$$

or to assuming that ES is parallel to MS; i.e., we are neglecting the angle ESM: this is referred to as "neglecting the solar parallax." From (12.2.9) we have

$$\frac{1}{\rho^3} - \frac{1}{R^3} = 3 \frac{r}{R^4} \cos \psi. \qquad (12.2.11)$$

Now i, expressed in radians, is approximately 0.09. For a first approximation we can ignore terms in i^2, in which case we can put $\cos i = 1$. Then substituting (12.2.9) and (12.2.11) into the expressions for the F's, we find, eventually,

$$F_r = \tfrac{1}{2}N^2r[1 + 3\cos 2(u - U)], \qquad (12.2.12)$$

$$F_b = -\tfrac{3}{2}N^2r \sin 2(u - U), \qquad (12.2.13)$$

$$F_n = -3N^2r \sin i \sin U \cos(u - U). \qquad (12.2.14)$$

Here we have put

$$N^2 = \frac{Sk^2}{R^3}, \qquad (12.2.15)$$

so that N is the mean motion of the Sun, assuming it to move in a circular orbit.

12.3   The Perturbation of the Nodes

The equation for the variation of Ω can be written

$$\frac{d\Omega}{dt} = \frac{nar}{\mu\sqrt{1 - e^2}} \frac{\sin u}{\sin i} F_n,$$

where $\mu = Ek^2$, E being the mass of the Earth. If n is the mean motion of the Moon, $\mu = n^2a^3$. Define m by

$$m = \frac{N}{n}; \qquad (12.3.1)$$

then $m = 0.0748$. Substituting from (12.2.14) and introducing m, we find

$$\frac{1}{n}\frac{d\Omega}{dt} = -3m^2 \frac{r^2}{a^2\sqrt{1-e^2}} \sin u \sin U \cos(u - U). \tag{12.3.2}$$

To find the first-order solution, we assume that all the elements involved in (12.3.2) are constant; then the left-hand side is $d\Omega/dM$. Also $u = \omega + v$ and $U = V + $ constant, where V applies to the orbit of the Sun. r, v, and V can be expanded in powers of e and e_1 (the eccentricity of the orbit of the Sun), using the series of Section 6.10, so that the right-hand side of (12.3.2) can be expanded in such a series. (Allowance should also be made for the fact that (12.2.15) is not valid for a non-circular orbit.) This is simple in principle but laborious, even for low powers of e. For present purposes we shall neglect the eccentricities entirely; since $e = 0.05$ and $e_1 = 0.02$, we should expect, by neglecting the e's and their powers, to run the risk of an error of up to 8 per cent. To this order of accuracy we have $r = a$, $v = M$, and $V = mM$, where we can put $U = V$. (12.3.2) becomes

$$\frac{d\Omega}{dM} = -3m^2 \sin u \sin U \cos(u - U),$$

which, after using some elementary trigonometry in order to sort out the constant from the purely periodic terms, we find to be

$$\frac{d\Omega}{dM} = -\tfrac{3}{4}m^2\{1 + \cos 2(u - U) - \cos 2u - \cos 2U\}.$$

Remembering the expressions for v and V, we can integrate this to give

$$\Omega - \Omega_0 = -\frac{3}{4}m^2\left\{M + \frac{1}{2(1 - m)}\sin(u - U) - \frac{1}{2}\sin 2u - \frac{1}{2m}\sin 2U\right\}. \tag{12.3.3}$$

The secular term is
$$-\tfrac{3}{4}m^2 M.$$

This gives a regression of the nodes through $2\pi\tfrac{3}{4}m^2$ per anomalistic month. (The *anomalistic month* is measured from perigee to perigee, or by a complete cycle of M; due to the motion of the line of apsides, it is approximately 0.233 of a day longer than a sidereal month.) Then the nodes will move through $2\pi\tfrac{3}{4}m$ per year, so that the time taken for a complete revolution is $4/3m$ years, or 17.8 years. The error here is about 5 per cent; well within the margin we allowed. To find a more accurate value, e and e_1 would have to be included. For a more accurate value still, we would proceed to a second-order solution, allowing for the variations of all the elements.

The remaining terms in (12.3.3) are all periodic. The term with largest amplitude is

$$\tfrac{3}{8}m \sin 2U,$$

which has period half an anomalistic year (measured from perihelion to perihelion) and amplitude $\frac{3}{8}m$ radians or $1°.6$.

The time elapsing between successive passages of the Moon through a node is called a *nodical* or *draconitic month*, its length being 27.212 days. Since an eclipse of the Sun or Moon can only occur when the Sun, Earth, and Moon are nearly in a straight line, it must happen when the Moon is near a node and is either new or full. The term "draconitic" is due to the theory held at one time that the Sun is swallowed by a dragon at a time of total eclipse. Since the Sun must be near the line of nodes for an eclipse to take place, the interval between two successive passages of the Sun through a node is important in the prediction of eclipses; this interval is called an *eclipse year* and is equal to 346.62 days. Now

$$19 \text{ eclipse years} \quad = 6585.78 \text{ days},$$

$$223 \text{ synodic months*} = 6585.32 \text{ days},$$

$$242 \text{ nodical months} \quad = 6585.35 \text{ days}.$$

The period $6585\frac{1}{3}$ days, or about 18 years and $11\frac{1}{3}$ days (depending on leap years), is called the *Saros*; it was known to ancient astronomers and, reputedly, used in the prediction of eclipses. It should not be confused with the period of the revolution of the nodes, although the two periods are indirectly related.

12.4   The Perturbation of the Inclination

The equation for the variation of i can be written

$$\frac{di}{dM} = \frac{ar}{\mu\sqrt{1 - e^2}} F_n \cos u.$$

After substitution for F_n, this becomes

$$\frac{di}{dM} = -3m^2 \frac{r^2}{a^2\sqrt{1 - e^2}} \sin i \sin U \cos u \cos(u - U). \qquad (12.4.1)$$

Ignoring the eccentricities as before and simplifying the right-hand side, we find

$$\frac{di}{dM} = -\frac{3}{4} m^2 \sin i \{\sin 2u + \sin 2U - \sin 2(u - U)\},$$

so that

$$i - i_0 = \frac{3}{8} m^2 \sin i \left\{ \cos 2u + \frac{1}{m} \cos 2U + \frac{1}{1 - m} \cos 2(u - U) \right\}. \qquad (12.4.2)$$

---

* The *synodic month* is measured from *new moon* to the next *new moon*, or by a complete cycle of $(u - U)$.

These terms are all periodic. That with largest amplitude is

$$\tfrac{3}{8}m \sin i \cos 2U,$$

which has period half an anomalistic year and amplitude approximately 9′.

12.5 The Perturbations of ω and e

Ignoring the square of the inclination, the equation for the variation of ω is

$$\frac{d\omega}{dM} = \frac{a^2\sqrt{1-e^2}}{\mu e}\left\{ -F_r \cos v + F_b\left(1 + \frac{r}{p}\right)\sin v \right\}$$

$$= \frac{1}{2}\,m^2\,\frac{\sqrt{1-e^2}}{e}\,\frac{r}{a}\left\{ -[1 + 3\cos 2(u - U)]\cos v \right.$$

$$\left. - 3\sin 2(u - U)\sin v\left(1 + \frac{r}{p}\right)\right\}. \quad (12.5.1)$$

To find the secular terms, it is simplest to make use of the fact that we know that ω *does* increase, so that over a long enough period of time (long, that is, compared with the period of rotation of the line of apsides), the terms with argument $2(u - U)$, or $2(\omega + v - U)$ in (12.5.1) will cancel themselves out and make no secular contribution (although they may be responsible for variations of long period). It follows that the secular variation comes only from

$$\frac{d\omega'}{dM} = -\frac{1}{2}\,m^2\,\frac{\sqrt{1-e^2}}{e}\,\frac{r}{a}\cos v. \quad (12.5.2)$$

Now

$$r\cos v = a(\cos E - e),$$

and

$$dM = dE(1 - e\cos E).$$

So,

$$d\omega' = -\frac{1}{2}\,m^2\,\frac{\sqrt{1-e^2}}{e}\,\{\cos E\,(1 + e^2) - e(1 + \cos^2 E)\}\,dE$$

$$= -\frac{1}{2}\,m^2\,\frac{\sqrt{1-e^2}}{e}\,\left\{\cos E\,(1 + e^2) - \frac{e}{2}\,(3 + \cos 2E)\right\}\,dE.$$

We reject all periodic terms on the right-hand side and put $E = M$ (since the difference between them is periodic), so that finally we find

$$\omega_{\text{sec}} = \omega_{0\,\text{sec}} + \tfrac{3}{4}m^2 M\sqrt{1 - e^2}. \quad (12.5.3)$$

Certainly the line of apsides advances; but the motion given by (12.5.3) is nearly the same, in magnitude, as that found for the nodes: yet, the line of apsides actually moves over twice as fast as the line of nodes. The inability of the first-order solution to explain the observed motion was recognized by Newton: for many years after his death he was reputed to have given up the problem as a bad job, but it was found later that he had accounted for most of the observed motion by taking second-order effects into consideration. The most seriously perturbed element is e, which changes altogether by some 40 per cent. In finding (12.5.3) we assumed that e was constant, and it is not surprising that the result is unreliable. It is usual to expand expressions in the lunar motion in powers of m; in the series for the rate of advance of perigee the first two terms are

$$\frac{3}{4} m^2 + \frac{225}{32} m^3;$$

this combination nearly accounts for the observed motion.

The right-hand side of (12.5.1) can be developed in powers of e in the form

$$\frac{A}{e} + B + Ce + De^2 + \cdots$$

and if

$$\omega = \frac{\omega_1}{e} + \omega_2 + \omega_3 e + \omega_4 e^2 + \cdots$$

then we have

$$\frac{1}{e} \frac{d\omega_1}{dM} = \frac{A}{e} = -\frac{1}{2} \frac{m^2}{e} \{[1 + 3 \cos 2(u - U)] \cos M + 6 \sin 2(u - U) \sin M\}.$$

Because of the appearance of e in the denominator, we should expect this to provide the largest periodic perturbations of ω. Substituting for u and simplifying, we find

$$\frac{1}{e} \frac{d\omega_1}{dM} = -\frac{1}{4} \frac{m^2}{e} \{2 \cos M - 3 \cos(2\omega - 2U + 3M) + 9 \cos(2\omega - 2U + M)\}$$

which can be integrated to give

$$\frac{1}{e} (\omega_1 - \omega_{10}) = -\frac{1}{4} \frac{m^2}{e} \left\{ 2 \sin M - \frac{3}{3 - 2m} \sin(2\omega - 2U + 3M) \right.$$

$$\left. + \frac{9}{1 - 2m} \sin(2\omega - 2U + M) \right\}.$$

Finally, neglecting m in the denominators, we find

$$\frac{1}{e} (\omega_1 - \omega_{10}) = -\frac{1}{4} \frac{m^2}{e} \left\{ 2 \sin M - \sin(2\omega - 2U + 3M) \right.$$

$$\left. + 9 \sin(2\omega - 2U + M) \right\}. \quad (12.5.4)$$

From inspection it can be seen that the right-hand side achieves its maximum numerical value of $12m^2/4e$ when $M = \pm 90°$ and $2(\omega - U) = 0$. The total amplitude of the oscillation is given by $\pm 3m^2/e$, or $\pm 17°.5$, which is too large by some 50 per cent.

The equation for the variation of e is

$$\frac{de}{dM} = \frac{a^2\sqrt{1 - e^2}}{\mu} \{F_r \sin v + F_b(\cos v + \cos E)\}$$

$$= \frac{1}{2} m^2 \sqrt{1 - e^2} \frac{r}{a} \{[1 + 3 \cos 2(u - U)] \sin v$$
$$- 3 \sin 2(u - U) (\cos v + \cos E)\}. \quad (12.5.5)$$

There are no secular terms. When powers of e on the right-hand side are ignored, this becomes

$$\frac{de}{dM} = \frac{1}{4} m^2 \{2 \sin M - 3 \sin(2\omega - 2U + 3M) - 9 \sin(2\omega - 2U + M)\}.$$

Integrating, and ignoring m in the denominators as before, we find

$$e - e_0 = \tfrac{1}{4}m^2 \{-2 \cos M + \cos(2\omega - 2U + 3M) + 9 \cos(2\omega - 2U + M)\}. \quad (12.5.6)$$

Here the right-hand side achieves its greatest numerical value when $M = 0$ or $180°$, and $2(\omega - U) = 180°$. But again the amplitude is too great, although (12.5.6) at least shows that substantial periodic perturbations of e are to be expected.

These results are very inaccurate and have no intrinsic value; they illustrate the danger of using rough solutions. From an inspection of the results for ω and e, we should expect that the largest fluctuation of each would have a period equal to half the time between two successive passages of the Sun through perigee, even when perigee is not fixed. This assumption is correct; the period of these variations is approximately 206 days.

If we assume that the Moon moves in an elliptic orbit, the first term in the equation of the center is

$$v - M = 2e \sin M$$
$$= (6° 17') \sin M.$$

But if periodic perturbations in ω and e are allowed for, we must add (to this order) the term

$$(1° 16') \sin(2\omega - 2U + M).$$

(The argument of this term appears reasonable from a consideration of the terms of largest amplitudes in the solutions (12.5.4) and (12.5.6).) This term causes very considerable periodic departures from elliptic motion, which were first noticed by Hipparchus; it constitutes the *evection*. The period is 31.81 days.

12.6 The Variation

The equation for the variation of a is

$$\frac{da}{dM} = \frac{2a^3}{\mu} \left\{ \frac{e}{\sqrt{1 - e^2}} F_r \sin v + \frac{a}{r} \sqrt{1 - e^2} F_b \right\}.$$

We are to neglect e, so the term in F_r vanishes, and we are left with

$$\frac{da}{dM} = -3m^2 a \sin 2(u - U). \tag{12.6.1}$$

Then

$$a - a_0 = \frac{3}{2} m^2 a \frac{1}{1 - m} \cos 2(u - U). \tag{12.6.2}$$

Hence a executes small oscillations with period half a synodic month.

a has its maximum value at new and full moon, and it is tempting to reason that the orbit is slightly elongated toward and away from the Sun, as though tidally distorted; but this reasoning is worthless because we have assumed that the radius vector at any time has the value a. In fact the reverse is the case, as can be seen in the following qualitative way. Assume that, solar perturbations apart, the orbit of the Moon would be circular. It can be seen from (12.2.12) and (12.2.13) that F_r has maxima at new and full moon and minima at the quarters; at each of these positions $F_b = 0$. This means that, as far as the Moon is concerned, there is less pull in the radial direction from the Earth at new and full moon than at the quarters; hence the curvature of its path will be least at new and full moon and greatest at the quarters, so that the orbit will be elongated, with its longer axis at right angles to the direction of the Sun.

We also see from the changing signs of F_b that the Moon will run late from new to the first quarter, but will then make up speed to full; it will again run late to the last quarter but will speed up and arrive at new on time. The gain or loss in longitude, compared with unperturbed motion, has period half a synodic month and can be written

$$(39') \sin 2(u - U).$$

This perturbation is known as the *variation*; it was discovered by Tycho Brahe (before the time of Newton).

12.7 The Perturbation of the Period and the Annual Equation

At any instant the Moon is apparently experiencing a radial attraction

$$\frac{Ek^2}{r^2} - F_r \tag{12.7.1}$$

toward the Earth. Supposing the Moon to move in a circular orbit, the average value of this radial force is, from (12.2.12),

$$\frac{Ek^2}{a^2} - \frac{1}{2} N^2 a$$

or

$$\frac{Ek^2}{a^2} \left(1 - \frac{1}{2} m^2\right).$$

So the Sun detracts, on the average, from the pull of the Earth on the Moon. (The average values of F_b and F_n are zero.) If this were forgotten, we might arrive at too low a value for $(E + M)k^2$ if we were to calculate it from the formula for the period,

$$P = 2\pi \frac{a^{3/2}}{k(E + M)^{1/2}}.$$

In effect, the action of the Sun seems to have decreased $(E + M)k^2$ by the factor $(1 - \frac{1}{2}m^2)$; alternatively it has the effect of increasing the period by the factor $(1 - \frac{1}{2}m^2)^{-1/2}$, or $(1 + \frac{1}{4}m^2)$, or 0.14 per cent. This amounts to nearly one hour; the correct figure is slightly over one hour.

Now let us continue to assume that the Moon moves in a circular orbit, but take into account that the Sun does not. Let a_1 be the semimajor axis of the Sun's orbit; then N^2 is no longer given by (12.2.15) but by

$$N^2 = \frac{Sk^2}{a_1^2} = \frac{Sk^2}{R^3} \left(\frac{R}{a_1}\right)^3$$

and

$$F_r = \frac{1}{2} N^2 \left(\frac{a_1}{R}\right)^3 r [1 + 3 \cos 2(u - U)].$$

The average value of the radial force, taken over one month (during which we assume R to be constant), is

$$\frac{Ek^2}{a^2} \left[1 - \frac{1}{2} m^2 \left(\frac{a_1}{R}\right)^3\right];$$

so we find the period of the Moon's orbit to be increased by the factor

$$1 + \frac{1}{4} m^2 \left(\frac{a_1}{R}\right)^3.$$

Now R varies by some 3 per cent during the course of the year; so the length of the month varies, becoming less from perihelion to aphelion (January to June) and then greater. This means that the Moon is apparently running ahead of time for the first six months and behind for the last six months of the (anomalistic) year. The resulting difference in longitude is given by

$$- (11' \, 16'') \sin V. \tag{12.7.2}$$

This is the *annual equation*.

12.8   The Parallactic Inequality

If terms in $(r/R)^2$ are included in (12.2.9) and the work following, then slight modifications will be called for in the results. The principal change is that a term is introduced into the longitude with period equal to a synodic month, and a coefficient that involves the ratio

$$\frac{E - M}{E + M} \frac{a}{a_1};$$

this term is called the *parallactic inequality*. An accurate observational determination of its value would lead to a value for a_1, the astronomical unit; the drawback to this is that the ratio M/E must be known first.

12.9   The Secular Acceleration of the Moon

The Moon's mean longitude is

$$l = nt + \epsilon. \tag{12.9.1}$$

If we neglect all periodic perturbations, we can take n as constant, and it remains to investigate the changes in ϵ. In an investigation of the Moon's mean motion, Halley used records of ancient eclipses and found l to be represented empirically by

$$l = l_0 + n_0 t + \sigma \left(\frac{t}{100}\right)^2 + \text{periodic terms.} \tag{12.9.2}$$

Here t is measured in Julian years (365.25 days) from some epoch. σ is called the coefficient of the *secular acceleration*; its value is approximately $11''$.

An explanation for this term was first given by Laplace. The average pull of the Earth on the Moon depends on the average value of F_r, which depends in turn on the average value of R^{-3}. This can be shown to depend on the eccentricity of the Sun's orbit, which is known to be gradually changing.

To put this into some sort of quantitative form, we see that if (12.9.1) and (12.9.2) are differentiated, then σ depends on the presence of a secular term in the expression for $d\epsilon/dt$. Neglecting the squares of i and e for the orbit of the Moon, the equation for $d\epsilon/dt$ (assuming n to be constant) is

$$\frac{d\epsilon}{dt} = -\frac{2nar}{\mu} F_r.$$

Ignoring periodic terms in F_r and giving r its mean value, we have

$$\frac{d\epsilon}{dt} = -m^2 n \left(\frac{a_1}{R}\right)^3.$$

The mean value of R^{-3} is

$$\overline{R^{-3}} = \frac{\int_0^{P_1} R^{-3}\, dt}{\int_0^{P_1} dt}$$

$$= \frac{1}{P_1} \int_0^{2\pi} \frac{1}{h_1} \frac{1}{R}\, dv$$

$$= \frac{1}{P_1 h_1 a_1 (1 - e_1^2)} \int_0^{2\pi} (1 + e \cos v)\, dv$$

$$= \frac{1}{a_1^3 (1 - e_1^2)^{3/2}}.$$

Hence over long periods we have

$$\frac{d\epsilon}{dt} = -\frac{m^2 n}{(1 - e_1^2)^{3/2}}. \tag{12.9.3}$$

This would be constant but for the fact that e_1 is slowly changing due to planetary perturbations. The value of e_1 is given, for the (astronomically) near future, by

$$e_1 = e_{10} - \alpha t, \tag{12.9.4}$$

where $e_{10} = 0.016771$ and $\alpha = 4.245\ 10^{-7}$, for the epoch 1850.0. Hence, expanding the right-hand side of (12.9.3) and ignoring α^2, we have

$$\frac{d\epsilon}{dt} = \text{constant} + 3m^2 n e_{10} \alpha t.$$

Integrating, we see that σ of (12.9.2) is given by

$$\sigma = \tfrac{3}{2}\ 10^4 m^2 n e_{10} \alpha. \tag{12.9.5}$$

The numerical evaluation of this is left to the student; the result is that σ is approximately equal to $10''.4$, and this appears to account satisfactorily for the observations.

The formula (12.9.4) is misleading; e_1 actually fluctuates periodically, the principal period being 24,000 years: the term αt in (12.9.4) is merely the first term in the expansion of some trigonometric function. Hence the secular acceleration will fluctuate with e_1.

We have seen how first-order results by themselves can be misleading. The apparent agreement between theory and observation found above was shown to be illusory by Adams. If higher order terms are taken into account, σ can be expanded as a power series in m, of which the right-hand side of (12.9.5) is the first term, which converges slowly; furthermore, the terms following the first are negative. Adams arrived at the value $5''.72$ for σ, and this does not fully account for the observations.

A formula of the type (12.9.2) assumes that t is the "evenly flowing" time always taken for granted in mechanics. But the eclipse observations used to determine σ use the rotating Earth as a clock, and the discrepancy between the values of σ can be explained if we assume that the rate of rotation of the Earth about its axis is gradually diminishing. This slowing down is now generally accepted. The usual explanation is that it is due to tidal friction in shallow seas between the sea beds and the water. Quantitative agreement has been found for this theory, but discussion on the subject is by no means closed.

It is of interest to consider the evolution of the Moon's motion in the light of the tidal theory for the slowing down of the Earth's rotation. At present the angular momentum lost to the Earth by tidal friction must be transferred to the orbital angular momentum of the Moon; the latter is therefore receding from the Earth, and the month is becoming longer. This will continue (in theory, at any rate) until the month and the day are of equal length, when the friction involved in the *lunar* tides must cease. But the *solar* tides will continue to cause friction, now robbing the Earth-Moon system of angular momentum, and causing the Moon to approach the Earth again. In the past, we go back to a time when the Moon was close to the Earth, and the day and month were short and nearly equal. It was the latter circumstance that was considered by Darwin to be the result of the Moon just having broken away from the Earth (a view that is not without its challengers today).

12.10 Theories of the Motion of the Moon

The history of theories of the motion of the Moon starts with the publication of the *Principia* by Newton in 1687, includes contributions from mathematicians such as Euler, Laplace, and Poisson, and culminates in the Hill-Brown lunar theory that has led to the very accurate expressions for the lunar motion used today in the almanacs.

Newton showed that the observed inequalities in the motion of the Moon were due to perturbations by the Sun, and he predicted some inequalities that had not been observed up to that time. He had difficulty over the motion of perigee, but eventually explained this to within 8 per cent of the observed motion by taking second-order terms into account. (Newton is reputed to have told Halley that the lunar theory "made his head ache and kept him awake so often that he would think of it no more".) His arguments were cast in abstruse geometrical form, but were almost certainly first worked out analytically, using the theory of fluxions.

Clairaut applied analytical methods to the problem and in 1749 succeeded in explaining the motion of perigee by using second-order approximations. In 1752 he published his *Théorie de la Lune* and in 1754 he published a set of numerical tables for the computation of the position of the Moon.

Euler published some tables in 1746. In 1753 he published a lunar theory that included a partial exposition of the method of variation of elements. His most significant contribution came in 1772 when he published his second lunar theory. In this his equations of motion were referred to axes rotating with the mean motion of the Moon.

Laplace's theory was evolved toward the end of the eighteenth century and published in 1802. He transformed the equations of motion so that the true longitude was the independent variable. His reference orbit was a Keplerian ellipse modified to avoid terms proportional to the time in the coefficients. He gave the explanation for the secular acceleration of the Moon noted above. Laplace's methods were carried to a higher degree of accuracy by several mathematicians, including Damoiseau, whose theory was published in 1827, and who published tables that were used until they were superseded by those of Hansen.

Another important theory stemming directly from the equations of motion, and carried through to a high degree of accuracy, was that published by de Pontécoulant in 1846.

Returning to chronological order, we come to one of the most important lunar theories, that of Hansen. His reference system is mentioned in Section 11.8. Hansen's work extended over forty years from 1829. His tables were published in 1857 and were used generally for over fifty years.

In 1860 Delaunay published the results of a lunar theory involving the removal, by analytical means, of the terms of the disturbing function, one by one, and the gradual building up of the solution. His expression for the disturbing function included 320 terms (including all terms of the seventh order of small quantities and some of the eighth). The analytical work took twenty years. The solution is not numerical but analytical, and can be applied not only to the motion of the Moon but also to any satellite motion (of the three-body type). It is the most perfect solution yet found for this type of motion. This theory was later made the basis of lunar tables.

In 1878 Hill published the first paper introducing a new method using rectangular coordinates based on axes rotating with the mean motion of the Sun. Hill first found a closed solution, symmetrical about the axes; this is an oval, with the longer axis perpendicular to the direction of the Sun (see Section 12.6.), and is known as Hill's *variational curve*. This curve was used as a reference orbit in describing the actual motion of the Moon. The work was further developed by Brown, who published tables in 1919 which have been used since 1923 in the preparation of lunar ephemerides. In the future his series solutions will probably be used for this purpose.

Problems

1. Prove that the locus of the point at which the attractions of the Sun and Earth are equal is a sphere whose radius is

$$R\,\frac{(SE)^{1/2}}{S - E}$$

and whose center is on the line joining the Sun and Earth, at the distance $ER/(S - E)$ from the center of the Earth, opposite to the Sun; where S and E represent the masses of the Sun and Earth, respectively, and R is the distance from the Sun to the Earth. Calculate these values and show that the Moon is always attracted more by the Sun than by the Earth. Why, then, does the Moon continue to move in orbit around the Earth?

2. Consider the problem of the motion of the Moon in terms of motion around the Sun disturbed by the Earth.

3. Prove that the ratio of the greatest disturbing effect of the Sun to the least disturbing effect of the Earth is approximately 0.0114.

4. Prove that the ratios of the maximum value of the Sun's disturbing force to the attractions of the Sun and Earth are 0.005 and 0.011, respectively.

5. Because it is the center of mass of the Earth-Moon system, which describes a Keplerian orbit about the Sun (neglecting planetary perturbations), the Sun, as observed from the Earth, will not apparently move in a Keplerian orbit, but will have displacements $\Delta\beta$ and $\Delta\lambda$ in latitude and longitude with respect to that Keplerian motion. Show that the former of these has period equal to the nodical month, and the latter has period equal to the synodic month, and that their observation can yield information about the ratio of the masses of the Earth and Moon. Taking this ratio as 81.27, find the amplitudes of $\Delta\beta$ and $\Delta\lambda$.

6. Find the secular perturbations caused by the Earth's oblateness on the motion of the Moon, and compare these with the perturbations produced by the Sun.

7. Investigate very approximately the perturbations produced by Jupiter on the motion of the Moon.

8. An artificial satellite revolving around the Earth, outside the atmosphere, is acted upon by the Earth's oblateness, the Sun, and the Moon, apart from the Newtonian attraction of the Earth, considered as a sphere. Assuming that it moves in a nearly circular orbit, compare the perturbations produced by the three effects for various major axes of the satellite's orbit. Find the ratio of the perturbations produced by the Sun and the Moon. Find the order of magnitude of the period of the satellite for which the perturbations produced by the Sun and Moon roughly equal in magnitude those produced by the Earth's oblateness.

9. Investigate the first-order motion of the Moon's nodes, taking into account the eccentricities of the orbits of the Sun and Moon.

10. (a) Derive a formula for the length of the nodical month in terms of the sidereal month and the rate of recession of the nodes. Check this with the numerical values.

    (b) Derive a formula for the length of the eclipse year in terms of the sidereal year and the motion of the nodes of the Moon's orbit. Check this with the numerical values.

    (c) Taking into account the precession of the equinoxes, find the time that will elapse between two successive passages of the ascending node through the vernal equinox.

    (d) Why is it the Saros, and not the period of nodal revolution, that can be used in predicting eclipses?

    (e) Derive a formula for the period of the evection in terms of the sidereal and anomalistic months. Check this with the numerical values.

11. Investigate the perturbation in the period by considering the secular perturbation of M.

12. Find the average value of F_r over an elliptic orbit. What modifications, if any, must be made to the work of Section 12.7 if the eccentricity of the Moon's orbit is taken into account?

13. The observed motion of the Moon might be used to relate the quantities $(E + M)$ with a, and one of these might be found from the other. If the perturbations due to the Sun are ignored (and therefore the resulting perturbation of the period), find the errors that might be introduced.

14. How will the secular acceleration of the Moon affect the time of an eclipse 4000 years ago as predicted by contemporary clocks, compared with the time recorded at the event?

15. Use first-order theory to find the annual equation. Compare your result with the formula (12.7.2).

16. Assuming that the discrepancy between the observed value of σ and Adams' value of σ is the result of a slowing down of the Earth's rate of rotation, and that the angular momentum lost to the Earth is added to the orbital angular momentum of the Moon, calculate the increases in a century of the Moon's mean distance from the Earth and the length of the sidereal month. Comment on the observability of these.

17. Assuming that the total angular momentum of the Earth-Moon system is conserved, investigate possible configurations in the past and future such that the lengths of the month and day are equal. If some angular momentum were lost through the tidal action of the Sun, what effect would this have on your results?

18. Assume that the orbit of the Sun is a circle, and neglect $(r/R)^2$ in the expression for the disturbing force. Define a system of rotating axes such that Ox always points toward the Sun, and Oz is perpendicular to the

ecliptic. Show that the equations of motion of the Moon with respect to these axes can be written

$$\ddot{x} - 2n_1\dot{y} - 3n_1^2 x = -\mu\frac{x}{r^3},$$

$$\ddot{y} + 2n_1\dot{x} \qquad = -\mu\frac{y}{r^3},$$

$$\ddot{z} \qquad + n_1^2 z = -\mu\frac{z}{r^3},$$

where n_1 is the angular motion of the Sun.

19. Write down the equations of motion of the Moon with respect to axes rotating with the mean motion of the Moon.

Chapter 13 ** THE EARTH AND ITS ROTATION

13.1 The Eulerian Motion of the Earth

The Earth is not a sphere, and in this chapter we shall consider some of the consequences of this. We shall assume that the Earth has symmetry about an axis and can be represented by a spheroid for which $a = b > c$; but the Earth is not homogeneous, and we must be wary of using the formulas for the field of a homogeneous spheroid. Let the moments of inertia of the Earth about the axes (the principal axes of inertia of the spheroid) be A, B, and C. Then $A = B < C$.

First we shall consider the rotation of the Earth when no outside forces are acting on it. Then, in Euler's equations, (5.2.7), $\boldsymbol{\Gamma} = 0$, and

$$A \frac{d\omega_1}{dt} - (A - C)\omega_2\omega_3 = 0, \qquad (13.1.1)$$

$$A \frac{d\omega_2}{dt} - (C - A)\omega_3\omega_1 = 0, \qquad (13.1.2)$$

$$C \frac{d\omega_3}{dt} = 0. \qquad (13.1.3)$$

From (13.1.3) we have

$$\omega_3 = \text{constant},$$

so that the spin of the Earth about its axis of symmetry is constant. Let

$$n = \frac{C - A}{A} \omega_3; \qquad (13.1.4)$$

then the first two equations become

$$\frac{d\omega_1}{dt} + n\omega_2 = 0$$

and

$$\frac{d\omega_2}{dt} - n\omega_1 = 0. \qquad (13.1.5)$$

Differentiating the first, and using the second to eliminate $d\omega_2/dt$, we find

$$\frac{d^2\omega_1}{dt^2} + n^2\omega_1 = 0,$$

and similarly,

$$\frac{d^2\omega_2}{dt^2} + n^2\omega_2 = 0.$$

The general solution of equations (13.1.5) is, then,

$$\left.\begin{aligned}\omega_1 &= \alpha\cos(nt + \beta), \\ \omega_2 &= \alpha\sin(nt + \beta).\end{aligned}\right] \tag{13.1.6}$$

The period of these terms, measured in sidereal days, so that $\omega_3 = 2\pi$, is

$$\frac{2\pi}{n} = \frac{A}{C - A}.$$

From other sources the value of this is known to be about 303, so that the period is 303 sidereal days, or 302 mean solar days. This is called the *Eulerian free period.*

A consequence can be considered as follows. Let P be a point on the Earth, and with origin at the center of the Earth, and Oz pointing along the direction of ω_3, let Ox meet the meridian through P. (See Figure 13.1.) The angular velocity of the Earth is

$$\omega_1\hat{\mathbf{x}} + \omega_2\hat{\mathbf{y}} + \omega_3\hat{\mathbf{z}},$$

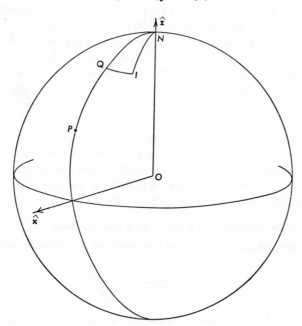

Figure 13.1

so that it has direction cosines proportional to ω_1, ω_2, and ω_3. Let the instantaneous axis of rotation cut the Earth near the north pole at I; then the equation of the line OI is

$$\frac{x}{\omega_1} = \frac{y}{\omega_2} = \frac{z}{\omega_3},$$

or

$$\frac{x}{\alpha\cos(nt + \beta)} = \frac{y}{\alpha\sin(nt + \beta)} = \frac{z}{\omega_3}. \tag{13.1.7}$$

Therefore the angle NI is α/ω_3, and the component of NI along NP is

$$NQ = \frac{\alpha}{\omega_3}\cos(nt + \beta).$$

Now the latitude of P, measured with respect to the axis of rotation, is nearly

$$90° - PQ = 90° - PN + \frac{\alpha}{\omega_3}\cos(nt + \beta). \tag{13.1.8}$$

PN is constant, so that the Eulerian oscillation should give rise to a variation in the latitude of P with period approximately ten months.

The latitude of a point can be found very accurately by astronomical observations, and it is known from these that it does, in fact, vary. But the empirical formula for the latitude demands two periodic terms (as opposed to one in (13.1.8)); one of these has amplitude $0''.09$ and period one year, and the other has amplitude $0''.18$ and period 14 months. The first is probably due to periodic changes in the moments of inertia of the Earth resulting from seasonal changes in the weather. The second might be the modification of the Eulerian free oscillation produced by the nonrigidity of the Earth. For, suppose the Earth had no rigidity, or that it was composed of nonviscous fluid; the two equal axes must always be perpendicular to the instantaneous axis of rotation: hence there can be no free oscillation of this sort. Therefore, as the rigidity of the Earth diminished, the Eulerian free period would increase until it became infinite for the case of no rigidity. There are, however, other possible explanations for the second term, and it may be that the actual Eulerian free oscillation simply has an amplitude too small to be detected.

13.2   The Couple Exerted on the Earth by a Distant Body

Consider MacCullagh's formula for the potential of a body at a distant point, (5.4.1):

$$V = -\frac{GM}{r} - \frac{G(A + B + C - 3I)}{2r^3}.$$

Let the origin be at the center of mass of the body, and let the axes be the principal axes of inertia. The force exerted on a distant unit mass at $\mathbf{r}$ is $-\nabla V$, and from Newton's third law the distant mass exerts an equal and opposite force on the body. This results in a couple of moment $\mathbf{r} \times \nabla V$ about the origin, exerted by the distant unit mass.

This couple is the result of the lack of spherical symmetry of the body, which expresses itself in the fact that V is not just a function of r, but involves x, y, and z in addition. Therefore, in finding the couple, we can ignore all those parts of V that are simply functions of r.

Now

$$I = \frac{Ax^2 + By^2 + Cz^2}{r^2}$$

and so provides the only part of V about which we need worry; call this

$$V_1 = \frac{3GI}{2r^3}$$

$$= \frac{3G}{2r^5} (Ax^2 + By^2 + Cz^2).$$

The evaluation of $\mathbf{r} \times \nabla V = \mathbf{r} \times \nabla V_1$ is straightforward; the couple is

$$\boldsymbol{\Gamma} = \frac{3G}{r^5} \left((C - B)yz, \quad (A - C)zx, \quad (B - A)xy \right). \tag{13.2.1}$$

13.3   The Couples Exerted on the Earth by the Sun and Moon

With origin at the center of the Earth, take axes Ex, Ey, and Ez such that Ex points toward the vernal equinox and Ez points toward the north celestial pole; also EX, EY, and EZ such that EX points toward the vernal equinox and EZ points toward the north pole of the ecliptic. (See Figure 13.2, page 300.) The relations between coordinates are

$$\left. \begin{array}{l} x = X, \\ y = Y \cos \epsilon - Z \sin \epsilon, \\ z = Y \sin \epsilon + Z \cos \epsilon. \end{array} \right] \tag{13.3.1}$$

Here ϵ is the obliquity of the ecliptic, assumed to be constant.

If Ω is the ascending node of the Moon's orbit, then

$$X\Omega = -gt + \text{constant},$$

where g is the rate of regression of the node in the ecliptic (all periodic perturbations being neglected).

Let k be the inclination of the Moon's orbit to the ecliptic; since it is small, we shall neglect k^2 so that $\sin k = k$ and $\cos k = 1$. To this order, we see that after a time t, Ω will regress through an angle gt with respect to the Moon's orbit.

Let n and n_1 be the mean motions of the Moon and Sun, respectively; then

$$XS = n_1 t + \alpha,$$
$$XM_1 = X\Omega + \Omega M$$
$$= nt + \beta,$$
$$\Omega M = nt + gt + \gamma,$$

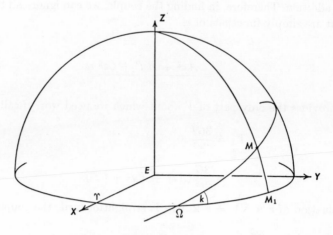

Figure 13.2

where α, β, and γ are constants, and the meridian through Z and M meets the ecliptic at M_1. Then

$$\sin MM_1 = \sin k \sin \Omega M$$
$$= k \sin(nt + gt + \gamma).$$

Let R and r be the distances (assumed constant) of the Sun and the Moon. Then we have the values of (X, Y, Z) for the Sun,

$$R(\cos(n_1 t + \alpha), \quad \sin(n_1 t + \alpha), \quad 0),$$

and for the Moon,

$$r(\cos(nt + \beta), \quad \sin(nt + \beta), \quad k \sin(nt + gt + \gamma)).$$

Then from (13.3.1) we find the values of (x, y, z)

$$R(\cos(n_1 t + \alpha), \quad \sin(n_1 t + \alpha) \cos \epsilon, \quad \sin(n_1 t + \alpha) \sin \epsilon) \qquad (13.3.2)$$

for the Sun, and

$$r(\cos(nt + \beta), \quad \sin(nt + \beta)\cos \epsilon - k \sin(nt + gt + \gamma) \sin \epsilon,$$
$$\sin(nt + \beta) \sin \epsilon + k \sin(nt + gt + \gamma) \cos \epsilon) \qquad (13.3.3)$$

for the Moon.

Let the masses of the Sun and Moon be M_s and M_m, and let them exert couples $_s\mathbf{\Gamma}$ and $_m\mathbf{\Gamma}$ on the Earth. From (13.2.1), using the property $A = B$, we find

$$_s\Gamma_x = \frac{3M_sG}{R^3}(C - A)\sin^2(n_1t + \alpha)\cos\epsilon\sin\epsilon,$$

$$_s\Gamma_y = \frac{3M_sG}{R^3}(A - C)\sin(n_1t + \alpha)\cos(n_1t + \alpha)\sin\epsilon,$$

$$_s\Gamma_z = 0.$$

(13.3.4)

These expressions are to be used in a moment to establish the existence of the precession of the Earth's axis of rotation; this takes 26,000 years for a complete cycle, so that we are certainly justified in neglecting the annual variations in the expressions (13.3.4). If we take the averages over one year, the y-component vanishes, and we are left with

$$_s\Gamma_x = \frac{3M_sG}{4R^3}(C - A)\sin 2\epsilon.$$

(13.3.5)

Similarly we have for the couple exerted by the Moon,

$$_m\Gamma_x = \frac{3M_mG}{r^3}(C - A)\{\sin^2(nt + \beta)\sin\epsilon\cos\epsilon$$
$$+ k\sin(nt + \beta)\sin(nt + gt + \gamma)\cos 2\epsilon\},$$

$$_m\Gamma_y = \frac{3M_mG}{r^3}(A - C)\{\cos(nt + \beta)\sin(nt + \beta)\sin\epsilon$$
$$+ k\cos(nt + \beta)\sin(nt + gt + \gamma)\cos\epsilon\},$$

$$_m\Gamma_z = 0.$$

Consider the mean values taken over one sidereal month. We have

$$\sin(nt + gt + \gamma) = \sin[(nt + \beta) + (gt - \beta + \gamma)]$$
$$= \sin(nt + \beta)\cos(gt - \beta + \gamma) + \cos(nt + \beta)\sin(gt - \beta + \gamma),$$

so that the mean values are

$$_m\bar\Gamma_x = \frac{3M_mG}{r^3}(C - A)\left\{\frac{1}{4}\sin 2\epsilon + \frac{k}{2}\cos(gt - \beta + \gamma)\cos 2\epsilon\right\},$$

$$_m\bar\Gamma_y = \frac{3M_mG}{r^3}(A - C)\frac{k}{2}\sin(gt - \beta + \gamma)\cos\epsilon.$$

(13.3.6)

Finally, if we average over the period of revolution of the nodes (still short compared with 26,000 years), the only nonzero term is

$$_m\bar{\bar\Gamma}_x = \frac{3M_mG}{4r^3}(C - A)\sin 2\epsilon.$$

(13.3.7)

Therefore the mean value of the total couple exerted by the Sun and Moon on the Earth, taken over a period of about nineteen years, acts along the x-axis and has magnitude

$$\bar\Gamma = \frac{3G}{4}(C - A)\sin 2\epsilon\left(\frac{M_m}{r^3} + \frac{M_s}{R^3}\right).$$

(13.3.8)

If we substitute numerical values for the masses and distances, we see that the Moon contributes about two-thirds of the total.

13.4 The Lunisolar Precession

In this section we shall consider analytically the consequence of the mean couple, (13.3.8), acting on the spinning Earth; this consequence is the lunisolar precession of the Earth's axis. But before doing this we shall consider a qualitative explanation for the precession.

From the reasoning in Section 12.3, we see that a close satellite of the Earth, moving in a circular orbit, would suffer a regression of its line of nodes, due to the perturbations of the Moon and Sun. The inclination of its orbit to the ecliptic would suffer no secular perturbation. Suppose the satellite initially had an orbit in the plane of the Earth's equator; the plane of the orbit would not remain equatorial but would lag behind. But now suppose the satellite to be fastened to the Earth; it would try to force the plane of the Earth's equator to regress, following the plane of its orbit.

Now consider the Earth as being made up of a sphere, with radius equal to the polar radius of the Earth, and a ring of extra material that is most concentrated around the equator. Consider this ring as being composed of a system of satellites; the plane of the orbit of each one will try to regress, and, if it were not attached to the Earth, it would succeed. As it is, each satellite in the ring will try to communicate this regression to the plane of the Earth's equator. They are partially successful, and as a result the plane regresses, while making a constant angle with the ecliptic (barring periodic variation); this is the phenomenon of precession.

If the satellites experienced no friction with the main body of the Earth, the precession of the bulge would be much faster than the actual precession. Also, if the Earth's crust floated on a liquid interior, the precession would still be too fast. Hence it is possible to conclude that the Earth's crust is rigidly attached to the interior.

Let us return to the consequence of the couple (13.3.8). We are to ignore fluctuations about the mean value; but these would be expected to cause periodic variations about the mean precessional motion with periods much less than 26,000 years. We shall also ignore the phenomenon of variation of latitude, and assume that the axis of rotation of the Earth is rigidly fixed along the shortest principal axis of inertia of a rigid Earth.

Let the spin of the Earth about its axis be n. Using the notation of Section 13.3, we see that the direction of the axis is $\hat{z}$; also

$$\hat{x} = \frac{\hat{z} \times \hat{Z}}{\sin \epsilon}.$$

The total angular velocity of the Earth is composed of this spin and the motion of the axis itself; so it is

$$n\hat{z} + \hat{z} \times \frac{d\hat{z}}{dt}.$$

Then the angular momentum of the Earth is

$$Cn\hat{z} + A\hat{z} \times \frac{d\hat{z}}{dt}$$

and its rate of change is

$$Cn\frac{d\hat{z}}{dt} + A\hat{z} \times \frac{d^2\hat{z}}{dt^2},$$

since n is constant. The equation for the rate of change of the angular momentum is, then,

$$Cn\frac{d\hat{z}}{dt} + A\hat{z} \times \frac{d^2\hat{z}}{dt^2} = \bar{\Gamma}\hat{x}$$

$$= \bar{\Gamma}\frac{\hat{z} \times \hat{Z}}{\sin \epsilon}. \qquad (13.4.1)$$

For the steady precession of $\hat{z}$ around $\hat{Z}$ with angular velocity $\omega\hat{Z}$, we have

$$\frac{d\hat{z}}{dt} = \omega\hat{Z} \times \hat{z},$$

and

$$\frac{d^2\hat{z}}{dt^2} = \omega^2\hat{Z} \times (\hat{Z} \times \hat{z})$$

$$= \omega^2(\hat{Z} \cos \epsilon - \hat{z}).$$

Substituting these conditions into (13.4.1), we see that such motion is possible, provided ω satisfies the quadratic equation

$$Cn\omega - A\omega^2 \cos \epsilon = -\frac{\bar{\Gamma}}{\sin \epsilon}$$

$$= -\frac{3}{2} G\left(\frac{M_m}{r^3} + \frac{M_s}{R^3}\right)(C - A) \cos \epsilon. \qquad (13.4.2)$$

The sum of the roots (which are real) is equal to $Cn/(A \cos \epsilon)$. If we take the day as the unit of time, this has the approximate value $2\pi/\cos \epsilon$. But the product of the roots is seen to be very small. Hence (13.4.2) has two real roots, of which one is of the order $2\pi/\cos \epsilon$ and the other is very small; obviously we must look to the second of these for terms relevant to the actual precession. We can neglect the square of this small root, so that we find

$$\omega = -\frac{3G}{2n}\frac{C - A}{C}\left(\frac{M_m}{r^3} + \frac{M_s}{R^3}\right) \cos \epsilon. \qquad (13.4.3)$$

Now let the unit of length be the astronomical unit, the unit of mass be the mass of the Sun, and the unit of time be the sidereal year. Then $G = 4\pi^2$ and $n = 2\pi \times 365.3$. Substituting these values and that of $\cos \epsilon$ into (13.4.3) we find

$$\omega = -2\pi\frac{C - A}{C} 1.19 \times 10^{-2}.$$

It is known that ω is negative (Υ recedes around the ecliptic), and if we adopt the period 25,800 years for the precession, we find

$$\frac{C - A}{C} = \frac{1}{308}.$$

A better value is 1/304, so that agreement with even this rough theory is satisfactory. A more refined theory would enable $(C - A)/C$ to be found from observation.

If the student is not aware of the elementary theory of spinning tops, he should consult any elementary mechanics text. The account given here is based on the methods used in Milne's *Vectorial Mechanics* (Ref. 15). We shall not investigate the stability of the precessional motion of the Earth's axis, but it can be shown to be stable by the use of elementary methods given in most texts.

13.5 Nutation

Let us forget, for the moment, about the terms in the expressions for the couples exerted on the Earth by the Sun and Moon which produce the mean value $\bar{\Gamma}$, (13.3.8), used to establish the lunisolar precession; we are left with certain periodic terms. We have seen that, as far as the couple is concerned, the Moon is more potent than the Sun, so that the most important of the periodic terms will be those arising from the motion of the Moon's node, for these have the largest amplitude and the longest period. The annual fluctuations due to the Sun and the monthly fluctuations due to the Moon will be ignored. From (13.3.6) and (13.3.7) we find the following relevant terms:

$$\Gamma'_x = \frac{3 M_m G}{2r^3} (C - A)k \cos 2\epsilon \cos(gt - \beta + \gamma),$$

and

$$\Gamma'_y = -\frac{3 M_m G}{2r^3} (C - A)k \cos \epsilon \sin(gt - \beta + \gamma).$$

Let

$$p = \frac{3 M_m G}{2r^3} (C - A)k;$$

then, if the time is measured from a suitable epoch, we can put

$$\left.\begin{array}{l} \Gamma'_x = p \cos 2\epsilon \cos gt, \\ \Gamma'_y = -p \cos \epsilon \sin gt. \end{array}\right\} \tag{13.5.1}$$

Consider the effects of this couple, isolated from the rest of the precessional motion; this is justified in a first approximation because all the effects are small. At some instant the component of the couple Γ'_x will be trying to induce a precession of the Earth's axis with angular velocity ω'_x, where

$$Cn\omega'_x = -\frac{\Gamma'_x}{\sin \epsilon}. \tag{13.5.2}$$

This will be true only instantaneously, but if we assume Γ'_x to remain constant for a time dt, then the Earth's axis will precess through an angle

$$\omega'_x \, dt,$$

and, according to the property of precession, this motion will be at right angles to the direction of the couple that is causing it. Hence the Earth's axis will move along the y-axis through an angle

$$-\frac{p}{Cn} \frac{\cos 2\epsilon}{\sin \epsilon} \cos gt \, dt.$$

So for general t we see that Γ'_x will result in simple harmonic motion along the y-axis with period $2\pi/g$, or 18.6 years. In exactly the same way, Γ'_y causes simple harmonic motion along the x-axis, with the same period but different amplitude. Combining the two, we see that the Earth's axis describes an ellipse in space with period 18.6 years.

The elliptic motion is superimposed upon the steady precessional motion already found; the result is that the Earth's axis describes a wavy path through space, the extra waviness being called the *nutation* (for "nodding").

We must emphasize that the account given here of precession and nutation only scratches at the surface of the problem. The student will find an adequate treatment in texts such as those of Plummer or Smart (Refs. 24, 25), but that requires an analytical approach involving theory outside the scope of this text. However, we have tried to show how elementary methods can be used to account for the grosser aspects of the phenomena, and may provide a geometrical understanding that is not perhaps so easily grasped from the analytical methods.

The constants involved in the formulas for precession and nutation are found basically from observation. But observations must be referred to an inertial system of reference, and this is extremely difficult to do. For example, positions of stars at different times might be used; but the stars have their own motions, and even if many stars were used so that their individual motions perhaps canceled out, there is still the possibility of some general drift that would not be affected. The motion of the Sun through space results in a general drift of stars away from the direction of motion, and a determination of the solar motion based on the observed positions of stars at different times involves a redetermination of the constants of precession and nutation. In the future it may be possible to define an inertial system with respect to the system of asteroids.

Problems

1. Prove that the mutual potential energy of two distant bodies is approximately

$$-\frac{G}{r}\left\{ MM' + \frac{M(A' + B' + C' - 3I')}{2r^2} + \frac{M'(A + B + C - 3I)}{2r^2} \right\},$$

where r is the distance between their centers of mass, and M and M' are their masses, etc.

2. The quadratic equation for the precessional motion has another solution; find it. Investigate the stability of the two solutions.

3. The boundary between the United States and Canada is, in part, defined by the 49th parallel of latitude. If this were measured with respect to the instantaneous north pole, find the extent (in meters) by which it would vary.

4. Investigate the precession of Jupiter, assuming it to be solid and homogeneous.

5. Investigate the precession of Saturn's rings.

6. An artificial satellite moves in a circular orbit, initially in the plane of the Earth's equator, just grazing the surface of the Earth. Assuming that the orbit is free from atmospheric friction, find the period and the time taken for a revolution around the ecliptic of the nodes of the orbit. (Consider the action of the Sun and Moon.)

7. Find the axes of the ellipse describing the nutation considered in Section 13.5. Sketch part of the path traced out on the celestial sphere by the Earth's axis as a result of precession and nutation; will this include loops?

Chapter 14 ** THE MOON AND ITS ROTATION

14.1 Cassini's Laws

It is well known that the Moon, roughly speaking, always points one face toward the Earth; as we shall see, this leads to a restriction on the possible figure of the Moon. This, and other regularities in the rotation of the Moon, are described in three laws due to Cassini. These laws have been confirmed observationally, but they are a simplification of the actual state of affairs, since there are additional small oscillations about the regular motion that they predict. The laws, together with these additional oscillations (when they can be observed), furnish data about the gravitational field of the Moon.

To consider Cassini's laws, let the Moon be at the center of the celestial sphere. Let Π_1 be the plane of the Earth's orbit around the Moon, with pole P. Let Π_2 be the plane through the Moon parallel to the ecliptic, with pole Z. Let Π_3 be the plane of the Moon's equator, with pole C. (See Figure 14.1, page 308.) The three laws are:

1. The Moon has uniform rotation about an axis fixed in the Moon, the period of rotation being equal to the sidereal period of the Moon.

2. The angle CZ is constant; about $1° 35'$.

3. While the node of the Moon's orbit regresses, its inclination remains constant; about $5° 9'$. As the node moves, the arc of the great circle PC always contains Z. This latter condition implies that the three planes Π_1, Π_2, and Π_3 meet in a line, and that Π_2 lies between Π_1 and Π_3.

In the following sections we shall establish these laws by showing that the oscillations about the steady motion that they predict are stable, subject to certain restrictions on the field of the Moon.

14.2 The Eulerian Equations

Let the principal axes of inertia of the Moon be the axes defining the coordinates (x,y,z). One of these must, by symmetry, nearly point toward the

Earth E; if G is the center of mass of the Moon (and therefore the origin of coordinates), let this axis be GA, or the x-axis. Also, one axis must point in nearly the same direction as the axis of rotation of the Moon; let this be GC, or the z-axis. With respect to these axes, let GZ and GE have direction cosines (p,q,r) and (λ,μ,ν), respectively; then p, q, μ, and ν are small quantities (the student should confirm this and find out just how small they are) whose squares will be neglected subsequently; also r and λ are nearly equal to one.

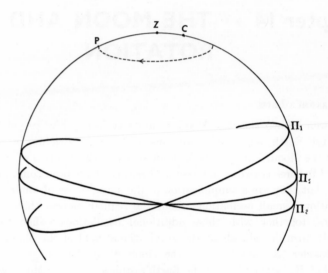

Figure 14.1

The couple exerted by the Earth on the Moon is small, and, in evaluating it, it is sufficient to assume that the Earth is a sphere and that it is a constant distance R from G. Let M be the mass of the Earth, and let A, B, and C be the principal moments of inertia of the Moon. Let the angular velocity of the Moon have components ω_x, ω_y, and ω_z about the x-, y-, and z-axes; the first two are small, and their squares and product will be neglected.

Euler's equations are, in full,

$$A\dot{\omega}_x - (B - C)\omega_y\omega_z = \frac{3MG}{R^3}(C - B)\mu\nu,$$

$$B\dot{\omega}_y - (C - A)\omega_z\omega_x = \frac{3MG}{R^3}(A - C)\nu\lambda,$$

$$C\dot{\omega}_z - (A - B)\omega_x\omega_y = \frac{3MG}{R^3}(B - A)\lambda\mu.$$

Neglecting second-order small quantities, we find

$$A\dot{\omega}_x - (B - C)\omega_y\omega_z = 0, \tag{14.2.1}$$

$$B\dot{\omega}_y - (C - A)\omega_z\omega_x = \frac{3MG}{R^3}(A - C)\nu, \tag{14.2.2}$$

$$C\dot{\omega}_z \qquad\qquad = \frac{3MG}{R^3}(B - A)\mu. \tag{14.2.3}$$

14.3 The Libration in Longitude

In the following sections we shall be concerned with the *physical* (as opposed to the *optical*) libration of the Moon. We note that if Cassini's laws held exactly, then there would be no physical libration. In this section we shall consider equation (14.2.3); this involves ω_z only, and so can be treated separately.

Let the line joining the Earth and Moon make an angle θ with some fixed direction, and let $\angle AGE = \phi$. (See Figure 14.2.) ϕ is a measure of the optical

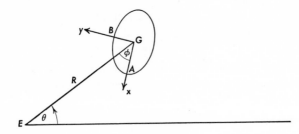

Figure 14.2

libration in longitude and is never more than about 7°; we will, therefore, feel justified in neglecting its square. The optical libration in latitude is also small; neglecting its square, we can say that GA makes an angle $(\theta + \phi)$ with the fixed direction. From Figure 14.2 we see that a positive ω_z would make $(\theta + \phi)$ decrease; hence

$$\omega_z = -\frac{d}{dt}(\theta + \phi).$$

Now

$$\mu = \cos\angle BGE = \sin\phi = \phi,$$

to the order of accuracy considered; so (14.2.3) becomes

$$\frac{d^2}{dt^2}(\theta + \phi) = -\frac{3GM}{R^3}\frac{B - A}{C}\phi. \tag{14.3.1}$$

Consider first the case when the orbit of the Earth around the Moon is circular, so that $d^2\theta/dt^2 = 0$. ϕ must always remain small, so that (14.3.1) describes simple harmonic motion and must be of the form

$$\frac{d^2\phi}{dt^2} + w^2\phi = 0. \tag{14.3.2}$$

This requires

$$w^2 = \frac{3MG}{R^3}\frac{B-A}{C}. \tag{14.3.3}$$

Then $B > A$, and for this to be so, $a > b$, where a and b are the lengths of the intercepts of the x- and y-axes with the Moon. The solution to (14.3.2) is

$$\phi = \alpha\cos(wt + \beta), \tag{14.3.4}$$

where α and β are arbitrary constants. If this oscillation could be observed, then its period would lead to a value for $(B - A)/C$; but it is too small to be detected.

Next we consider the consequences of the fact that the Moon's orbit is not a circle. If Cassini's first law were accurate, then

$$\dot\theta + \dot\phi = n, \quad \text{a constant,}$$

and

$$\theta = \phi = nt + \epsilon.$$

If t is measured from perigee, then ϵ is a small quantity of the same order as ϕ; θ is the true anomaly. In order to allow for periodic deviations from Cassini's law, put

$$\theta + \phi + \chi = nt + \epsilon, \tag{14.3.5}$$

so that (14.3.1) becomes

$$\ddot\chi = -w^2(\chi + \theta - nt - \epsilon)$$

or

$$\ddot\chi + w^2\chi = -w^2(\theta - nt - \epsilon). \tag{14.3.6}$$

Now $(\theta - nt)$ is the equation of the center for a Keplerian orbit and can be expanded accordingly. But we must allow for the fact that the orbit of the Moon is not even Keplerian. Then the right-hand side of (14.3.6) can be expanded in a series

$$\sum H\sin(ht + h'),$$

which will include all the periodic inequalities in the Moon's motion. (We neglect the secular acceleration of the Moon.) To solve (14.3.6), consider the equation

$$\ddot\chi + w^2\chi = -w^2H\sin(ht + h').$$

The complementary function is $\alpha\cos(wt + \beta)$, and the particular integral is of the form

$$X\sin(ht + h'),$$

where, by substitution, we find

$$X = \frac{w^2 H}{w^2 - h^2}.$$

Hence the solution is

$$\chi = \alpha \cos(wt + \beta) + w^2 \frac{H}{w^2 - h^2} \sin(ht + h').$$

Then the complete solution of (14.3.6) is

$$\chi = \alpha \cos(wt + \beta) + w^2 \sum \frac{H}{w^2 - h^2} \sin(ht + h'). \tag{14.3.7}$$

We have seen that the complementary function, giving the free oscillations, is too small to be observed. The terms in the particular integral are the forced oscillations; for any one to be appreciable, it must have large H or small h. The two most promising inequalities are the elliptic inequality (the first term in the expansion of the equation of the center), for which

$$H = 22639''.1 \quad \text{and} \quad \frac{2\pi}{h} = \text{the anomalistic month,}$$

and the annual equation, for which

$$H = -668''.9 \quad \text{and} \quad \frac{2\pi}{h} = \text{the anomalistic year.}$$

Now, $(B - A)/C$ is very small, and so, therefore, is w; and it is the annual equation that provides the larger forced oscillation. This can be observed, although not very accurately, and from observations of its amplitude the value of $(B - A)/C$ can be found.

We have now shown that Cassini's first law is true in the sense that oscillations about the state which it describes are small and stable, provided $a > b$. We shall next establish the other two laws in the same way.

14.4   Other Oscillations

In Figure 14.3, page 312, the dotted line represents the path of the Earth on the celestial sphere (with the Moon at its center), and N is its ascending node. The great circle through Z and E cuts Π_2 at H. Then $EH = l$ is the latitude of E. Neglecting the effects of precession on the position of Υ, we can write

$$\Upsilon N = -gt + \text{constant,}$$

where g is the rate of regression of the nodes. Let the orbit of the Earth be inclined at an angle k to Π_2; in the course of the time interval t, N will regress through an angle $gt \cos k$ with respect to the Earth's orbit; but k is small, so this may be taken as gt.

We have finished with equation (14.2.3). In considering equations (14.2.1) and (14.2.2) we need not concern ourselves with variations in ω_3, which we

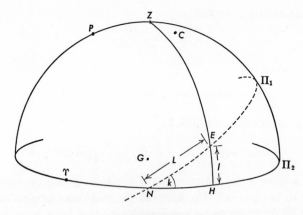

Figure 14.3

shall now take to be n; nor are we interested in μ or ϕ; so we can assume that the Earth moves in a circular orbit with angular motion n. Then

$$NE = L = nt + gt + \gamma,$$

where γ is a constant. Now

$$\cos ZE = p\lambda + q\mu + r\nu$$
$$= p + \nu,$$

approximately. Also

$$\cos ZE = \sin l$$
$$= \sin k \sin L$$
$$= k \sin L,$$

approximately. Hence

$$\left.\begin{array}{l} \nu = k \sin L - p \\ = k \sin(nt + gt + \gamma) - p. \end{array}\right] \tag{14.4.1}$$

Before solving the equations of motion, we shall find the condition for P, Z, and C to lie on a great circle, as required by Cassini's third law. N is the pole of the great circle PZ, so if C lies on this circle, GN must be perpendicular to GC. In the work following, $\hat{\mathbf{C}}$ will stand for the direction of $\mathbf{GC}$, and so on. Cassini's third law requires

$$\hat{\mathbf{C}} \cdot \hat{\mathbf{N}} = 0.$$

To find $\hat{\mathbf{N}}$, resolve along $\hat{\mathbf{H}}$ and $\hat{\mathbf{H}} \times \hat{\mathbf{Z}}$, so that

$$\hat{\mathbf{N}} = \hat{\mathbf{H}} \cos L + \hat{\mathbf{H}} \times \hat{\mathbf{Z}} \sin L,$$

to the required order of accuracy, since we are putting $\cos k = 1$. Now

$$\hat{\mathbf{H}} = \frac{\hat{\mathbf{Z}} \times (\hat{\mathbf{Z}} \times \hat{\mathbf{E}})}{\sin ZE}$$

$$= \frac{\hat{\mathbf{Z}} \cos ZE - \hat{\mathbf{E}}}{\sin ZE}$$

$$= \hat{\mathbf{Z}} \cos ZE - \hat{\mathbf{E}},$$

approximately, since $\sin ZE = \cos l$, and l is small. Hence

$$\hat{\mathbf{N}} = \cos L(\hat{\mathbf{Z}} \cos ZE - \hat{\mathbf{E}}) + \hat{\mathbf{Z}} \times \hat{\mathbf{E}} \sin L,$$

so that

$$\hat{\mathbf{C}} \cdot \hat{\mathbf{N}} = \cos L(r \cos ZE - \nu) + \sin L(p\mu - q\lambda)$$
$$= \cos L(\cos ZE - \nu) - q \sin L,$$

approximately. But $\cos ZE = p + \nu$; so

$$\hat{\mathbf{C}} \cdot \hat{\mathbf{N}} = p \cos L - q \sin L. \tag{14.4.2}$$

Let d/dt represent rate of change with respect to the moving axes GA, GB, and GC; then, since $\hat{\mathbf{Z}}$ is fixed in space,

$$\frac{d\hat{\mathbf{Z}}}{dt} + \boldsymbol{\omega} \times \hat{\mathbf{Z}} = 0.$$

Resolving, we find

$$\dot{p} - \omega_z q + \omega_y r = 0,$$
$$\dot{q} - \omega_x r + \omega_z p = 0,$$
$$\dot{r} - \omega_y p + \omega_x q = 0,$$

or, to the first order,

$$\left. \begin{array}{l} \dot{p} - nq + \omega_y r = 0, \\ \dot{q} - \omega_x r + np = 0, \\ \dot{r} \qquad\qquad = 0. \end{array} \right] \tag{14.4.3}$$

Differentiating the first two of these, and using the third, we find

$$\left. \begin{array}{l} \dot{\omega}_y = -\ddot{p} + n\dot{q}, \\ \dot{\omega}_x = \ddot{q} + n\dot{p}, \end{array} \right] \tag{14.4.4}$$

since $r \sim 1$.

We can now substitute for ω_x and ω_y and their derivatives in (14.2.1) and (14.2.2), when we find

$$\ddot{q} + n\dot{p} - \left(\frac{B-C}{A}\right)n(nq - \dot{p}) = 0,$$

$$-\ddot{p} + n\dot{q} - \left(\frac{C-A}{B}\right)n(\dot{q} + np) = -\frac{3MG}{R^3}\left(\frac{C-A}{B}\right)(k \sin L - p).$$

Put

$$\frac{C - B}{A} = \sigma, \quad \text{and} \quad \frac{C - A}{B} = \tau;$$

then, since $MG/R^3 = n^2$, the equations are

$$\ddot{q} + n\dot{p}(1 - \sigma) + n^2\sigma q = 0, \qquad (14.4.5)$$

$$-\ddot{p} + n\dot{q}(1 - \tau) - 4n^2\tau p = -3n^2\tau k \sin L. \qquad (14.4.6)$$

The solution of these equations will consist of a complementary function, representing free oscillations, and a particular integral, emanating from the term in $\sin L$, giving the forced oscillations. The free oscillations must be stable, and we shall now find the conditions for this to be so.

Put

$$p = Fe^{st}, \quad \text{and} \quad q = Ge^{st};$$

then substitution into (14.4.5) and (14.4.6) gives

$$Gs^2 + nsF(1 - \sigma) + n^2\sigma G = 0,$$

$$Fs^2 - nsG(1 - \tau) + 4n^2\tau F = 0,$$

since we are ignoring the term in $\sin L$. Eliminating the ratio F/G, we find

$$(s^2 + n^2\sigma)(s^2 + 4n^2\tau) + n^2s^2(1 - \sigma)(1 - \tau) = 0,$$

or

$$s^4 + s^2n^2(1 + 3\tau + \sigma\tau) + 4n^4\sigma\tau = 0.$$

Consider this as a quadratic for s^2. For the oscillations to be stable, the two roots must be real and negative. The condition for them to be real is

$$(1 + 3\tau + \sigma\tau)^2 - 16\sigma\tau > 0,$$

which is certainly true. For the roots to be negative, their sum must be negative, or

$$-n^2(1 + 3\tau + \sigma\tau) < 0,$$

which is true, and their product must be positive, or

$$\sigma\tau > 0;$$

i.e.,

$$(C - A)(C - B) > 0.$$

So C is either greater or less than both A and B; therefore the axis along Gz, of length c, is either less or greater than both a and b. Hence the axis of rotation is either the longest or the shortest axis of the Moon.

Now consider the forced oscillations. Try a solution

$$p = P \sin L, \quad q = Q \cos L.$$

By substitution (remembering that $dL/dt = n + g$), we find

$$\left.\begin{array}{l} Q\{-(n + g)^2 + n^2\sigma\} + Pn(n + g)(1 - \sigma) = 0, \\ P\{(n + g)^2 - 4n^2\tau\} - Qn(n + g)(1 - \tau) = -3n^2\tau k. \end{array}\right] \qquad (14.4.7)$$

Solving for Q/P, we find

$$\frac{Q}{P} = \frac{n(n+g)(1-\sigma)}{(n+g)^2 - n^2\sigma}$$

$$= \frac{\left(1 + \frac{g}{n}\right)(1-\sigma)}{1 + 2\frac{g}{n} - \sigma}$$

$$= \left(1 + \frac{g}{n} - \sigma\right)\left(1 - 2\frac{g}{n} + \sigma\right)$$

$$= 1 - \frac{g}{n}, \tag{14.4.8}$$

where products of small quantities have been ignored at each stage. Similarly we find

$$P = \frac{3nk\tau}{3n\tau - 2g}. \tag{14.4.9}$$

Now

$$CZ^2 = p^2 + q^2$$

$$= P^2\left(\sin^2 L + \left(\frac{Q}{P}\right)^2 \cos^2 L\right)$$

$$= P^2\left(1 - \frac{g}{n} - \frac{g}{n}\cos 2L\right). \tag{14.4.10}$$

Hence, apart from a small oscillation with period half a nodical month, CZ is constant. This proves Cassini's second law; we shall return to it in a moment, after proving the third law.

From (14.4.2),

$$\hat{\mathbf{C}}\cdot\hat{\mathbf{N}} = (P - Q)\cos L \sin L$$

$$= \frac{Pg}{2n}\sin 2L. \tag{14.4.11}$$

This oscillates with small amplitude about zero, so that, apart from this oscillation, it is zero, and P, Z, and C lie on a great circle. This also follows if the complementary functions are included in the evaluation of $\hat{\mathbf{C}}\cdot\hat{\mathbf{N}}$.

It remains to find the condition for Z to lie between P and C. Consider the situation when we put $L = 90°$ in the solution; then the Earth E lies on the great circle PZC, and we have (see Figure 14.4, page 316)

$$EP > EZ.$$

If the x-axis cuts the celestial sphere at A, then we know that A very nearly lies on the great circle $PZCE$, and since $AC = 90°$, the condition that Z should lie between P and C is

$$AZ > 90°.$$

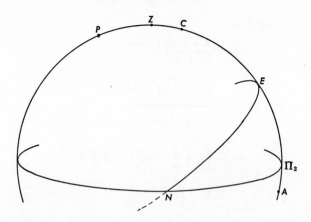

Figure 14.4

Therefore $\cos AZ$ is negative; but $\cos AZ = p = P \sin 90°$, so that

$$P = \frac{3k\tau}{3\tau - 2\dfrac{g}{n}} < 0.$$

It will be established in a moment that τ is numerically less than $2g/3n$, so that we must have

$$\tau > 0,$$

as the condition for Z to lie between P and C. But this implies

$$C - A > 0,$$

or

$$c < a.$$

Hence c is the shortest of the three axes, and we have

$$a > b > c.$$

    Now

$$CZ = |P|\left(1 - \frac{g}{2n}\right),$$

ignoring oscillations. P is small, so we can take

$$CZ = |P| = \left|\frac{3k\tau}{3\tau - 2\dfrac{g}{n}}\right|. \qquad (14.4.12)$$

Substituting the observed values

$$CZ = 91'.4, \quad k = 308'.7, \quad \text{and} \quad \frac{g}{n} = 0.00402,$$

we find
$$\tau = 0.00061.$$

Problems

1. Find the amplitudes of the two forced oscillations discussed in Section 14.3.
2. Find the periods of the free oscillations of (14.4.5) and (14.4.6).
3. Write down the equation for the variation of longitude, taking into account the secular acceleration of the Moon. Discuss the solutions and the orders of magnitude of any modifications to the earlier theory.
4. If the center of mass of the Moon is constrained to describe a circle, with a uniform angular velocity n about a fixed center of force O attracting according to Newton's law, show that the axis GA of the Moon will oscillate on each side of GO or will make complete revolutions relative to GO, according as the angular velocity of the Moon about its axis at the moment when GA and GO coincide in direction is less or greater than $(n + w)$, where w has the meaning given to it in Section 14.3. Find also the extent of the oscillations.
5. A body free to turn about its center of gravity, which is fixed, is in stable equilibrium under the attraction of a distant fixed particle M' at distance R. Show that the axis of least moment is turned toward the particle. Show also that the times of the principal oscillations are

$$2\pi\left\{\frac{BR^3}{3M'G(C - A)}\right\}^{1/2} \quad \text{and} \quad 2\pi\left\{\frac{CR^3}{3M'G(B - A)}\right\}^{1/2}.$$

If the body be the Earth, and M' the Sun, show that the smaller of these two periods is about ten years.

Appendix A ** PROPERTIES OF CONICS

A1. General Equations

This is in no way an adequate summary of the properties of conics; we are concerned only with the description of some of the properties that are useful in celestial mechanics. If the student has some grounding in analytical geometry, these sections may serve for review or for reference. A student who is not familiar with the subject at all should consult in addition any standard text on analytical geometry.

The word "conic" comes from the phrase "conic section," meaning any plane section of a right circular cone. The cone (which in the limit could be a cylinder or a straight line) is assumed to extend from either end of the apex; then any plane section cuts the cone in the figure of a conic, and any conic can be obtained in this way. (See Figure A.1, page 320.) This definition is not very helpful here, but there are many alternatives.

The general equation of the second degree in cartesian coordinates is a conic, and any conic can be represented by a cartesian equation of the second degree. This is a possible definition, and the properties of conics can be discussed through the properties of quadratic forms. In this context it appears that the conic is the next simplest geometrical figure after the straight line (which has a linear cartesian equation). A property of the general quadratic equation in two variables is that, by a suitable change of axes, we can *usually* reduce it to the form

$$ax^2 + by^2 + c = 0. \tag{A1.1}$$

If this is possible, the origin of coordinates is called the *center* of the conic, and the axes of coordinates are the axes of the conic; they are axes of symmetry. Normally, if we are to work in cartesian coordinates, it is simplest to use these axes.

Another definition, which leads at once to the general equation in polar coordinates, is that a conic is the locus of a point such that the ratio of its distance from a fixed point to its distance from a fixed line is constant. The fixed point is called a *focus*, the fixed line is a *directrix*, and the constant ratio is the *eccentricity* of the conic. To find the equation in polar coordinates, choose the focus as origin, and let the polar angle v be measured from the line OD perpendicular to the

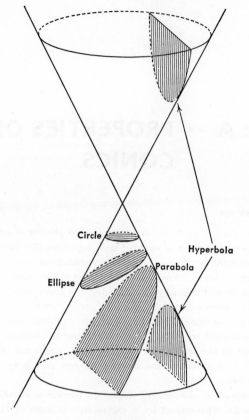

Figure A.1

directrix, which is at a distance k from the focus. Let $P(r,v)$ be a point on the conic; then from the definition,

$$r = e(k - r \cos v)$$

or

$$\frac{p}{r} = 1 + e \cos v, \qquad (A1.2)$$

where e is the constant ratio, or eccentricity. $p = ek$ is called the *parameter* of the conic. e determines the shape of a conic, while p determines its size. If polar coordinates are to be used, then it is wise to choose a focus as origin.

The line OD, being an axis of symmetry, is an axis of the conic; the minimum value of r (and the maximum, if it exists) occurs on OD. The chord through O, perpendicular to OD, is called the *latus rectum* and has length $2p$. p is often referred to as the *semilatus rectum*.

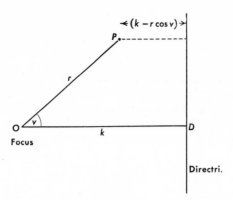

Figure A.2

A.2   The Ellipse

The ellipse is a conic for which $0 \leqslant e < 1$. If $e = 0$, the ellipse becomes a circle. From the polar equation we see that r is bounded, so that the ellipse is a closed figure. It follows from the theory of quadratic forms that the cartesian equation of an ellipse can be put into the form

$$\frac{x^2}{a^2} + \frac{y^2}{b^2} = 1. \tag{A2.1}$$

a and b are positive, and a is invariably chosen to be greater than or equal to b. The x- and y-axes are the major and minor axes of the ellipse, respectively, and a and b are the *semimajor* and *semiminor axes*.

From an examination of the polar equation, (A1.2), we see that the focus used as origin lies on the x-axis, and that the directrix is parallel to the y-axis. Let the focus be S; then, by symmetry, there must be another focus S' such that the center C bisects SS'. Let the axes meet the ellipse at A, A', B, and B' (see Figure A.3, page 322); then it is easily verified that

$$CA = CA' = a,$$
$$CB = CB' = b,$$
$$SA = q = a(1 - e),$$
$$SA' = q' = a(1 + e),$$
$$CS = CS' = ae,$$
$$p = a(1 - e^2),$$
$$b^2 = a^2(1 - e^2),$$
$$SB = a.$$

The polar equation can be written

$$\frac{a(1 - e^2)}{r} = 1 + e \cos v. \tag{A2.2}$$

These formulas should all be memorized.

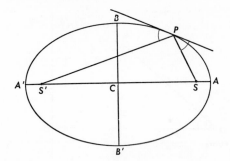

Figure A.3

Another definition of the ellipse is that it is the locus of P such that

$$SP + S'P = \text{constant},$$

where S and S' are fixed points; clearly these are the foci, and the constant has the value $2a$. We also note without proof that the lines SP and $S'P$ make equal angles with the tangent at P.

From the form of the cartesian equation of the ellipse, (A2.1), it follows that the ellipse is the orthogonal projection of a circle of radius a; this is the *auxiliary circle*. Alternatively, draw a circle of radius a, and choose any diameter AA'. From any point Q on the circumference, drop a perpendicular QR onto AA', and construct P on QR such that

$$\frac{PR}{QR} = \frac{b}{a}.$$

Then P will trace out the ellipse with semiaxes a and b.

It is easily verified from this property that the area of the ellipse is

$$\pi ab.$$

Let $\angle QCA = E$; then the cartesian coordinates of P are

$$x = a \cos E, \quad y = b \sin E. \tag{A2.3}$$

E is called the *eccentric angle* of P.

A.3   The Parabola

The conic with $e = 1$ is the parabola. If we let e tend to one for an ellipse, then a tends to infinity. Although some properties of the parabola can be deduced from corresponding properties of the ellipse by letting $e = 1$ and $1/a = 0$, this may lead to expressions that are meaningless; as, for instance, if it is applied to (A2.2). However, if we remember that the pericentron distance, $q = SA$, remains finite, and write (A2.2) as

$$\frac{q(1 + e)}{r} = 1 + e \cos v,$$

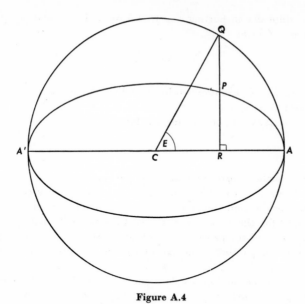

Figure A.4

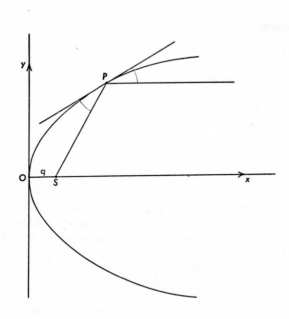

Figure A.5

then there is no difficulty in putting $e = 1$, and we find the polar equation of the parabola in the usual form:

$$r = q \sec^2 \frac{v}{2}.$$ (A3.1)

The size of a parabola is usually given by q. (All parabolas have the same shape.) The semilatus rectum is $2q$.

The cartesian equation can be put into the form

$$y^2 = 4qx.$$ (A3.2)

There is only one focus, at $(q,0)$, and one axis, the x-axis.

Return for a moment to the ellipse, and let e tend to one. The second focus tends to infinity, and the theorem that the tangent at P makes equal angles with SP and $S'P$ becomes, for the parabola, that the tangent at P makes equal angles with SP and the axis of the parabola. This leads to the well-known property that a ray of light traveling parallel to the axis of a parabolic mirror passes through the focus after reflection.

Sometimes it is convenient to consider a curve as traced out by the variation of a single variable, or *parameter*; the equations (A2.3) are an example of this; they are one form (out of many possibilities) of the *parametric equations* of the ellipse. There are many possible representations of the parabola; perhaps the simplest is

$$x = qt^2, \quad y = 2qt.$$ (A3.3)

A.4   The Hyperbola

The hyperbola is defined by $e > 1$. From the polar equation we see that the curve is not bounded, since r can become arbitrarily large. When r does become large, v tends to one of the values given by

$$v_a = \cos^{-1}\left(-\frac{1}{e}\right).$$ (A4.1)

The cartesian equation can be put into the form

$$\frac{x^2}{a^2} - \frac{y^2}{b^2} = 1.$$ (A4.2)

In this text both a and b are taken as positive. a is sometimes (and at times more conveniently) taken as negative; whatever convention the student may adopt, he should stick to it consistently. When x and y become large, (A4.2) is nearly the same as

$$\left(\frac{x}{a} + \frac{y}{b}\right)\left(\frac{x}{a} - \frac{y}{b}\right) = 0,$$ (A4.3)

which is the equation of two lines through the origin. The larger r becomes, the more nearly the curve resembles these two lines; they are called *asymptotes*. The directions given by the values of v_a, from (A4.1), must be parallel to these asymptotes, and we deduce that the angle between the asymptotes is

$$2\cos^{-1}\left(-\frac{1}{e}\right) \quad \text{or} \quad \cos^{-1}\left(\frac{2}{e^2}-1\right).$$

From (A4.2) we see that there is no point on the hyperbola for which $-a < x < a$; therefore the hyperbola has two branches; the polar equation gives only one of these. (See Figure A.6.) Comparing the gradients of the asymptotes, (A4.3), with the formula for v_a, we find

$$\tan^{-1}\frac{b}{a} = \cos^{-1}\frac{1}{e}$$

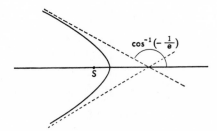

Figure A.6

from which we deduce

$$b^2 = a^2(e^2 - 1).$$

b can be less or greater than a; Figures A.7(a), (b), and (c) show hyperbolas for which b is less than, equal to, and greater than a. If $b = a$, then the figure is a *rectangular hyperbola*.

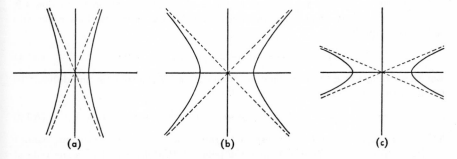

(a)   (b)   (c)

Figure A.7

In the notation of Figure A.8, we see that

$$CA = a,$$
$$AS = q = a(e - 1).$$

The tangent at A cuts the asymptotes in points $(-a, \pm b)$. The semilatus rectum is

$$p = a(e^2 - 1).$$

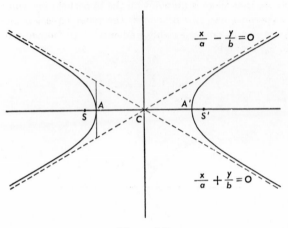

Figure A.8

The hyperbola can be defined as the locus of P such that the difference between SP and $S'P$ is constant, S and S' being fixed points. These are the foci, and to recover the equations given above, the constant difference must be equal to $2a$, so that

$$SS' = 2c = 2ae.$$

The cartesian coordinates of any point on the hyperbola with equation (A4.2) are given by the parametric equations

$$x = \pm a \cosh F, \quad y = b \sinh F. \tag{A4.4}$$

A5. Pole and Polar

This section is required for the interpretation of Hamilton's theorem, Section 4.9.

Let $P(x_1, y_1)$ be any point from which real tangents can be drawn to a conic with the general equation

$$ax^2 + 2hxy + by^2 + 2gx + 2fy + c = 0. \tag{A5.1}$$

Let these tangents meet the conic at points Q and R; then it is not difficult to establish that the equation of the line QR is

$$x(ax_1 + hy_1 + g) + y(by_1 + hx_1 + f) + gx_1 + fy_1 + c = 0. \tag{A5.2}$$

This line is the polar of P with respect to the conic. Even if real tangents cannot be drawn from P, (A5.2) still defines the polar of P. Conversely, P is the pole of the line with equation (A5.2).

The student will be able to verify without difficulty that the focus and directrix are pole and polar.

If P lies on the conic, then (A5.2) is the equation of the tangent at P.

The most interesting properties of poles and polars involve projective geometry, which the student is encouraged to pursue further; but it is outside the scope of this text.

Appendix B ** THE ROTATION OF AXES

If a system of right-handed rectangular axes is rotated positively through θ about the x-axis, the new coordinates, (x',y',z'), of a point are related to the old, (x,y,z), by

$$x' = x,$$
$$y' = y \cos \theta + z \sin \theta,$$
$$z' = -y \sin \theta + z \cos \theta.$$

These equations can be written in matrix notation as

$$(x'y'z') = (x\ y\ z) \begin{pmatrix} 1 & 0 & 0 \\ 0 & \cos \theta & -\sin \theta \\ 0 & \sin \theta & \cos \theta \end{pmatrix}$$
$$= (x\ y\ z)\ P(\theta),$$

where

$$P(\theta) = \begin{pmatrix} 1 & 0 & 0 \\ 0 & \cos \theta & -\sin \theta \\ 0 & \sin \theta & \cos \theta \end{pmatrix}.$$

Similarly, a positive rotation through θ about the y-axis leads to new coordinates given by

$$(x'y'z') = (x\ y\ z)\ Q(\theta),$$

where

$$Q(\theta) = \begin{pmatrix} \cos \theta & 0 & \sin \theta \\ 0 & 1 & 0 \\ -\sin \theta & 0 & \cos \theta \end{pmatrix}.$$

And a positive rotation through θ about the z-axis leads to new coordinates given by

$$(x'y'z') = (x\ y\ z)R\ (\theta),$$

where

$$R(\theta) = \begin{pmatrix} \cos \theta & -\sin \theta & 0 \\ \sin \theta & \cos \theta & 0 \\ 0 & 0 & 1 \end{pmatrix}.$$

For a combination of two rotations, let us say $R(\theta)$ and then $P(\phi)$, we have

$$(x'y'z') = (x \; y \; z) \; R \; (\theta) \; P(\phi)$$

$$= (x \; y \; z) \begin{pmatrix} \cos\theta & -\sin\theta & 0 \\ \sin\theta & \cos\theta & 0 \\ 0 & 0 & 1 \end{pmatrix} \begin{pmatrix} 1 & 0 & 0 \\ 0 & \cos\phi & -\sin\phi \\ 0 & \sin\phi & \cos\phi \end{pmatrix}$$

$$= (x \; y \; z) \begin{pmatrix} \cos\theta & -\sin\theta\cos\phi & \sin\theta\sin\phi \\ \sin\theta & \cos\theta\cos\phi & -\cos\theta\sin\phi \\ 0 & \sin\phi & \cos\phi \end{pmatrix}.$$

In the same way the matrix describing any number of rotations can be found by straightforward matrix multiplication. For example, to rotate from axes in a cometary orbit with Ox pointing toward perihelion and Oz along $\hat{\mathbf{h}}$, to equatorial axes with Ox pointing toward the vernal equinox and Oz toward the north celestial pole, we have the matrix

$$R(-\omega) \; P(-i) \; R(-\Omega) \; P(-\epsilon).$$

Special care should be taken that the signs of the rotations are correct.

These formulas apply equally well to infinitesimal rotations. Their use will often obviate the need for spherical trigonometry.

Appendix C ** NUMERICAL TABLES

C1. Elements of Planetary Orbits

Planet	a		Sidereal Period		Synodic Period	e
	AU	10^6 km	Tropical years	Days	Days	
Mercury ☿	0.387 098	57.91	0.240 85	87.969	115.88	0.205 615 + 0.000 02
Venus ♀	0.723 331	108.21	0.615 21	224.701	583.92	0.006 818 − 0.000 05
Earth ⊕	1.000 000	149.60	1.000 04	365.256		0.016 750 − 0.000 04
Mars ♂	1.523 679	227.9	1.880 89	686.980	779.94	0.093 310 + 0.000 09
Jupiter ♃	5.202 7	778.3	11.862 23	4 332.588	398.88	0.048 335 + 0.000 16
Saturn ♄	9.546	1428	29.457 74	10 759.21	378.09	0.055 892 − 0.000 34
Uranus ♅	19.20	2872	84.018	30 687	369.66	0.047 0 + 0.000 2
Neptune ♆	30.09	4498	164.78	60 184	367.49	0.008 7 + 0.000 04
Pluto ♇	39.5	5910	248.4	90 700	366.74	0.247

C2. Physical Elements of Planets

Planet	Equatorial Radius R_e	Ellipticity $\dfrac{R_e - R_p}{R_e}$	Mass, (excluding satellites)	Mean Density
	km		⊕ = 1	gr/cm
Mercury	2 420	0.0	0.053	5.3
Venus	6 200	0.0	0.815	4.95
Earth	6 378	0.0034	1.000	5.52
Mars	3 400	0.0052	0.107	3.95
Jupiter	71 400	0.062	318.00	1.330
Saturn	60 400	0.096	95.22	0.687
Uranus	23 800	0.06	14.55	1.56
Neptune	22 300	0.02	17.23	2.27
Pluto	7 200		0.9?	4?

Epoch	1900.0 + T Centuries		Mean Longitude at 1950 Jan. 0.5 UT
i	Ω	$\tilde{\omega}$	
′ ″ ″	° ′ ″ ″	° ′ ″ ″	° ′ ″
0 10.6 + 6.3T	47 8 43 + 4266T	75 53 54 + 5596T	33 10 6
23 37.1 + 4.5T	75 47 1 + 3260T	130 9 8 + 5065T	81 34 19
		101 13 11 + 6180T	99 35 18
51 1.1 − 2.3T	48 47 12 + 2786T	334 13 6 + 6626T	144 20 7
18 31.4 − 20.5T	99 26 36 + 3638T	12 43 15 + 5796T	316 9 34
29 33.1 − 14 T	112 47 25 + 3143T	91 5 54 + 7050T	158 18 13
46 20.9 + 2.3T	73 28 38 + 1795T	169 3 + 5800T	98 18 31
46 45.3 − 34.3T	130 40 53 + 3956T	43 50 + 2400T	194 57 8
8 44 − 20 T	108 57 17 + 4889T	222 48 + 5000T	165 36 9

Surface Gravity		Velocity of Escape	Rotation Period (equatorial)	Inclination of Equator to Orbit
Attractive	Equator centrifugal			
cm/sec^2		km/sec		
360	− 0.00	4.2	87.969 days	
850	− 0.00	10.3	Unknown	
982	− 3.39	11.2	23^h 56^m 4.1^s	23° 27′
376	− 1.71	5.0	24^h 37^m 22.6^s	25° 12′
2 600	− 225	61	9^h 50^m.5*	3° 7′
1 120	− 176	37	10^h 14^m*	26° 45′
940	− 62	22	10^h 49^m	97° 59′
1 500	− 28	25	15^h 40^m	29°
800?		10?	16^h	

The period of rotation becomes longer toward the poles.

C3. Satellites

Planet and Satellite	Distance from Planet		Sidereal Period	Orbit Inclination	Orbit Eccentricity	Radius of Satellite	Reciprocal Mass	Mass
	10^3 km	10^{-3} AU	Days	°		km	$\dfrac{1}{\text{planet}}$	10^{24} gm
Earth								
Moon	384.4	2.571	27.321 661	5.1 E	0.0549	1738	81.3	73.4
Mars								
1 Phobos	9.4	0.0627	0.318 910	1.8 P	0.019	8		
2 Deimos	23.5	0.1570	1.262 441	1.4 P	0.003	4		
Jupiter								
1 Io	421.8	2.8196	1.769 138	0 P	small	1660	24 000	79
2 Europa	671.4	4.4862	3.551 181	0 P	and	1440	39 800	47.8
3 Ganymede	1 071	7.1559	7.154 553	0 P	vari-	2470	12 400	153
4 Callisto	1 884	12.5865	16.689 018	0 P	able	2340	21 000	90
5	181	1.207	0.498 179	0 P	0.003	80		
6	11 500	76.605	250.62	28.5 B	0.155	60		
7	11 750	78.516	259.8	28.0 B	0.207	20		
8	23 500	157.20	738.9	R 33 B	0.38	20		
9	23 700	158	755	R 24 B	0.25	11		
10	11 750	78.5	260	28.3 B	0.140	10		
11	22 500	150.834	696	R 16.6 B	0.207	12		
12	21 000	140	625	R	0.13	10		

Saturn							
1 Mimas	185.7	1.2401	0.942 422	1.5 P	0.0196	260	15 000 000	0.038
2 Enceladus	238.2	1.5909	1.370 218	0.0 P	0.0045	300	8 000 000	0.07
3 Tethys	294.8	1.9694	1.887 802	1.1 P	0.0000	600	870 000	0.65
4 Dione	377.7	2.5224	2.736 916	0.0 P	0.0021	650	550 000	1.03
5 Rhea	527.5	3.5226	4.517 503	0.3 P	0.0009	900	250 000	2.3
6 Titan	1 223	8.1660	15.945 452	0.3 P	0.0289	2500	4 150	137
7 Hyperion	1 484	9.8929	21.276 665	0.6 P	0.110	200	5 000 000	0.11
8 Iapetus	3 563	23.798	79.330 82	14.7 P	0.029	600	100 000	5
9 Phoebe	12 950	86.593	550.45	R 30.	0.166	150		
Uranus							
1 Ariel	191.8	1.2820	2.520 38	0 P	0.007	300		
2 Umbriel	267.3	1.7859	4.144 18	0 P	0.008	200		
3 Titania	438.7	2.9303	8.705 88	0 P	0.023?	500		
4 Oberon	568.6	3.9187	13.463 26	0 P	0.010?	400		
5 Miranda	130.1	0.87	1.414					
Neptune							
1 Triton	353.6	2.3635	5.876 83	R 20 P	0.000	2000	3 000 000	150
2 Nereid	6 000?	40?	500		0.7?	150	700	0.05

R means that the satellite is retrograde. *E* means that the inclination is measured from the ecliptic. *P* means the the inclination is measured from the planet's equator. *B* means that the inclination is measured from the planet's orbit.

Dimensions of Saturn's Rings

Radius (limiting values quoted), 10^3 km

	138
Outer *A* ring: moderately bright	120
Cassini division: dark	116
Main *B* ring: very bright	90
Gap: dark	89
Crape or *C* ring: faint	71

Thickness of rings, less than 20 km.

Mass of rings $4 \times 10^{-5} \times$ the mass of Saturn.

C4. The Earth

Length of the Year

Tropical	365.242 198 78 − 0.000 006 16T ephemeris days
Sidereal	365.256 365 56 + 0.000 000 11T ephemeris days
Anomalistic	365.259 641 34 + 0.000 003 04T ephemeris days
Eclipse	346.620 031 + 0.000 032T ephemeris days
Julian	365.25 days.

Length of the Day

Mean solar day	24^h 03^m $56^s.555$ sidereal time
or	1.002 737 91 sidereal days.
Sidereal day	23^h 56^m $4^s.091$ mean solar time
or	0.997 269 57 mean solar days.

Dimensions

Equatorial radius	$a = 6\ 378.388$ km
Polar radius	$c = 6\ 356.912$ km
Depression from spheroid at lat. 45°	3.2 meters
Mass	$M = 5.977 \times 10^{27}$ gm

Moment of Inertia

about rotation axis $\quad C = 8.11 \times 10^{44}$ gm cm^2

$\qquad\qquad\qquad\qquad = 0.3340\ Ma^2$

about equatorial axis $\quad A = 0.3329\ Ma^2$.

C5. The Moon

Length of the Month

Sidereal period	27.321 661 0 − 0.000 000 2T days
Synodic month	29.530 588 2 − 0.000 000 2T days
Anomalistic month	27.554 550 5 − 0.000 001 4T days
Nodical month	27.212 220 days
Tropical month (♈ to ♈)	27.321 581 7 − 0.000 000 2T days

Orbit

Mean distance from the Earth	384 405 km
or	0.002 570 AU
Inclination of orbit to ecliptic	5° 9′
Inclination of lunar equator to ecliptic	1° 32′
Eccentricity of orbit	0.054 90
Period of node	18.60 tropical years.

Dimensions

Radius	1738.0 km
Mass	7.380×10^{25} gm
or	mass of Earth/81.31
Mean density	3.342
Surface gravity	162.0 cm/sec^2
Escape velocity	2.38 km/sec

(Radius directed toward Earth) − (polar radius)
$$a - c = 1.08 \text{ km}.$$

(Radius directed toward Earth) − (radius in direction of orbit)
$$a - b = 0.2 \text{ km}.$$

Moment of inertia about rotation axis, $C = 0.397 \, Mb^2$, where M is the mass of the Moon.

Moment of inertia differences,

$$\frac{C - A}{C} = 0.000 \ 622,$$

$$\frac{B - A}{C} = 0.000 \ 12.$$

C6. The Sun

Radius	6.960×10^{10} cm
Mass	1.991×10^{33} gm
Angular velocity at equator	2.90×10^{-6} radian/sec
Moment of inertia	5×10^{53} gm cm^2
Mean equatorial horizontal parallax	8″.80
Mean distance from Earth	1.4960×10^{13} cm.

C7. Physical Constants

Speed of light	$c = 2.997 \ 91 \times 10^{10}$ cm/sec
Gravitation constant	$G = 6.668 \times 10^{-8}$ dyne cm^2 gm^{-2}
Gaussian gravitation constant	$k = 0.01720 \ 209895$
Obliquity of ecliptic	$\epsilon = 23° \ 27' \ 08''.26 - 46''.85T$

Invariable plane of the solar system,
$$\Omega = 106° \ 35' \ 01'' + 3452''T$$
$$i = \quad 1° \ 34' \ 59'' - \quad 18''T$$

Constant of nutation	9″.207
Constant of aberration	20″.49
Constant of precession	$5493''.6 - 0''.0036T.$

C8. Miscellaneous Data

1 foot	= 30.4800 cm
1 mile	= 1.609 344 km
1 nautical mile	= 6080 ft = 1.853 km
Seconds in a day	= 86 400
Seconds in a tropical year	= $3.155 \ 6926 \times 10^7$
1 mile/hour	= 44.704 cm/sec
	= 1.4667 ft/sec

1 radian	$= 57°295\ 7795$
1°	$= 0.017\ 453\ 2925$ radian
π	$= 3.141\ 5927$
e	$= 2.718\ 2818$

Appendix D ** MISCELLANEOUS EXPANSIONS IN SERIES

D1. f **and** g **Series**

$$f = 1 - \tfrac{1}{2}\sigma t^2 + \tfrac{1}{2}\sigma\tau t^3 + \tfrac{1}{24}\sigma(3\omega - 2\sigma - 15\tau^2)t^4 - \tfrac{1}{8}\sigma\tau(3\omega - 2\sigma - 7\tau^2)t^5$$

$$+ \tfrac{1}{720}\sigma\{(630\omega - 420\sigma - 945\tau^2)\tau^2 - (22\sigma^2 - 66\sigma\omega + 45\omega^2)\}t^6 + \cdots$$

$$g = t - \tfrac{1}{6}\sigma t^3 + \tfrac{1}{4}\sigma\tau t^4 + \tfrac{1}{120}\sigma(9\omega - 8\sigma - 45\tau^2)t^5 - \tfrac{1}{24}\sigma\tau(6\omega - 5\sigma - 14\tau^2)t^6 + \cdots$$

where

$$\sigma = \frac{1}{r_0^3}, \quad \tau = \frac{\dot r_0}{r_0}, \quad \omega = \frac{\dot{\mathbf{r}}_0 \cdot \dot{\mathbf{r}}_0}{r_0^2}.$$

D2. Elliptic Motion

The following series apply to elliptic motion for which e is less than 0.663.

$$E = M + 2\sum_{n=1}^{\infty}\frac{1}{n}J_n(ne)\sin nM.$$

$$\cos E = -\frac{1}{2}e + 2\sum_{n=1}^{\infty}\frac{1}{n}J_n'(ne)\cos nM.$$

$$\sin E = \frac{2}{e}\sum_{n=1}^{\infty}\frac{1}{n}J_n'(ne)\sin nM.$$

$$\sin v = 2\sqrt{1 - e^2}\sum_{n=1}^{\infty}J_n'(ne)\sin nM.$$

$$\cos v = -e + \frac{2(1 - e^2)}{e}\sum_{n=1}^{\infty}J_n(ne)\cos nM.$$

$$v - M = (2e - \tfrac{1}{4}e^3)\sin M + (\tfrac{5}{4}e^2 - \tfrac{11}{24}e^4)\sin 2M$$
$$+ \tfrac{13}{12}e^3\sin 3M + \tfrac{103}{96}e^4\sin 4M + \cdots$$

The J_n and J'_n are Bessel functions. The first few are given by

$$J_1(e) = \tfrac{1}{2}e(1 - \tfrac{1}{8}e^2 + \tfrac{1}{192}e^4 - \tfrac{1}{9216}e^6 + \cdots),$$

$$J_2(2e) = \tfrac{1}{2}e^2(1 - \tfrac{1}{3}e^2 + \tfrac{1}{24}e^4 - \tfrac{1}{360}e^6 + \cdots),$$

$$J_3(3e) = \tfrac{9}{16}e^3(1 - \tfrac{9}{16}e^2 + \tfrac{81}{640}e^4 - \cdots),$$

$$J_4(4e) = \tfrac{2}{3}e^4(1 - \tfrac{4}{5}e^2 + \tfrac{4}{15}e^4 - \cdots),$$

$$J_5(5e) = \tfrac{625}{768}e^5(1 - \tfrac{25}{24}e^2 + \tfrac{625}{1344}e^4 - \cdots),$$

$$J_6(6e) = \tfrac{81}{80}e^6(1 - \tfrac{9}{7}e^2 + \tfrac{81}{112}e^4 - \cdots),$$

and

$$J'_1(e) = \tfrac{1}{2}(1 - \tfrac{3}{8}e^2 + \tfrac{5}{192}e^4 - \tfrac{7}{9216}e^6 + \cdots),$$

$$J'_2(2e) = \tfrac{1}{2}e(1 - \tfrac{2}{3}e^2 + \tfrac{1}{8}e^4 - \tfrac{1}{90}e^6 + \cdots),$$

$$J'_3(3e) = \tfrac{9}{16}e^2(1 - \tfrac{15}{16}e^2 + \tfrac{189}{640}e^4 - \cdots),$$

$$J'_4(4e) = \tfrac{2}{3}e^3(1 - \tfrac{6}{5}e^2 + \tfrac{8}{15}e^4 - \cdots),$$

$$J'_5(5e) = \tfrac{625}{768}e^4(1 - \tfrac{35}{24}e^2 + \tfrac{375}{448}e^4 - \cdots),$$

$$J'_6(6e) = \tfrac{81}{80}e^5(1 - \tfrac{12}{7}e^2 + \tfrac{135}{112}e^4 - \cdots).$$

In general,

$$J_n(ne) = \frac{e}{2}\left(\frac{ne}{2}\right)^{n-1}\frac{1}{(n-1)!}\left\{1 - \frac{n^2e^2}{2\cdot(2n+2)} + \frac{n^4e^4}{2\cdot4\cdot(2n+2)(2n+4)} - \cdots\right\},$$

and

$$J'_n(ne) = \frac{1}{2}\left(\frac{ne}{2}\right)^{n-1}\frac{1}{(n-1)!}\left\{1 - \frac{n+2}{n}\frac{n^2e^2}{2(2n+2)} + \frac{n+4}{n}\frac{n^4e^4}{2\cdot4\cdot(2n+2)(2n+4)} - \cdots\right\}.$$

Appendix E ✶✶ THE GREEK ALPHABET

Name	Sign Capital	Sign Small	Name	Sign Capital	Sign Small
Alpha	A	α	Nu	N	ν
Beta	B	β	Xi	Ξ	ξ
Gamma	Γ	γ	Omicron	O	o
Delta	Δ	δ	Pi	Π	π or $\tilde{\omega}$
Epsilon	E	ϵ	Rho	P	ρ
Zeta	Z	ζ	Sigma	Σ	σ or ς
Eta	H	η	Tau	T	τ
Theta	Θ	θ	Upsilon	Y	υ
Iota	I	ι	Phi	Φ	ϕ
Kappa	K	κ	Chi	X	χ
Lambda	Λ	λ	Psi	Ψ	ψ
Mu	M	μ	Omega	Ω	ω

Appendix F ** BIBLIOGRAPHY

Chapter 1

For the student in search of stimulating literature on astronomy there is still no substitute for the popular works of Eddington and Jeans (now happily being reprinted in paperback editions), in spite of the fact that much of the subject matter is out of date. Similar books written recently include notably the popular books by Gamow and Hoyle. (The student should not become cynical about the diversity of theories described; the progress in astronomy over the past thirty years has fully matched that in any other subject.)

For a survey of astronomical discovery and ideas see

1. De Vaucouleurs, G. *Discovery of the Universe*. New York: Macmillan, 1957.

   Elementary and readable books about the solar system include

2. Whipple, F. L. *Earth, Moon and Planets*. Philadelphia: The Blakiston Company, 1941.

3. Watson, F. G. *Between the Planets*. (Revised edition.) Philadelphia: The Blakiston Company, 1956.

The student will also find a wealth of information in the books by P. Moore on the Moon and planets.

A discussion and summary of the main properties of the planets and satellites in the solar system is given in

4. Ehricke, K. A. *Space Flight*. New York: Van Nostrand, 1960.

Students new to astronomy should procure a text such as

5. Baker, R. H. *Astronomy*. (7th edition.) New York: Van Nostrand, 1959.

More advanced works dealing with the solar system include:

6. Jeffreys, H. *The Earth*. (3rd edition.) Cambridge, England: Cambridge University Press, 1952.

7. Kuiper, G. P. (Editor) *The Atmospheres of the Earth and Planets*. Chicago: University of Chicago Press, 1952.

8. Kuiper, G. P. (Editor) *The Earth as a Planet*. (Volume two of *The Solar System*.) Chicago: University of Chicago Press, 1954.

9. Urey, H. C. *The Planets, Their Origin and Development*. New Haven: Yale University Press, 1952.

10. De Vaucouleurs, G. *Physics of the Planet Mars*. New York: Macmillan, 1954.

11. Peek, B. M. *The Planet Jupiter*. New York: Macmillan, 1958.

A text recommended for spherical astronomy is

12. Smart, W. M. *Spherical Astronomy.* (4th edition.) Cambridge, England: Cambridge University Press, 1944.

Apart from texts and reference books, the student should make use of the journals on astronomy. Those of a popular nature include:

Sky and Telescope. Sky Publishing Company, Harvard College Observatory, 60 Garden Street, Cambridge 38, Mass.

The Journal of the British Astronomical Association. Burlington House, London, W.1., England.

More advanced journals include:

The Astronomical Journal. (*A.J.*) American Institute of Physics, 335 East 45 Street, New York 17, N.Y.

Publications of the Astronomical Society of the Pacific. (*P.A.S.P.*) 675 Eighteenth Avenue, San Francisco 21, Calif.

Monthly Notices of the Royal Astronomical Society. (*M.N.*) Burlington House, London, W.1., England.

If the student is new to journals, he should approach them through references and through the indexes, remembering that authors as well as subjects are guides to the papers in which he may be interested. He should remember that every paper contains a summary and usually a list of references; he can, through the latter, rapidly build up an extensive bibliography.

Chapter 2

Many texts on mechanics include introductions to vectors; an example is

13. Pars, L. A. *Introduction to Dynamics.* Cambridge, England: Cambridge University Press, 1953.

Separate texts include:

14. Rutherford, D. E. *Vector Methods.* (8th edition.) New York: Interscience Publishers, 1954.

15. Milne, E. A. *Vectorial Mechanics.* New York: Interscience Publishers, 1948.

Chapter 3

The student should consult references such as 13, 14, and 15.

Chapter 4

The student will find accounts of central orbit theory in most texts on mechanics such as 13, or the following:

16. Ramsey, A. S. *Dynamics.* (Parts one and two.) Cambridge, England: Cambridge University Press, 1946.

17. Whittaker, E. T. *Analytical Dynamics.* (4th edition.) Cambridge, England: Cambridge University Press, 1959. (Now available in a paperback edition.)

18. Moulton, F. R. *An Introduction to Celestial Mechanics.* (2nd edition.) New York: Macmillan, 1914.

Chapter 5

Much of the material in this chapter is based on

19. Ramsey, A. S. *Newtonian Attraction.* Cambridge, England: Cambridge University Press, 1949.

See also 15. Discussions on the figures of rotating and tidally distorted masses, with applications to astronomy are given in

20. Jeans, J. H. *Problems of Cosmogony and Stellar Dynamics*. Cambridge, England: Cambridge University Press, 1919.
21. Jeans, J. H. *Astronomy and Cosmogony*. Cambridge, England: Cambridge University Press, 1928.

Chapter 6

See 12 and 18, and, for a generous collection of formulas appropriate to two-body motion, 4. See also

22. Baker, R. M. L. and Makemson, M. W. *Astrodynamics*. New York: Academic Press, 1960.

This is an excellent introduction to the applications of celestial mechanics to the new problems of space flight, and to some of the new methods being developed. It includes an extensive bibligraphy of recent papers.

23. Porter, J. G. *Comets and Meteor Streams*. London: Chapman and Hall Ltd., 1952.

The following are more advanced works:

24. Smart, W. M. *Celestial Mechanics*. New York: Longmans, Green & Co., 1953.
25. Plummer, H. C. *Dynamical Astronomy*. Cambridge, England: Cambridge University Press, 1918. Now available as a paperback: New York: Dover Publications, 1960.
26. Brouwer, D., and Clemence, G. M. *Methods of Celestial Mechanics*. New York: Academic Press, 1961.

This book is invaluable for the theoretical and practical aspects of the subject, and is useful as a text or as a reference book.

Chapter 7

The student should consult

27. Herget, P. *The Computation of Orbits*. University of Cincinnati. Published privately by the author, 1948.
28. Dubyago, A. D. *The Determination of Orbits*. New York: Macmillan, 1961.
29. *Notes of the Summer Institute in Dynamical Astronomy at Yale University. July 1959*. Published by the Yale University Observatory, New Haven, 1960.
30. Williams, K. P. *The Calculation of Orbits of Asteroids and Comets*. Bloomington, Indiana: The Principia Press, 1934.
31. Watson, J. C. *Theoretical Astronomy*. Philadelphia: J. B. Lippincott Co., 1896.

See also 18, 22, and 25.

Chapter 8

See 18, 25, 26, and, for more advanced work, 17. There are also discussions in

32. Finlay-Freundlich, E. *Celestial Mechanics*. New York: Pergamon Press, 1959.
33. Kurth, R. *Introduction to the Mechanics of the Solar System*. New York: Pergamon Press, 1959.

Chapter 9

See, in particular, 24, 25, and 26. For an advanced consideration of this and other problems in celestial mechanics see

34. Wintner, A. *The Analytical Foundations of Celestial Mechanics*. Princeton: Princeton University Press, 1947.

A discussion of the practical applications of the equations to the solar system is given by

35. Porter, J. G. *A Comparative Study of Perturbation Methods*. A.J., 63, 405.

(The numbers denote volume and number and page, respectively.) This is one of the papers read at a conference on celestial mechanics. All the papers will be found in *A.J.*, 63, 401–464

Chapter 10

See 26, 27, 29, and 30. For the theory see

36. Bennett, A. A., Milne, W. E., and Bateman, H. *Numerical Integration of Differential Equations*. New York: Dover Publications, 1956.

The student will find full instructions together with appropriate tables in

37. *Interpolation and Allied Tables*. Great Britain, Her Majesty's Nautical Almanac Office, 1956.

See also

38. *Planetary Coordinates for the Years 1960–1980*. Great Britain, Her Majesty's Nautical Almanac Office, 1958.

Chapter 11

See 4, 22, 23, 24, 25, 31, 33, and 35, but especially, see 26, 27, 29, and 38. See also

39. Brown, E. W. *An Introductory Treatise on the Lunar Theory*. Cambridge, England: Cambridge University Press, 1896. Now available in a paperback edition: New York: Dover Publications, 1960.

40. Brown, E. W., and Shook, C. A. *Planetary Theory*. Cambridge, England: Cambridge University Press, 1933.

Hansen's method for perturbations is described in 26. See also 38 and

41. Musen, P. *Modified Formulae for Hansen's Special Perturbations*. A.J., 63, 426.

The planetary equations are used to solve the problem of motion in the field of a slightly oblate planet in

42. Kozai, Y. *The Motion of a Close Earth Satellite*. A.J., 64, 367.

Herrick's method for the variation of parameters is given in

43. Herrick, S. *A Modification of the "Variation of Constants" Method for Special Perturbations*. P.A.S.P., 60, 321.

He applies his method, and gives a general discussion of other methods in

44. Herrick, S. *Icarus and the Variation of Parameters*. A.J., 58, 156.

Herrick gives a discussion of the integral for M in

45. Herrick, S. *The Mean Longitude or Mean Anomaly in Perturbations by Variation of Constants*. A.J., 56, 186.

Merton's method is given in

46. Merton, G. *A Modification of the Perturbation-of-Elements Method. M.N.*, 109, 421:

For a description of the theory of the adjoint equations see

47. Kopal, Z. *Numerical Analysis.* New York: Wiley, 1955.

For its application to ballistics see

48. Bliss, G. A. *Mathematics for Exterior Ballistics.* New York: Wiley, 1944.

Chapter 12

See 39; also 24, 25, 26, and 29.

Chapters 13 and 14

See 6, 24, 25, 33 and many texts on mechanics, including

49. Routh, E. J. *Advanced Dynamics of a System of Rigid Bodies.* New York, Dover Publications, 1955.

Appendix C

The most comprehensive book of tables, etc., is

50. Allen, C. W. *Astrophysical Quantities.* University of London, The Athlone Press, 1955.

A very useful set of tables is always included in the *Handbook of the British Astronomical Association,* which is published annually.

INDEX